Precalculus

A Modeling Approach

PRELIMINARY EDITION

Patrick J. Driscoll
U.S. Military Academy

David H. Olwell
U.S. Military Academy

WCB
McGraw-Hill

Boston, Massachusetts   Burr Ridge, Illinois   Dubuque, Iowa
Madison, Wisconsin   New York, New York   San Francisco, California   St. Louis, Missouri

WCB/McGraw-Hill
A Division of The McGraw-Hill Companies

Precalculus: A Modeling Approach
Preliminary Edition

This book is printed on acid-free paper.

1 2 3 4 5 6 7 8 9 0 DOC DOC 9 0 0 9 8 7

ISBN 0-07-017867-4

Editorial Director: Kevin Kane
Publisher: Tom Casson
Sponsoring editor: Maggie Rogers
Development editor: Paul Murphy
Marketing manager: Michelle Sala
Project manager: Michelle Lyon
Production supervisor: Richard DeVitto
Cover designer: Nicole Leong
Printer: R.R. Donnelley & Sons Company

Library of Congress Catalog Card No.: 97-061746

http://www.mhhe.com

CONTENTS

LIST OF FIGURES

LIST OF TABLES

About the Authors

Pat Driscoll is originally from Buffalo, New York. He holds a B.S. in Engineering from the U.S. Military Academy at West Point, both an M.S. in Operations Research and an M.S. in Engineering Economic Systems from Stanford University, and a Ph.D. in Industrial and Systems Engineering from Virginia Tech. Pat has been an Academy Professor in the Department of Mathematical Sciences at West Point since 1991. He actively consults throughout the United States on multimedia restructuring of both educational and professional development courses, specializing in Web-based next-generation methods. He is currently serving as the Associate Dean of Information and Educational Technology at West Point. He has a wonderful bride (Marie), two great children (Ryan and Patrick), and six interesting cats (Loki, Peaches, Pixel, Penrose, Cocoa, and Jamocha). This book is lovingly dedicated to all of them.

Dave Olwell is originally from Seattle, Washington. He graduated with distinction from the U.S. Military Academy at West Point. Dave earned Masters degrees in mathematics and statistics and a Ph.D. in statistics from the University of Minnesota. He is currently an associate professor in the Department of Mathematical Sciences at West Point. Dave consults extensively across the U.S. and Europe on statistical modeling. He and his wife, Karen, have three very active sons and a golden retriever.

CHAPTER
1

THE
PRELIMINARIES

The mind contains furniture into which the guests must fit.

Morris Kline

Chapter Goals

⇒ Understand the role of precalculus as a bridge course in mathematics.

⇒ Understand the effects that technology has on teaching and learning mathematics.

⇒ Understand the authors' perspective on the material in this book.

⇒ Understand the rationale behind the sequencing of mathematics courses in secondary education.

Ok, let's be perfectly honest here: There is no such thing as "precalculus" as a mathematical topic. If you look in any math history book, you will not find some "pre-Newton" person having a "pre-apple" fall on their head, spurring the development of "pre-calculus." However, there are a good deal of concepts and ideas that are beneficial to know prior to taking calculus, and they are typically not covered in algebra, geometry, or trigonometry. So, there is a need to have some course that acts as a bridge between secondary and post-secondary mathematics. It might as well be called precalculus, because the topics need to be addressed before studying calculus, and this is our attempt to expose some of these mathematical ideas to you.

We should state that precalculus is not a review course for high school mathematics prior to proceeding to collegiate mathematics. Even if you have taken an advanced placement calculus course during your secondary education, there is a very high likelihood that you have not seen the material in the manner in which we present it here. Nor should this course be the last course you ever take in mathematics. This is the starting point where mathematics gets real: translating the real world into mathematical language, applying real tools to real problems, and understanding what mathematics is really about.

Many of the mathematical ideas are captured in strong visual images that you can consistently rely on for correct intuition—visual images that either we create for you or you create on your own with some direction from us and your instructor. Some concepts will simply illuminate a new perspective of material that you have previously studied. All will focus your attention on the style of mathematics you will encounter in post-secondary education and the real world.

Calculus is simply about change, how to represent change in mathematical expressions, and how to get some important information from these expressions once you have them. The mathematical concepts of integrals, derivatives, and limits that are introduced in calculus all capture aspects of the behavior of something engaged in moving from one state to another. Precalculus, on the other hand, is about *changing*: changing the way we think about mathematics.

We introduce a number of techniques in this book for obtaining solutions from mathematical models. These techniques emphasize developing the "big four" categories of skills that are used in mathematics: numerical, analytical, graphical, and descriptive. These are the basics of some very useful tools that you will learn more about in later courses.

However, instead of focusing on simply doing calculations, we examine issues such as such as: *How* did we find the answer(s)? *What* questions did we ask in the process? Will these same questions help us to find the answers to other problems? Instead of seeing mathematics as "a collection of individual tools that work fine when applied to math problems, but what do they have to do with the real world?" we want to start seeing math for what it *really* is: a language. It is a very special language with its own symbols and rules that seem to be just right for describing the world that we live in.

Our long-term goal in studying mathematics is to be able to describe—and maybe predict—real world events such as earthquakes, payoffs from investments, acoustics, epidemics, and freight deliveries using this language of symbols. Pre-calculus is a great place to begin seeing mathematics in this light because you need this perspective to succeed in collegiate mathematics.

1.1   A NEW PERSPECTIVE

Some of the ideas introduced in this book will come naturally, and some require a little discussion between you and others before you really get the picture. The point is, however, that we have to change our perspective either now or later—and the sooner, the better.

In this book, we focus on developing mathematical abilities, which are uniquely human skills. These are *modeling* skills. The ability to make observations and gather data based on our senses, the ability to reason and make connections between seemingly unrelated ideas, and the ability to communicate the results of our analysis to others are a few of the important skills that computers cannot do, and that we can.

This book takes a slightly different lean from others you may have seen. It is not intended to be a one-stop reference for all the mathematics addressed within the chapters. We think of it as a guide to seeing mathematics differently, pushing you toward exploration and discovery. With this in mind, it is possible that you may occasionally need to look back on previous material you have studied to refresh your memory. This is natural. However, we think that this need will be minimal because of the stand-alone nature of our approach.

In this textbook, we rely on a computer algebra system (CAS) called *Derive* to illustrate many graphical and analytical techniques. However, it is not necessary to use *Derive* to use this book. If you have familiarity with some other CASs such as Mathematica, Maple, MathCad, Scientific Notebook, etc., you will easily be able to accomplish the same type exploration as we do with *Derive*. Just to help reinforce this point, we've also included some of the output graphics of these programs where appropriate.

As may be apparent from a few of the output illustrations, we didn't pick

Derive because of its beautiful graphics. We picked *Derive* because it is an inexpensive, powerful CAS that is easy to use and convenient for exploring the ideas we are after. Its graphics are effective and easy for a student to manipulate and understand. It is also not a RAM memory glutton. In fact, *Derive* is the resident software program on Texas Instrument's TI-92, an inexpensive and excellent advanced calculator for exploring mathematics. We consider the TI-92 as a viable option to explore the ideas in this book in lieu of a computer, if such a choice need be made.

Most important, a CAS provides the freedom to examine ideas and effects, and to develop individual visualizations (pictures) of important mathematical concepts. We want to minimize the time spent performing routine calculations and manual graphing, because *Derive* performs these tasks quickly and accurately. So, instead of simply solving equations, we focus on analyzing them, understanding where they originate, examining why certain solution techniques work for particular cases, and determining what their solutions imply.

EXPLORATION   This is what we mean by "exploration": considering the answer to each mathematical problem as a starting point, a treasure to be uncovered, rather than as a final result. Along the way, each person discovers and observes various things that are usually different from those someone else sees. Like a tour guide in a new city, we point out many of the major attractions, leaving many things for you to discover on your own so that you develop ingenuity, creativity, and critical problem solving. If you discover a topic that interests you and we move on to a new subject, you can use the references at the end of the chapter to find out more information.

1.2   A SEA CHANGE IN COMPUTING

When we began writing this book, computing was about powerful calculation being able to expose powerful ideas. In response to the needs of education, various companies developed and released mathematical software such as Mathematica, Maple, MathCad, Matlab, *Derive*, and Theorist, just to name a few. Nearly every quantitative collegiate course we were aware of was using some computer application to help students understand the topics presented.

Each software package could perform the calculations and graph the plots we needed very well. So, we selected a package to support our courses based mainly on cost and the amount of effort it took a student to learn the software. A powerful software application that requires a lot of effort to learn may be great for research, but the students' interest will die in a New York minute. *Derive* was an easy choice because of its menu-driven environment and relatively small requirement for computer memory.

Enter the Internet. Enter the World Wide Web. Enter cheap RAM chips. Enter applications such as Java, X-Lisp Stat, and Shockwave that allow very focused illustrations, demonstrations, and communications to occur as we need them, when we need them, without having to own a personal version of the mathematical software. It is now possible to wrap the little piece of the application we need inside some code (called an *applet*), and pull it down over the Internet. Now, computing is about *connecting* to the resources we need, whether they are on some local area network at our school, or at some remote university on the other side of the world.

The only question left to be resolved (and it is not resolved as of yet) is exactly what material we should cover in text form and what we should post to a Web site for readers to learn on their own. Once a book is published, it becomes a fixed media product. Web-based resources can easily be modified to respond to input from students and instructors alike. We're partially solving this dilemma by setting up a McGraw-Hill Web site for the support of this course, and we will OUR WEB update it constantly. The general Web site at McGraw-Hill under which you can SITE find our Web page is http://www.mhcollege.com/math/pcama/index.htm.

We think that this book is a movement in the right direction. The topics that we believe require a perspective change on your part, we have kept in the text. The topics that you can easily pick up on your own by just playing, we moved to the Web.

We really didn't want to leave Web surfers on their own. So, we've created a frequently asked questions (FAQ) page that will continue to grow as time goes on, along with direct e-mail support to instructors for discussion and exchange of ideas. Instructors will also have restricted access to a source for a complete set of solutions and suggestions for covering the book's material. We believe that a combination of these components will eventually evolve into a standard approach for all educational courses, whether they are distance-learning courses or resident courses. We also believe that we are not quite there yet. There are technological issues, copyright issues, learning issues, teaching issues, and cost issues that remain to be resolved before this approach becomes standard practice.

We strongly believe that a modeling emphasis within mathematics actively promotes the kind of things we long for as a mathematics community:

active self-learning by students, interdisciplinary cooperation among instructors for developing syllabi and courses, and a realism that recognizes the service orientation of mathematics after students leave academia. However, we realize that we don't have a monopoly on good ideas, and wholeheartedly welcome both student and instructor comments on the material in this book. Until the McGraw-Hill Web site is complete, you can reach us via the Web at

(David): http://www.dean.usma.edu/math/resource/faculty/olwell.htm

(Pat): http://www.dean.usma.edu/math/resource/faculty/driscoll.htm

or, by e-mail at

olwell@euler.math.usma.edu

ap5543@exmail.usma.edu

The Web site at McGraw-Hill will have active links to both of our web pages so that you will not have to search to find us.

The rest of this introductory chapter is optional. We wrote the material for both the instructor and student to motivate the rest of the book and to explain our point of view. We discuss some of the implications of going from high school to collegiate mathematics. We also introduce some of the background issues surrounding the use of a CAS for exploration and discovery of fundamental ideas embedded in collegiate mathematical thinking. Our focus is to provide a "big picture" of mathematics education: one that will persist throughout the many changes that will occur as teaching methods continue to evolve and improve.

1.3   OUR POSITION ON LEARNING

Applying language of mathematics to the real world (also called "doing mathematics") is a strictly human way of organizing, describing, and analyzing events we observe in the physical world in such a way that our minds can develop, recognize, and understand patterns. These patterns link ideas. For most people, these links tend to be visually based, although not necessarily so. For example, we often link certain smells to the coming of a rainstorm or a fire. It is not a coincidence that we often find ourselves saying, "Oh, now I see!" when we finally understand an idea.

Developing your own mental pictures of mathematical concepts is important for two reasons. First, you will retain these pictures for a long time, well past the point when the details of doing some calculation or procedure have been forgotten. Second, you have to have your own picture of a concept before you can understand it. Sure, it's possible that groups of people can have the same picture in their minds of a certain mathematical concept. Typically, this is not the case. As teachers, we try to show you as many different ways of looking at a topic as we can. Sometimes we run out before you "get it." Throughout this book we use drawings, screen captures from computer renderings, discussion questions, and exercises to present various perspectives, hoping that at least one will trigger a pattern in your brain.

In-class discovery and exploration are being used in mathematics courses far more frequently today than ever before. These techniques rely heavily on computers and graphing calculators to answer "what if" types of questions, and to examine problems from symbolic, numerical and graphical perspectives. Not surprisingly, this parallels a practice deeply ingrained in business. Without computational power, individual businesses easily lose their competitive edge in today's global markets. However, the insights they get using the same techniques we introduce in this book enable them to develop far-reaching strategies.

Up front, we have to admit a truth: Even with the tools afforded by technology, learning mathematics remains an inefficient process. Education is not training. Training is very efficient. We can train you to perform calculations. We cannot train you to think mathematically. You have to learn that on your own. We can point to patterns that have succeeded in the past, but this is not a guarantee for the future.

As a language, mathematics is a language much like any other language. In this sense, it is possible to learn a great deal of the vocabulary of mathematics without really understanding how the vocabulary pieces together to reveal the meaning of the underlying concepts. It is often said that a true measure of proficiency in a language is demonstrating the ability to express humor in that language. Humor is very conceptual; situational humor such as a funny story must be carefully crafted and presented so that a listener can visualize the situation or the humor will be lost. In the same fashion, if you can explain mathematical ideas from a conceptual perspective, you will find yourself more in control of the mathematical language.

By its very nature, learning cannot be a one-sided effort. It takes a certain amount of maturity on the part of the student to make the effort required to understand the ideas we have included and learn the language of mathematics. To complement such a student, we rely on teachers to enhance the presentation of material with their experience and perspective. In concert with this textbook, these elements form critical three-pronged foundation necessary for dynamic learning to take place.

1.4   PROBLEM SOLVING AND PRECALCULUS

A large part of doing mathematics is asking the right type of questions. Finding exact numerical answers is sometimes secondary to the goals we set out to achieve. In fact, determining that no solution exists is an answer that is equally as valuable as finding one! The approach we take to problem solving is critical, and the results we obtain directly depend upon the approach we use.

Effective problem solving follows a pattern. This is not to say that it adheres to some lockstep sequence without variation, but rather that there are fundamental components of the problem solving approach. Pilots use pre-flight checklists, builders use blueprints, and chefs use recipes. However, like a chef creating an entree, the level of creativity, ingenuity and experience that go into solving problems significantly affect the end product.

A good problem solving approach can be described simply. First, there is an unorganized mess that we see at the start. From this mess, we extract a workable definition of the problem we are going to attempt to conquer. We do some data gathering and attempt to express the problem *as we see it* in mathematical terms. Then, we see if we can identify information about a solution to this mathematical formulation. Last, assuming that we were able to do something worthwhile, we translate our analytical results in mathematical language back into the language of the real world, and determine if they make sense (notice our role as interpreters). If they do, we may have gained some useful information and insights into the problem at hand, and we need to communicate our results. If not, maybe we can alter what we did, or attempt a completely new approach, as time permits. In all of this, notice the predominant role that the word "if" plays. This is how the real world of mathematics operates. Successfully getting beyond the "if's" is the name of the game.

The good news is that you probably have quite a bit of experience in solving pre-made mathematical problems. Standardized tests and textbook exercises still stress this skill. However, with the advent of computer algebra systems (CASs), this skill loses some of its value. In today's world, the ability to perform routine calculations accurately is worth about the price of a good cup of coffee. There are inexpensive desktop computers that are capable of performing thousands, millions, even billions of calculations per second to any reasonable degree of accuracy. Since most real world calculations are well beyond our ability to solve by hand in a reasonable amount of time anyway, let's focus on aspects of problem solving in which we have a distinct advantage over machines.

For all of our limitations, we are still the most valuable link in the problem solving process: We possess the unique ability to think. We make observations, gather data, develop models, obtain solution information (We hope!), analyze results, and communicate our newly acquired information and insights to other people in the hope that we are actively contributing to some body of knowledge. These are the essential skills of this course and for applying mathematics in the real world today. So, why have you spent so much time on other mathematical skills so far in your education?

1.5   THE SEQUENCING OF MATHEMATICS

Think of yourself as someone being trained as a carpenter. Up to this point in your education, the mathematics courses you have been taking have been adding tools to some sort of "math toolbox" that you have been carrying around. Just like any apprentice, you have been able to work on small projects that use these tools individually: algebra for algebra problems, geometry for geometry problems, and trigonometry for trigonometry problems. But, in the real world, tools seldom are used in this manner. Most carpentry problems require all sorts of tools to get the job done. Different carpenters may use different tools for the same task, or perhaps the same tools in a different order. It depends upon their experience. This is true of mathematics tools and mathematics problems also. We never know what we are going to need until we take a look at the problem. Precalculus provides a bridge that allows us to begin to build new things (models) with our math toolbox in the same way. So, let's look back at algebra, geometry and trigonometry for a few moments to develop a big picture of what we have done.

Usually underrated at first, algebra is full of complex ideas that make it one of the most challenging topics in early mathematics. The overall idea behind algebra is to manipulate objects (variables) according to the same rules that we previously applied only to numbers. However, because variables do not necessarily combine to give a new variable like numbers combine to give a new number, we shifted our attention to the rules themselves (associative, communicative, ALGEBRA and distributive properties) and their limitations. If we did not make this jump to using variables, we might have missed this opportunity.

Also in algebra, we extend the number system from simply what we need for counting (the natural, or whole number system), to what we need for manipulating these new objects (the real number system and the complex number system). Instead of just getting an answer, algebra requires us to consider *how* a solution is obtained. It is the first time that we see that we have options available when solving problems, and, although we are limited to using algebra tools, the goal is to pick the most efficient option for a particular situation.

GEOMETRY

For the most part, geometry seems to be about shapes, lines, bisectors, angle relationships, and other tools used to compare triangles, squares, quadralaterals, etc. It is actually much more than that. By requiring us to do short mathematical proofs, geometry tries to extend our reasoning from using intuition ("It seems correct"), to using *logic* to support our arguments. It may be interesting to point out that the logic system used in geometry is called an *axiomatic system*, and is completely based on five *postulates*, or fundamental truths, proposed by the philosopher and mathematician Euclid (300 B.C.). This is an important point to realize, because the ideas that Euclid assumes to be true (a line has no width, two parallel lines do not intersect, among others) may be the most common, but are not fixed as absolutely true. By changing one or more of Euclid's postulates, entirely new rules of geometry are created that are equally as valid. This is precisely what Nikolai Lobachevsky (1793–1856) and David Hilbert (1862–1943) did. As a result, new geometries were introduced that are fascinating and far reaching in their own right.

Many areas within the mathematical sciences rely heavily on geometry to gain insights into what is known as *problem structure*, a concept we will later revisit. For example, a group of equations that are linked together, called a *system of equations*, is often viewed first from an algebraic standpoint that pictures the equations as just expressing relationships between variables. Geometry recognizes each individual equation as defining an underlying geometric surface (a line, a plane, a curve, etc.). Examining the intersection of these surfaces often provides more insight into the problem at hand than does the algebra. It is often this geometric structure that inspires new theories and solution procedures. In fact, several of today's advanced technologies in computing–such as parallel processing, decomposition, and distributed processing, all of which make previously impractical calculations commonplace–were first inspired by geometry.

Trigonometry combines pieces of algebra and geometry to give us a first exposure to associating mathematics with the physical world. Largely based on mathematics originating in Egypt and Babylonia, trigonometry introduces ideas associated with basic engineering mathematics. The properties of angles and angle measurement are introduced much like the properties of numbers and equations in algebra. Quite unsurprisingly, we revisit trigonometric concepts in both this course and calculus.

Our emphasis in precalculus builds a bridge to college-level calculus courses. It brings together, or *synthesizes*, the tools acquired in previous courses, and introduces several new ones. By exploring the ideas of precalculus, we learn to ask the type of questions that show us what tools can be used, how to build mathematical models using these tools, and how to solve these models, if a solution exists. Since much of a mathematician's success depends upon effective communication of results, we also want to hone these skills in the process. A very wise person once said, "You understand what you can explain." We have finally realized the truth in this statement with regard to mathematics.

Last, just in case you still think that all math problems have solutions, we repeat the point that, in some cases, demonstrating that a solution is not possible is doing proper mathematics, and may be the best we can do. The challenge when this occurs is to discover and explain why a solution could not be found, and whether changing our assumptions, collecting new data, or changing our approach would help.

1.6 SUMMARY

Applying mathematics to the real world generally requires three steps. First, we must isolate and mathematically describe an event or problem that we want to better understand. This step is part of a *modeling process* that is a major theme of this book. Second, we must apply our mathematical tools to extract information from the mathematical description we formulate. This is commonly called *solving* the model. Third, we must interpret these results in the setting of the original problem, gaining insights, and communicating our results to others.

Before precalculus, a majority of our effort went to learning the various solution techniques for typical problems in algebra, geometry and trigonometry. Now, we focus on the first and third steps, the human steps, and let *Derive* handle the second.

As crazy as it may seem nowadays, back when we were in high school, we learned how to calculate square roots of numbers by hand, spending about a week mastering the mechanics of the technique. We never learned why someone would want to find square roots, or how the calculation might be useful for real world problems. We simply memorized the procedure. When we were tested, we simply had to accurately calculate the square root of some number, typically a simple whole number whose answer provided no insight into a real problem. Consequently, when personal computers and hand-held calculators became available, we promptly forgot the method. For all of our effort, we were ultimately left with something of very little value. We think your experience will be different with this precalculus course.

Discussion Ideas

These questions ask you to examine your readiness to take this course and to encourage you to begin the maturation process we discussed in this introduction.

⇒ How do you see this course fitting into your educational plan?

⇒ What do you feel are your mathematical strengths and weaknesses?

⇒ How do you know when you understand a mathematical topic? Is this indication the same as what you use in other subjects? How is it different; why is it different; and, more important, should it be different?

⇒ How comfortable are you with using a personal computer or graphing calculator?

⇒ Which do you consider a more important goal: earning a good grade, or fully understanding the material of a course? If you had to sacrifice one for the other, which would it be?

⇒ Do you think that you learn better by (1) reading text, (2) looking at pictures and illustrations, or (3) performing calculations? What is it in your past experience that has conditioned you into having this preference for learning?

⇒ Can you draw a simple bubble diagram with circles and arrows that illustrates the major topics in algebra, geometry, and trigonometry and how they are linked? Do you notice any one theme that is consistent in all of the courses?

⇒ Do you keep your mathematics notebooks after a course is over, or are they not worth keeping? If you keep them, how often have you referred back to them? If they are not worth keeping, what is wrong with them? Is this the same for all of your courses?

⇒ Prior to taking big exams, do you reexamine the material covered in the course to date and look for themes, separating calculation techniques from major concepts? If not, you should. This is how a syllabus is developed and examinations are written.

⇒ If you had to teach one of the mathematics courses you have taken so far, how would you teach it differently from the way you experienced it? How would you make the classroom an active place for interaction? What would you have emphasized? What would you have ignored?

⇒ Pick one of the mathematics courses that you have experienced to date. If you had to create a video game that would subliminally teach a lot of the mathematical ideas of that course, how would you do it? What would the game be? Are there any mathematical ideas that could not be taught this way? Which ones?

1.7   COMPLEMENTS

Our vision for the role of this course has largely been shaped by our experiences in helping students with vastly different mathematical abilities to adapt to the demands of college mathematics within the changes caused by technology growth. As the reformation of calculus enters its tenth year, many of our institutions either have felt, or are just beginning to feel, the shock waves of this movement. Some of these changes are universally agreed upon and are easily adopted by educators. Some of the changes are controversial and are still being hotly debated.

Regardless of the outcome of concensus-building among educators, for the students' sake we believe that it is about time to focus on developing their mathematical thought processes at an earlier age, rather than waiting. The current situation is not fair: We change the type of questions and the expectations of students' understanding and performance in college mathematics, without their having previous experience to rely on. This "sink or swim" approach may work fine in some situations, but the upshot for the field of mathematics is that we lose a lot of young talent who could have made great contributions to our discipline.

The challenge we face, and will continue to face, is adequately illustrated in a summary of student evaluations at a notable post-secondary institution:

"In December 1996, our students said that we were enthusiastic, encouraging, organized, concerned, difficult to understand, and a bit boring instructors who taught very conceptual, very deep, very demanding, very rigorous, but irrelevant courses with well understood goals and objectives, fair tests, terrible textbooks, and long assignments."

The emphasis we place on conceptual mathematical modeling has largely been influenced by the work of Gil Strang, John Casti, Frank Giordano, and Russell Ackhoff. We are grateful to our fellow faculty members in the Department of Mathematical Sciences at the United States Military Academy at West Point, who have done much to reinforce our belief in the future of mathematics and the potential of the student.

CHAPTER
2

BASIC
TOOLS

The purpose of computing is insight, not numbers.

Richard Hamming

Chapter Goals

⇒ Understand the development of computer algebra systems (CASs).

⇒ Understand the difference between numerical and symbolic solutions, exact and approximate solutions, and the primary sources of error.

⇒ Understand the difference in capabilities between CASs, spreadsheets, and advanced scientific calculators (ASCs).

In this chapter, we want to develop some familiarity with the computational tools we will be using to explore the ideas of precalculus. The three that we are going to focus on are the computer algebra system (CAS) *Derive*, a spreadsheet such as Excel or QuattroPro, and advanced scientific calculators in general. Our intention is to examine some of the capabilities and limitations of each tool, and

how they influence the approach we choose for "doing mathematics." We don't
want to turn this chapter into a tutorial on each of these computational tools for
several reasons. However, using this chapter in conjunction with the user's guides
provided by each of these tools will be more than sufficient for us to develop a
good level of proficiency.

2.1   COMPUTER ALGEBRA SYSTEMS

2.1.1   A little history

Humans have consistently sought tools to make calculations easier. As early as
1650 B.C., the Egyptians used simple written tables of equivalents for unit fractions to avoid having to recompute these values each time they were needed.
One of the first computational devices was called an *abacus*. The earliest written reference to the abacus seems to come from Babylonia around 1500 B.C.
Similar references appear in Chinese literature beginning around 75 A.D. The
abacus consists of a simple board with various counters or pebbles that can be
manipulated to keep track of algebraic operations. For its time, the abacus was
a wonderful device, allowing easy addition and subtraction, and supporting multiplication and division. Amazingly, in many parts of the world, the abacus is
still being used to support merchants' trade calculations; probably because it is
simple to use, durable, and never needs batteries!

HISTORY

By the 17th century, mathematicians had developed an immense amount of
knowledge based upon numerical sequences. However, advancing computational
devices required a technique that could replace the operation of multiplication
with addition in an efficient manner. In 1614, the mathematician John Napier
(1550–1617) partially achieved this goal with the publication of his work *Mirifici
logarithmorum canonis descriptio*. Henry Briggs, a Professor of mathematics
in London, completed the efforts of Napier with the publication of *Arithmetic
logarithmica* in 1624.

It was Edmund Gunter (1561–1626) who started the real revolution. In the
second decade of the 17th century, he transformed the tables of logarithms to
occur along a straight line. Shortly afterward, William Oughtred (1574–1660)
modified Gunter's approach by introducing the idea that the different scales
could slide along each other, either in a straight-line configuration, or in a circular
pattern. Around the middle of the 17th century, Edmund Wingate (1593–1656)
and Seth Partridge (1603–1686) introduced a ruler that slid between two pieces

of fixed wood. It was this invention that led to the mass production and use of the *slide rule* in the 19th century.

Blaise Pascal[†] invented the first actual calculating machine as we know it in 1642. It differed from the abacus in that it carried 10's to the next column automatically without requiring the operator to manually move beads.

Over the next 200–300 years, calculating machines continued to improve. By World War II, the first modern computers were being used to aid in both cryptography (breaking the secret codes of the Axis powers) and in the solution of ballistic missile trajectories. Even with the advent of these new tools, mathematicians and scientists still lacked the ability to manipulate symbols and to generate useful graphs. Two large numbers could be multiplied together accurately, but it was not yet possible to symbolically manipulate a simple equation such as $ax + by = c$ to solve for x, for example.

All of this has changed with the rapid development of powerful computing devices and supporting software programs. Hand-held calculators replaced the slide rule in the late 1960s and early 1970s. As with any new technology, these calculators were limited in what they could do, and were quite expensive. The ones now commonly available in grocery stores are actually far better and much less expensive than these early models.

The personal computer then began to dominate the technological computing world in the late 1970s and early 1980s. By the mid-1980s, several commercial vendors developed powerful software called computer algebra systems (CASs) for mathematics that began to fully use the capabilities of these new computers. To keep pace (and save their businesses!), calculator vendors incorporated graphing and symbolic capabilities into their hand-held machines. For the first time, it was possible to own a computing device capable of manipulating symbols as well as numbers, and to graphically see the results of mathematics in action. The effect? The computing revolution hit mathematics like a ton of bricks. How to best use this new technology remains an open issue even today. There is no doubt, however, that the opportunity is ripe for exploring the ideas of mathematics much like scientists in chemistry and physics have done for centuries: within a

---

[†]For this contribution, the computer language Pascal was named in his honor. Pascal made many other contributions to probability, geometry, science, and engineering. He also designed the first mass transit bus system for Paris, using horse drawn carriages.

laboratory environment in which "what if?" questions could be addressed.

2.1.2 The case today

Several excellent software programs are available today for just such an exploration. The five most common in use in academia are *Derive*, Mathematica, Maple, Matlab, and MathCad. Each of these are available for use on a variety of computer operating systems (Macintosh, Windows, DOS, UNIX). And, although each program clearly operates differently, they all possess the major capabilities we look for in a CAS today:

- MULTIPLE CAPABILITIES. They perform numerical calculations to a level of accuracy that can be specified by the user, symbolically manipulate expressions, and display both two- and three-dimensional graphics.

- WORKBENCH APPROACH. They allow the user to rapidly adjust parameter values, expressions, and model design to examine the effects of change and answer "what if?" questions.

CAPABILITIES

- MULTIPLE GRAPHING ENVIRONMENTS. They allow the user to examine several plots at the same time, in both two and three dimensions.

- ABILITY TO IMPORT CODE OR CALL TO AN EXTERNAL SOFTWARE PROGRAM. Although this is usually not needed by precalculus students, it is useful when working with other programs or computer code (e.g., FORTRAN or C) in later courses.

Simplicity of use, powerful algorithmic routines, low cost, and memory space considerations lead us to favor *Derive* for use in precalculus.

As an example of the use of *Derive*, consider the problem of solving the system of two equations in two unknowns given by

$$3x + 4y = 7$$

$$5x - 4y = \pi$$

We can use *Derive* to solve this system symbolically, numerically, or graphically. The *Derive* screen illustrating our options appears in Figure 2.1. The two equations are entered as lines 1 and 2. These equations are converted to slope-intercept form in lines 3 and 4 (we just did this for convenience; it was not necessary), and plotted in the upper right window. The intersection point (why do we know

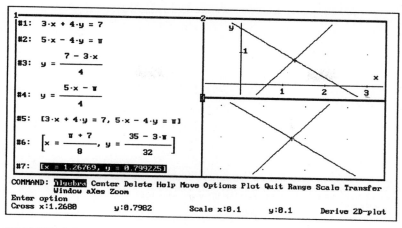

FIGURE 2.1
Three methods of exploration using *Derive*.

that there is only one intersection point?) can be found by looking at the graph. We next created a lower right window, zooming in on the intersection of the two lines. We can easily get the approximate coordinates of this intersection point by moving the cursor to the intersection and checking the coordinates of the cursor, located at the bottom of the *Derive* screen. On lines 5 and 6, the exact solution is found in symbolic form. On line 7, we found a numerical approximation to the exact symbolic solution. Notice that it does not agree exactly with the values given by the cursor coordinates. If we wanted to improve the accuracy given by the cursor coordinates, we could easily change the scale of the plot in order to zoom in closer on the intersection point. We will do a lot of this style of exploration later. Read on, MacDuff.

2.1.3   Numerical versus symbolic computations

It is safe to assume that prior to this course you have encountered both numerical and symbolic calculations. Numerical calculations give you a result in the form of a number. As is obvious from the previous example, this number can either be an *exact solution* or an *approximate solution* to the problem that you are NUMERICAL working with. On the other hand, a symbolic calculation yields a result in terms of the *symbols* that orginally appeared in the expressions you were manipulating. A symbolic solution does not necessarily involve numbers. This distinction between numerical and symbolic calculations is important. The examples that

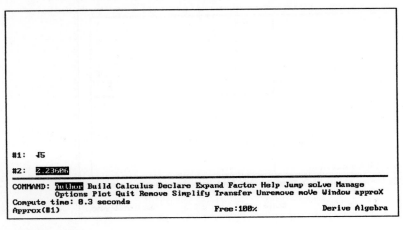

#1:   √5
#2:   2.23606

COMMAND: **Author** Build Calculus Declare Expand Factor Help Jump soLve Manage
         Options Plot Quit Remove Simplify Transfer Unremove moVe Window approX
Compute time: 0.3 seconds
Approx(#1)   Free:100%   Derive Algebra

FIGURE 2.2
Numerical approximation in *Derive*.

follow illustrate the distinction we are making.

Example 2.1. Suppose we need to approximate $\sqrt{5}$.

Solution. This is a numerical calculation. We could find an answer with whatever number of significant digits and to any desired accuracy we need. Of course,
left alone, $\sqrt{5}$ *is* a number all by itself. By approximating $\sqrt{5}$, we are finding a
decimal approximation to an irrational number. The *Derive* screen in Figure 2.2
illustrates the approximation of $\sqrt{5}$ to 6 digits (2.23606). To get this result, we
simply enter $\sqrt{5}$ using the Author menu option, which is then displayed (here on
line 1). We obtain the result on line 2 using the approX menu option. The *Derive*
default numerical precision is 6 digits, which can be easily changed, if desired.

Example 2.2. As opposed to seeking a numerical solution, let's look at simplifying the expression $\sqrt{(a^2 - 2ab + b^2)}$ in a symbolic fashion.

Solution. Here, we are working with the symbols a and b, and the solution,
$|a - b|$, is in terms of those symbols. After authoring the expression in *Derive*, we
obtain the symbolic result using the *Derive* menu option Simplify. Figure 2.3
shows the steps used.

SYMBOLIC

Notice that a symbolic result still contains unknown quantities in what we
are calling the solution. Symbolic calculations allow us to find what is known
as a *general solution* expression. This means that all possible solutions for an
expression of the type we are trying to solve take on the form we obtained as a
result. This analogy may help get the idea across.

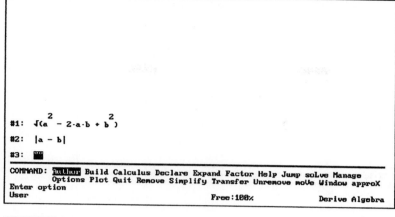

#1: $\sqrt{(a^2 - 2 \cdot a \cdot b + b^2)}$

#2: $|a - b|$

#3:

COMMAND: Author Build Calculus Declare Expand Factor Help Jump soLve Manage
         Options Plot Quit Remove Simplify Transfer Unremove moVe Window approX
Enter option
User
                              Free:100%   Derive Algebra

FIGURE 2.3
Symbolic solutions in *Derive*.

Example 2.3. Think of a general solution as a template, or pattern, similar to a pattern for men's trousers, for instance. A company that manufactures men's trousers doesn't want to start over from scratch just because it needs to make a certain style of trousers in different sizes, say small, medium, and large. It uses a single style template to make all the men's trousers of a particular style. By simply changing certain numerical values (waist, inseam, loose-fit, etc.), it can make different size trousers that *all look the same*! The template represents a general solution. Once the company substitutes specific values for the different unknowns, say waist = 33, inseam = 31, and loose-fit = yes, the machinery will manufacture a specific solution for the problem of manufacturing men's trousers.

So, to obtain a specific solution from a general mathematical solution such as the type we obtain from symbolic calculations, we substitute specific numbers for the unknown symbols in the general solution. Changing the numbers we substitute allows us to change the specific solution. The next example is a classic illustration of this idea.

Example 2.4. We can use symbolic calculations to derive the quadratic formula. Given the symbolic equation $ax^2 + bx + c = 0$, we can find the roots of the equation in terms of a, b, and c using *Derive*.

Solution. The quadratic formula, a general solution for the roots of a quadratic equation, is given by

$$x = \frac{-b \pm \sqrt{b^2 - 4ac}}{2a}$$

The symbolic solution to $ax^2 + bx + c = 0$, or general solution, is found very easily by *Derive*, as illustrated in Figure 2.4. Using this general solution, we can find the roots of any specific quadratic equation simply by substituting

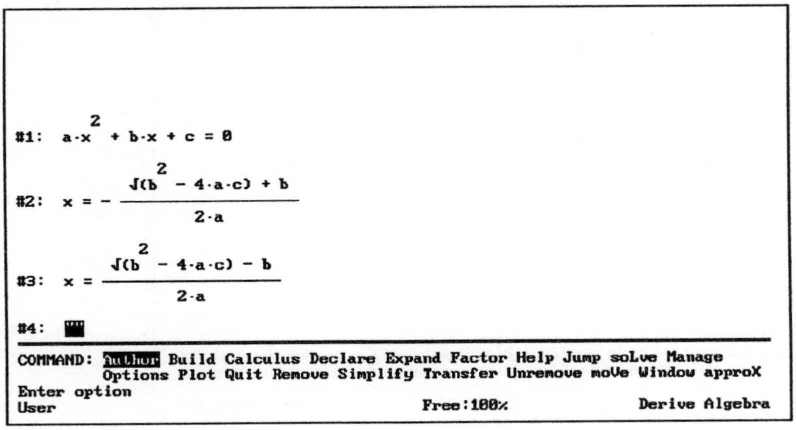

```
#1:   a·x  + b·x + c = 0
         2


            2
         √(b  - 4·a·c) + b
#2:   x = - ─────────────────
              2·a


            2
         √(b  - 4·a·c) - b
#3:   x = ─────────────────
              2·a


#4:   ▓

COMMAND: ▓Author▓ Build Calculus Declare Expand Factor Help Jump soLve Manage
         Options Plot Quit Remove Simplify Transfer Unremove moVe Window approX
Enter option
User                                    Free:100%           Derive Algebra
```

FIGURE 2.4
Solutions to quadratic equation.

the appropriate values of a, b and c.[‡] To get the same general solution using *Derive*, we first enter the given equation using the Author menu option, which is displayed on line 1. Next, using the soLve menu option, we obtain the general solution for two roots of this quadratic equation in symbolic form. These are shown on lines 2 and 3. Notice that the format (called the *syntax*) for these roots is slightly different from the usual expression, but the answer is correct.

2.1.4 Approximate versus exact modes

There is a very good reason why we are stressing the difference between approximate and exact solutions: It is not always necessary (or possible) to seek an exact solution to every mathematical problem, especially when an approximate one will suffice. For example, suppose that we require a decimal value for $\sqrt{5}$. Since $\sqrt{5}$ is an *irrational* number, it does not have an exact decimal representation. In Example 2.1, we found a 6-digit approximation for $\sqrt{5}$. How many digits are enough, knowing that however many we choose the answer will always contain some degree of *error*? Usually, the number of digits chosen is determined by the context of the problem. If we are cutting 6 × 6 wooden posts to support

---

[‡]The first known solution of a quadratic equation is from the Middle Kingdom of Egypt, circa 2160–1700 B.C. The general rule for the solution of the quadratic equation was known to the Hindu mathematician Brahmagupta (ca. 628). The quadratic formula as we know it had to await the development of good notation, and is generally credited to Euler (1707–1783).

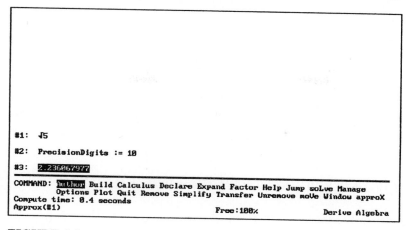

```
#1:  √5

#2:  PrecisionDigits := 10

#3:  2.236067977
```
```
COMMAND: Author Build Calculus Declare Expand Factor Help Jump soLve Manage
         Options Plot Quit Remove Simplify Transfer Unremove moVe Window approX
Compute time: 0.4 seconds
Approx(#1)                            Free:100%            Derive Algebra
```

FIGURE 2.5
Approximation to 10 digits.

an outside deck for a house, then we probably can assume that we have a good
degree of tolerance for error, and plus or minus a half inch is probably good
enough. If we are off by more than we wanted, we could either trim the post
more, or shim the support with some other piece of wood. However, if we are
making incisions for a radial keratotomy surgical procedure to correct a condition of nearsightedness in a human eye, a thousandth of an inch might make the
difference in whether that person's vision improves.

> **Example 2.5.** Returning to Example 2.1, select `Options`, `Precision`. Notice the
> default setting for the number of digits is 6. To change this setting, say to 10, use
> the **tab** key to move to the `Digits` item, and type in the new precision. After
> returning to the main menu, we use the up-arrow key to highlight the numbered
> *Derive* expression with $\sqrt{5}$, and obtain a new approximation using `approX`. The
> resulting approximation is shown in Figure 2.5.

2.1.5 Computational error

If you subtract the 10-digit approximation to $\sqrt{5}$ from the exact value of $\sqrt{5}$,
you will not get 0 for a result. This nonzero leftover amount is called the *error*. Although there are several sources of error that can occur when applying
mathematics to real-world problems, let's limit our attention here to three po-   ERROR
tential sources of error. Two of these sources are inherent in numerical computer
calculations: *truncation error* and *rounding error*. The third source of error is
called *measurement error*, and is commonly introduced when generating data
from scientific measurements. Let's take a closer look at these.

TABLE 2.1

16-bit computer storage of 6.625.

0	1	1	0	1	0	1	0	0	0	0	1	0	0	1	1

Most calculators and computers today use what is known as a *floating point* binary representation for numbers containing decimal points. Each digit of a *decimal* floating point number is the coefficient of some power of 10. For example, the number 22.341 can be expressed in the form

$$(2 \times 10^1) + (2 \times 10^0) + (3 \times 10^{-1}) + (4 \times 10^{-2}) + (1 \times 10^{-3})$$

By multiplying by 10^n, we move, or *float*, the decimal point to the left ($n < 0$) or right ($n > 0$); hence, the expression *floating point* representation.

BINARY
POINT

Each digit in a *binary* representation of a floating point number is a coefficient involving powers of 2. We use a subscript to denote a base other than base 10. Using a base 2 representation, the decimal point is referred to as a *binary point*. Those digits to the left of the binary point are coefficients of non–negative powers of 2, and those to the right are coefficients of negative powers of 2.

Example 2.6. The binary floating point number 110.101_2 represents

$$(1 \times 2^2) + (1 \times 2^1) + (0 \times 2^0) + (1 \times 2^{-1}) + (0 \times 2^{-2}) + (1 \times 2^{-3})$$

and has the decimal value

$$4 + 2 + 0 + \frac{1}{2} + 0 + \frac{1}{8} = 6.625$$

This binary representation can equivalently be written as

$$0.110101_2 \times 2^3$$

where the binary point has been floated by multiplying the number 110.101_2 by 2^3 in the same way that we can float the decimal point in base 10 numbers.

Although we prefer to work in base 10, computers naturally operate in base 2 using binary floating point representations. In general, a computer stores the value of each binary floating point number in a fixed number of storage places called *bits*. Typically, this fixed number is 16, and these bits are divided into two groups in order to store the *mantissa* and the *exponent* in base 2 representation. For our example, the mantissa 0.110101_2, and the exponent $3 = 11_2$ could be stored as shown in Table 2.1.

Difficulty arises because not all real numbers can be exactly represented using this 16-bit scheme. Placing a storage limitation on the representation of real numbers forces a computer to occasionally round off a number to the nearest binary floating point number. A computer must always round off when representing irrational numbers such as $\sqrt{5}$, because the decimal representation does not terminate. The difference between the exact number and the rounded-off representation that results is called *roundoff error*. This roundoff error does not just occur with irrational numbers. It can occur with very simple whole numbers also. ROUNDOFF ERROR

In the next example, don't get wrapped up in the details of the calculations. Just follow along and you will get the point we're trying to make with regard to error: All computers generate some degree of error when faced with calculation.

Example 2.7. Consider the integer 300. In base 10, we can equivalently write 300 as 0.3×10^4. For a computer, a 16-bit base 2 representation of 0.3 is given by 0.0100110011001101_2, a number with only 16 digits past the binary point. However, an infinite-bit base 2 decimal representation of 0.3 is

$$0.0100110011\ldots0011\ldots$$

By limiting the number of binary digits to 16, we have introduced a roundoff error in the last binary digit. How big is the roundoff error? In this case, by subtracting the two quantities (infinite digit minus the 16-digit representation), we see that the error, or amount left unaccounted for, is

$$0.0000000000000000100110011\ldots0011\ldots_2$$

which is about 0.00000915527 in base 10. We usually do not know the roundoff error, but we do know that it is no bigger than the gap between the two possible values, which is $(1/2)^{16} = 1.52587 \times 10^{-5}$. Is this bad? Again, it depends on the individual problem.

Suppose in the case of an irrational number, such as $\sqrt{5}$ or π, we decide that we need only four digits past the decimal point. By simply stopping the stream of numbers at four digits, as opposed to rounding the last digit, we introduce what is called *truncation error* into our calculations. Obviously, if a particular number can be exactly represented by the number of digits we choose to use, then truncation error is not a problem.

Discussion Ideas

⇒ The choice to build computer microprocessors such as the Intel Pentium chip and the PowerPC chip using base 2 originates from the electronic device called the *transistor*. A transistor works like a gate for electric current. Either the gate is open, or it is closed. When it is open, current passes through the transistor unchanged, retaining its identity. So, a number "1" is used to represent the current being "on," or the transistor being "open." A "0" then represents the current being "off" and the transistor being "closed." A computer microprocessor is made up of many millions of these transistors. By working in base 2, which uses only 1's and 0's, computer scientists can then program operations, commands, and numerical representations in a way that these microprocessors are able to use. So, numbers are pretty straightforward to convert to base 2. But, what about letters of the English alphabet? And what about special characters such as &, $, and @? Computer keyboards have all these characters and more. Can you think of how programmers are able to get a computer to recognize these characters using base 2?

⇒ *Derive* uses an interesting variation called *approximate rational arithmetic* to perform numerical operations (see the *Derive* User Manual). All irrational numbers are approximated and stored as mentioned above. However, in **Exact** mode, rational numbers are not approximated, and as much memory as necessary is used to store rational numbers. Are there some rational numbers that could cause problems for this strategy? In what way? Is rounding still occurring, even with this approach?

ERROR
FROM
MEASURE

The last source of error we want to discuss is called *measurement error*. The name seems to imply that this error is introduced by the sloppy use of some instrumentation. Although that may be the case in some situations, it also happens through no fault of our own. Measurement error always occurs as a result of the fact that every measuring instrument is limited in accuracy and can never provide more than an estimate or approximation of some true value. Most of the time, this approximation is more than sufficiently accurate, such as in surveying roads, determining the distance between cities, taking body temperature, or tuning a musical instrument. We commonly weigh ourselves using a bathroom scale. Although the scale may indicate a certain number of pounds, this is certainly not our true weight. The difference between the reading on the scale and our true weight is due to measurement error caused by the manufactured precision of the scale.

As fast and powerful as modern computers are becoming, these three types of error can still exist in our calculations. However, faced with this situation, we like to be able to describe the amount of error present in an estimate or approximation because it influences how we interpret the results we get. There are two definitions we use to specifically identify the amount of error involved in problem solving.

Definition 2.1. Absolute Error. Letting X represent the measured value of some quantity, and X_T represent the true value of this quantity, then the *absolute error* is defined as

$$\text{absolute error in } X = |\text{ true value } - \text{ measured value }|$$
$$= |X_T - X|$$

Definition 2.2. Relative Error. Letting X represent the measured value of some quantity and X_T represent the true value of this quantity, then the *relative error* is given by

$$\text{relative error in } X = \left| \frac{\text{true value } - \text{ measured value}}{\text{true value}} \right|$$
$$= \left| \frac{X_T - X}{X_T} \right|$$

Notice that the numerical value of absolute error has the same units as the quantity being measured or approximated. For example, if the true value of the quantity we are interested in is 7.35 microns, and we measure 7.45 microns, then the absolute error is $|7.35 - 7.45| = 0.10$ microns.

Relative error, on the other hand, is *dimensionless*. That is to say, the units we are using to label the numerical value cancel in the expression for relative error. For this reason, relative error is usually expressed as a percentage. For example, the relative error of the same measurements noted earlier is given by

$$\left| \frac{7.35 \text{ microns } - 7.45 \text{ microns}}{7.35 \text{ microns}} \right| = \left| \frac{0.10 \text{ microns}}{7.35 \text{ microns}} \right|$$
$$= 0.014 \text{ or } 1.4\%$$

The distinction between these two measures of error is important. Of the two, relative error is more commonly used as an indicator of the quality of a particular measurement or approximation. This is because absolute error is insensitive to the size of the quantities being compared; it simply gives the absolute difference between the two quantities. To clarify this point, consider the wood-cutting and surgical example mentioned earlier. In both cases, say that we make an absolute error of 0.002 inches. For the case of cutting wood for a deck, suppose we needed a cut length of 48.5 inches (true length), and we cut to 48.498 inches. The relative error in the lumber cut is rather insignificant at 0.004 percent. However, suppose the length of the surgical cut required (true length) is 0.02 inches, and we have the same amount of absolute error, 0.002 inches. The relative error for the surgical cut is 10%, which is definitely not insignificant. The relative error indicates the true impact of error *relative* to the size of the measurements involved.

2.2   PLOTTING GRAPHS

If the increase in speed for numerical calculations and the ability to symbolically manipulate expressions were not enough to do the trick, then the ability to rapidly plot two- and three-dimensional curves and surfaces sealed the union of technology and mathematics forever. Visualization provides insights into problem solving in ways not readily available otherwise. Although both computers and graphing calculators possess the ability to produce the type of images that we are interested in, our bias is toward using computers to accomplish this task, primarily because of the power of mathematical software such as *Derive*.

In this section, we examine both discrete (not connected) point plotting and graphing of continuous curves and surfaces in *Derive*. *Derive* frees us from the repetitive tedium of hand-drawing graphs and plotting points, thereby allowing us to concentrate on analyzing the plots instead. Notice that we are not saying that we do not need to understand what *Derive* is doing when it so rapidly plots these surfaces. After all, it is mathematics that enables the software program to produce the plots. However, the nice aspect of letting the computer do all the drawing is that we need only a basic understanding of the Cartesian coordinate system to interpret the visual results.

2.2.1   Plotting

All computer plots are essentially plots of individual points that are connected with straight line segments. The more points used, consequently the smaller the connecting straight line segments, the better that curved surfaces appear. All computer screens are composed of discrete image boxes of fixed sizes, called *pixels*, that divide up the usable screen space. High resolution monitors possess a large number of very small pixels, and consequently give the curves and surfaces

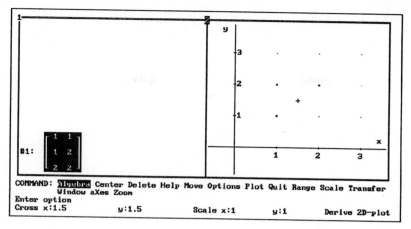

FIGURE 2.6
Plotting discrete data points in *Derive*.

plotted by software the appearance of smoothly connected objects. Low resolution screens, with a smaller number of larger pixels, leave the images more jagged. All images are really just strings of dots created by the pixels. Our eyes do not have the resolution to detect the actual pixels (more on our senses in Chapter 3).

In the computer environment, plotting lists of discrete points is quite a natural task. This is very fortunate for us, since we begin to attack a lot of the interesting problems we face in the real world by first collecting numerical information or *data sets* that are simply lists of numbers. Typically, we plot these data sets just to see what we are up against, and to check if the data sets exhibit any patterns that we can exploit. Much more on this later. Let's first examine how to plot lists of points in *Derive*, and then move on to plotting curves and surfaces specified by equations. In both cases, the software requires that we must first specify either the list of points, or the equation for the curve or surface prior to it producing a plot.

> **Example 2.8.** Let's start with a simple task. Suppose we have the following list of three points to plot: { (1, 1), (1, 2), (2, 2) }. In *Derive*, we can enter the list using the Author menu option, typing the expression [[1, 1], [1, 2], [2, 2]] using square brackets as shown. Individual points must be enclosed by these square brackets. We then plot this list of points using the Plot menu option. The *Derive* screen display for this is shown in Figure 2.6.

To plot a two- or three-dimensional curve represented by an expression, *Derive* previously required us to write the expression in terms of one variable, such

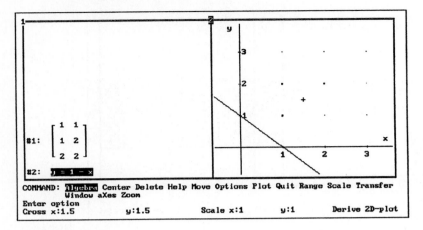

FIGURE 2.7
Continuous and discrete data plot.

EXPLICIT

as $y = (x+1)^2$, $p = \sqrt{d - y^2 + 5}$, or $z = 22y - x$. This form is called an *explicit* expression. Earlier versions of *Derive* would not plot an *implicit* expression of the form $x + y = 1$, but would plot its equivalent explicit expression $y = 1 - x$.[§] We prefer one form over the other for mathematical reasons that are best left unexplained for just a short while. Let's assume for now that our preference is to use explicit forms. In this particular case, we can **Author** either the complete equation $y = 1 - x$ or just the expression $1 - x$. If we plot this new expression without removing any of the other expressions that we previouly have plotted, *Derive* superimposes the new plot over whatever currently is plotted. Figure 2.7 shows the expression $1 - x$ plotted over the discrete list of points from the earlier example.

Sometimes we will not want to clutter up the plot screen with several different plots. However, having the capability to plot multiple expressions on the same screen is often extremely useful. The next example shows some of the possible uses.

Example 2.9. Suppose that we own and operate a factory that assembles and sells portable CD players. By analyzing financial data collected over the years,

---

[§]*Derive* version 3.0 will create implicit plots of the form $f(x, y) = 0$, where $f(x, y)$ represents an expression involving two variables, but they are typically very slow. It is still better to enter the expression in explicit form $y = f(x)$ or $x = f(y)$ by isolating one variable, and then plot the expression.

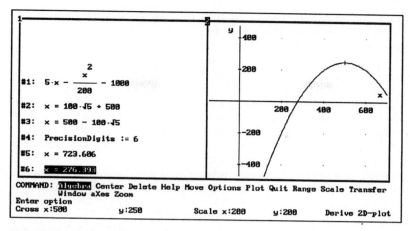

FIGURE 2.8
Profit function and maximum.

suppose that we determine that our profit can be predicted from the number of CD players we assemble and sell, according to the formula

$$P = 5x - \frac{x^2}{200} - 1000$$

where the variable P represents profit, and the variable x represents the number of CD players assembled and sold during a specific time period. In this case, let's assume that the time period is one year. Assuming that we do not want to make more CD players than we can sell, it would be helpful to identify the range of production that allows us to be profitable, and the production level that yields the most profit. So, let's call the goal of finding out this information our *research objective*.

Solution. The first step we take is to plot the profit equation to see what it looks like. In this case, notice that we have conveniently used an explicit expression involving the variable P isolated. This assumes that the values of P depend upon the values of x that are substituted into the right-hand side of the expression. To denote this dependency, let's use the notation $P(x)$, which will be shorthand for "P depends upon the variable x." Stated another way, the notation makes it clear that P is a *dependent* variable, and x is an *independent* variable. *Derive* plots the dependent variable on the vertical axis, and uses the horizontal axis for independent variables.

To get a useful perspective for viewing the curve, we change the menu selection Options, Scale until we get a satisfactory view. We can then use the *Derive* crosshairs to locate the point(s) where the curve crosses the x-axis. This is a visual approximation of the values. Since the vertical axis represents P, or profit, the portion of the curve above the x-axis indicates positive profit (this is good). The portion of the curve below the x-axis indicates negative profit, or loss (this is not so good). The points where the curve crosses the x-axis correspond to zero profit, and therefore also the roots of the profit expression. We could alternatively use the soLve menu option to find the same roots algebraically while in the algebra window. This would yield the same information as our visual technique using the crosshairs, within the preset precision.

For the second part of our research objective, "finding the production level that yields the most profit," we can again use the plot of the profit expression to get a visual approximation of this information. Moving the crosshairs to what appears to be the highest point of the curve, we can Zoom the screen in until we are satisfied that the cursor location accurately represents the maximum height.[¶] We can read the production level x that corresponds to this maximum profit value from the coordinates of the selected point displayed at the bottom of the *Derive* screen, as illustrated in Figure 2.8. So, we solved for the roots of the profit equation symbolically in the left window, and found the maximum profit information graphically in the right window. Note the scale used to obtain a useful perspective at the bottom of the *Derive* screen: $x : 200$, $y : 200$. (We used an old screen for this; the variable y is the same as P).

Our results indicate that the factory is profitable when we assemble and sell between $500 \pm 100\sqrt{5}$ CD players. Making a fractional number of CD players does not make sense in our problem. Rounding this result indicates that we should produce between 277 and 723 CD players to be profitable. The coordinates of the crosshairs on the graph in the right window is identified at the bottom left of the screen as $x = 500$, $y = 250$. This indicates that the graphically estimated maximum profit is $P = \$250$ when $x = 500$ CD players are produced.

In a later chapter, we will use actual historical data from a manufacturing plant to determine profit equations such as the one used in this example. Without giving too much away, we plan to do this by plotting the discrete data points on a graph and using *Derive* to find the curve that best describes, or *best fits* them. Using this fitted curve as the approximate profit expression, we can then repeat the process of determining maximum profit amounts that depend upon production levels. The nice thing is that the numerical, symbolic and graphical capabilities of *Derive* allow us to work real world problems with all their complexity. Otherwise, we would have restricted our attention to much simpler problems to accommodate hand calculations.

Exploration Exercises

2.1. Place each of the following six expressions in explicit form, and plot the resulting expression. For each of the expressions, assume that the research objective is to identify the approximate minimum and maximum value(s) the expression achieves, and its approximate root(s). If it is not possible to determine this information for a particular curve, explain why in your own words.

[¶]Be careful when using Zoom! Restricting the view of a curve can sometimes cause you to miss valuable information and lead you to an incorrect conclusion.

1. $y + 2x^2 - 2 = x^4$, over the interval $-1 \le x \le 1$
2. $q + 1 - x^3 = -x$, over the interval $-1 \le x \le 2$
3. $yx - x^2 = 2$, over the interval $1 \le x$
4. $r(k^2 + 1) = 4k$, over the interval $-4 \le k \le 4$
5. $y + 3 = x^4 + x$, over the interval $-2 \le x \le 2$
6. $y + 2x - 2 = x^4 - 2x^3 - x^2$, over the interval $-1 \le x \le 2$

2.2. *Revenue* is defined as the amount of money taken in by a company for doing what they do as a business. Their *costs* are the monies paid out by this same company in the course of doing business. The company's *profit* is the difference between its revenues and costs. In equation form, Profit = Revenues − Costs. Let x denote the level of production of the company. Assuming that revenue, cost, and therefore profit depend upon the number of items produced (x), we can express this profit equation as $P(x) = R(x) - C(x)$. For the revenue and cost expressions $R(x) = 9x$ and $C(x) = x^3 - 6x^2 + 15x$, with $x \ge 0$,

1. Determine what level of production (x) yields the greatest profit.
2. Plot both $R(x)$ and $C(x)$ on the same graph. Explain what their intersection point(s) indicate.
3. Write the two equations as a single equation $R(x) - C(x)$ and simplify the expression. Solve for the approximate roots of this new expression, and compare the values to the intersection point(s) previously determined.
4. If a particular set of equations $R(x)$ and $C(x)$ intersect, explain why there will exist roots to the expression $R(x) - C(x)$.

2.3. Repeat the previous exercise using $R(x) = 70x$ and $C(x) = x^3 - 6x^2 + 45/x$ with $x \ge 0$.

2.4. For the two profit expressions $P(x)$ used in the previous exercise, find their exact roots algebraically by using the *Derive* soLve menu option.

2.2.2   Change of variables

In the previous section, when we needed to get a more precise estimate for an extreme value of the curve (maximum or minimum), we could change the scale of the plot to zoom in on an appropriate region of the curve. This automatic *scaling* adjusts the distance between the axis tick marks displayed on a plot. It SCALING allows us to look in greater or less detail at a portion of a particular curve by zooming out or zooming in. When you first start using these automatic options to examine different aspects of a computer plot, you might be surprised by how the appearance of the plot changes as you increase or decrease the resolution.

This scaling effect can also be achieved using a mathematical technique called a *change of variables*, which has been around for quite a long time as a useful technique. By making a change of variables to alter the scale of a plot, none of the plot settings in *Derive* are changed. Prior to computers, this was the only way of accomplishing scale changes.

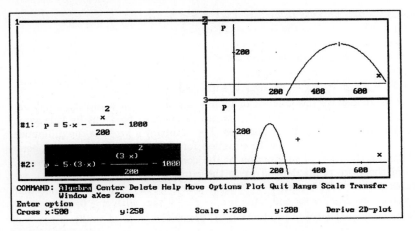

FIGURE 2.9
Scaling effects on the profit expression.

We can also shift the plot of a curve to the left, to the right, up or down on the screen using a slightly different change of variables, called a *translation*, which we will also explore. For convenience, we will drop the notation $P(x)$ temporarily, and return to using just P. Although it technically doesn't make a difference, at this stage of the book you might be more comfortable seeing a dependent-variable notation like that you have seen in earlier math courses. Later, we'll go back to using the other notation.

2.2.2.1   SCALING.

The basic idea of a change of variables is to substitute a new variable or a new expression for a specific variable wherever it appears in an expression. Substituting a new expression for an independent variable will change the reference units for a plot. For instance, if we substitute the new expression $3x$ for the independent variable x in the profit expression of Example 2.9, $P = 5x - \frac{x^2}{200} - 1000$, we cause an interesting effect. The portion of the plot between $[0, 1]$ after the substitution will cover as much detail as the plot between $[0, 3]$ in the original plot. The plot of the profit curve shrinks or contracts in the horizontal direction when we perform this type of change of variables. It is the multiplication by a number greater than 1 that is causing this contraction. The plot will contract even further if we substitute the expression $10x$ for x, or $30x$ for x. The next example illustrates this effect in more detail.

Example 2.10. Consider again the parabola given by

$$P = 5x - \frac{x^2}{200} - 1000$$

which is plotted in the upper right window of Figure 2.9 using the *Derive* scale settings $x : 200$, $y : 200$, as in Example 2.9. Line 2 of the algebra window displays the result of substituting $3x$ for x. To accomplish this substitution, we used the *Derive* menu options Manage, Substitute. The plot of this rescaled expression appears in the lower right window of the figure. Notice how the new plot is contracted horizontally.

So, if we perform a change of variables using a new expression that has multiplication by a constant greater than 1, we know that the resulting new plot will appear horizontally contracted if we plot the new curve on the same set of coordinate axes as the original plot. What would happen to the plot if we were to substitute a new expression that had multiplication by a constant *less* than 1, such as $x/3$ for x? Both of these substitutions involved the independent variable. What would happen if we were to perform a change of variables using the *dependent* variable? Does the resulting plot change in its horizontal appearance, or its vertical appearance? And is there a similar relationship that exists between the size of the multiplication constant used in a new dependent variable expression and the resulting plot effect as there was with the independent variable? Let's explore.

Exploration Exercises

2.1. Describe the effect that occurs when substituting a new expression that has multiplication by a constant less than 1 for the original independent variable. Try substituting the term $(x/3)$ for x in the original equation of Example 2.10. Verify your answer with an appropriate *Derive* plot. You may want to split the screen as we did just for convenience.

2.2. Here's your chance to try writing your own theorem. Specify your own rule that describes the effects on the plot of an expression when substituting constant multiples of the original independent variable. Your rule should cover three cases: when the multiplication constant is (1) less than 1, (2) equal to 1, and (3) greater than one. What assumption do you need to hold true for your rule to work? (*Hint*: the assumption is contained in the last paragraph before these exercises.)

2.3. Now for the dependent variable. Can you conjecture, or guess, what happens to the appearance of the original plot if we substitute the new expression $3P$ for P in the original profit expression of Example 2.10? Check to see if your conjecture was correct using *Derive*.

2.4. What effect is caused by using a multiplicative constant less than 1 in a change of variables substitution for a dependent variable? Again, use the original profit expression of Example 2.10 as an example.

2.5. Here's a chance to write your second theorem. Specify your own rule that describes the effects on the plot of an expression when substituting constant multiples of the original dependent variable. Again, your rule should cover three cases: when the multiplication constant is (1) less than 1, (2) equal to 1, and (3) greater than one. Does the same assumption used in your first theorem have to hold true for this rule to work?

2.6. Do your theorems still hold true if we were to allow *negative* constants as multipliers in the new expressions? Demonstrate your answer using examples.

2.7. Try to combine both of the theorems you specified into a single theorem. Then check to see if your new Change of Variables theorem is correct by substituting new expressions for *both* dependent and independent variables at the same time.

2.8. The previous exercise raises an interesting point: Does it matter whether we substitute new expressions for both dependent and independent variables simultaneously, or sequentially (one followed by the other)? In other words, is final plot resulting from a change of variables scaling dependent upon the order in which we perform the substitutions?

2.9. The fact that we were working with a quadratic profit expression motivates another question: Are the theorems you specified still valid if the original expression that you are working with is of higher order (cubic, quartic, etc.)? Demonstrate your answer using examples.

2.10. The fact that we were working with a quadratic profit expression motivates yet another question: What kind of effects result from the change of variable substitutions we used if the original expression was only first order?

2.11. Based on all your exploration, consolidate your findings into a single, concise rule that captures the effects of scaling by variable substitution in expressions.

2.2.2.2 TRANSLATION OF CURVES.

In the previous section, all of the effects of performing a change of variables resulted in either contractions or expansions of the original curve. What if we didn't want the curve to contract or expand, but simply wanted to shift its
TRANSLATE   location? Or, what if we want to have both effects happen at the same time, that is a contraction and a shift, or an expansion and a shift? For us to accomplish this, we need to be able to *translate* the plot of an expression.

Translating a curve involves adding a positive or negative amount the new expression we substitute using a change of variables. A translation of this type moves the original plot of an expression left or right, or up or down, depending on whether we substitute for the independent variable or the dependent variable.

So, for example, we could substitute the new expression $x + 3$, or $x - 10$ for the independent variable x in the original expression. Or we could substitute $P - 6$ or $P + 5$ for the dependent variable P in the profit expression $P =$

$5x - \frac{x^2}{200} - 1000$ we used as an example. Or, we could do both simultaneously, or one after the other. Does it matter? We will see soon.

If you check, you will notice that we left these options out of all the different effects you explored in the previous exercise set. But now, the door is wide open to examine all sorts of effects. Besides isolating the effects of performing a single translation, can we identify and control the effects of a change of variables using expressions that involve both multiplication by a constant *and* addition or substraction of some amount?

By following a pattern of exploration similar to that of the previous exercise set, you will have no problem identifying the various effects of translation. So, rather than bore you with repetition, we'll leave these ideas for discovery in the next set of exercises.

Exploration Exercises

2.1. Can you conjecture, or guess, the effect that occurs to the original plot by substituting the new expression $(x - 3)$ for x in the profit expression of Example 2.9? What about if you use the new expression $(x + 3)$? Check your answer using *Derive*. If your initial guess was incorrect, can you explain why your intuition might have led you to make a faulty conjecture?

2.2. Now, based on your experience with the previous question, make a conjecture about the effect that will occur by substituting the new expression $(P - 3)$ for P in the original profit expression. What about if you use the new expression $(P + 3)$? Verify your answer using *Derive*.

2.3. Does the size of the constant added to a new expression have a similar effect to that noted for multiplication? That is, with multiplication it matters whether the constant multiplier is less than 1 (expansion) or greater than 1 (contraction). Does translation ever change into some other effect?

2.4. Here's yet another chance to practice writing your own theorem. Specify your own rule that describes what happens to the original plot of an expression when substituting a new expression that has a constant added or subtracted from it.

2.5. In the theorem that you wrote in the previous exercise, do you need the assumption to hold that the new plot appears on the same set of coordinate axes as the original plot? Explain your answer and use some example plots to demonstrate.

2.6. As in the previous exploration exercise, we have the question: Does it matter whether we substitute new expressions for both dependent and independent variables simultaneously, or sequentially (one followed by the other)? In other words, is the final plot resulting from a change of variables translation dependent upon the order in which we perform the substitutions?

2.7. The fact that we used a quadratic profit expression motivates the same question as the earlier exploration with scaling: Is the theorem you specified still valid if the original expression is of higher order (cubic, quartic, etc.)? Demonstrate your answer using examples.

2.8. The fact that we were again using a quadratic profit expression motivates the question: What kind of effects result from the change of variable translation substitutions we used if the original expression was only first order?

Here is an important summary question involving scaling and translation using a change of variables: Do the operations of scaling and translating preserve algebraic relationships?

Suppose that the original profit expression is given by $P = x^2 + 3x - 9$. It is a fact from algebra that the equation: $4x - 8 = 2(2x - 4)$ is true. However, we can view this equation differently now that we have seen the change of variables technique.

We can think of the right hand side of this equation as a new expression being constructed first by a scaling and a translation $(2x - 4)$ then by another scaling $2(2x - 4)$; whereas, the left hand side is composed of a scaling and a translation $(4x-8)$. Algebraically, the result is the same. We can also verify that a resulting plot of both sides is also the same (you should check this). The question that needs to be answered is whether the final plot of the profit expression is the same regardless of the order in which we accomplish a change of variables: simply substituting the new expression $(4x - 8)$ directly for x in the profit expression $P = x^2 + 3x - 9$, or by first performing the scaling and translation substitution $(2x - 4)$ for x, and then performing the scaling substitution $(2x)$ for x. Intuition would seem to suggest that it does not matter. Is intuition correct? Is our answer still valid if we increase or decrease the order of the profit expression?

Before we depart this section, let's leave you with one practical example of why we might want know how to do translations. It's based on the idea that we generally try to simplify an expression that we are working with. Indirectly, it will set the stage for application ideas that we'll introduce in later chapters. We're tossing the idea out to you here as a tool for you to use as you see fit while you're working with the ideas of precalculus.

Example 2.11. We saw earlier that substituting the new expression $(x - 3)$ for x in the profit expression $P = 5x - (x^2/200) - 1000$ causes the original plot to shift to the right 3 units. Substituting $(P - 3)$ for P in the same expression causes the original plot to shift upward by 3 units. OK, but this understanding has us focused on how the plot of the expression moves from being centered on the point $(0, 0)$ to a new location 3 units up and 3 units to the right. Let's take another approach. And just to generalize things a bit for you, we'll use y instead of P for the dependent variable in the expression we are working with.

Suppose that the original plot of our expression was centered on the point $(4, 7)$ instead of $(0, 0)$. This means that the expression would initially look as if a substitution had already been performed:

$$y - 7 = 5(x - 4) - \frac{(x-4)^2}{200} - 1000$$

Does this look familiar? We typically arrive at an expression such as this after factoring an expression. It surely would be nice to be working with an expression that was centered on one or both of the axes if for no other reason than making our calculations simpler.

If we think not of shifting the plot of the expression from one location to another, but of *shifting the underlying axes* instead, we have exactly the concept we need!

Each x-coordinate needs to move to a new coordinate 4 units to the right: $\bar{x} = x - 4$, and each y-coordinate in the original plot needs to move to a new coordinate 7 units up: $\bar{y} = y - 7$. Taken together, we have accomplished what is known as a *translation of coordinates* into a new coordinate system in which each point is given by $(\bar{x}, \bar{y})$ using the translation relationships

$$\bar{x} = x - 4$$

$$\bar{y} = y - 7$$

If we substitute $\bar{x}$ and $\bar{y}$ for $(x - 4)$ and $(y - 7)$ where they appear in the factored expression, we get a much simplified expression

$$\bar{y} = 5\bar{x} - \frac{\bar{x}^2}{200} - 1000$$

to work with. The relationships noted above then provide a direct means of translating some results in the new $(\bar{x}, \bar{y})$ system back to variables in the original (x, y) system.

For example, the highest point achieved by the parabola in the $(\bar{x}, \bar{y})$ system is given by $(\bar{x}, \bar{y}) = (500, 250)$. In the original system, the highest point we are looking for is given by $x = \bar{x} + 4 = 500 + 4 = 504$, and $y = \bar{y} + 7 = 250 + 7 = 257$, or $(x, y) = (504, 257)$.

This idea of moving information between coordinate systems is one concept behind the mathematical idea of a *tranformation*, which you will see later in your education.

2.2.2.3   USING THE ZOOM.

A question naturally arises as to why we would use a change of variables for scaling changes instead of simply using the *Derive* Zoom plot menu option. The answer relates scaling to some of the error issues discussed previously. It also illustrates the strength of mathematics.

Example 2.12. In the trigonometric equation $y = \sin(1/x)$, as x gets very small, the fraction $1/x$ gets very large. The value of $\sin(1/x)$ varies rapidly between $y = -1$ and $y = 1$.

As we zoom in on the area around the point $(0, 0)$, the plot of $\sin(1/x)$ oscillates wildly.

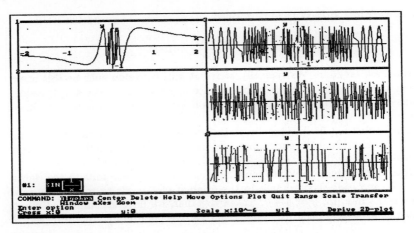

FIGURE 2.10
Effects of changing the horizontal scale.

Figure 2.10 shows a *Derive* display in which we have split the screen into five windows. Window 1 shows a plot of $\sin(1/x)$ with each x-axis tick mark equal to one unit. Window 2 displays the original expression. Window 3 has an x scale of 0.01 units per tick mark. Window 4 has an x scale of 0.0001 units per tick mark, whereas window 5 has 0.000001 units per tick mark. If the appearance of this *Derive* screen is different, it is because we have set Options Display to "small text" for convenience.

Since $y = \sin(1/x)$ represents a smooth curve, why do we see such an irregular, jagged curve being displayed? The answer is that three sources of error are present.

First, *Derive* uses a stepwise calculation, called an *algorithm*, to produce an approximate value for the expression $\sin(x)$. When x changes slowly, the error involved with the approximation changes slowly. When x changes rapidly, the approximation error changes rapidly. The expression $1/x$ changes *very* rapidly near the origin.

Second, as we continue to zoom in, we eventually are looking at points that are smaller than the limit of our machine arithmetic. This introduces the type of rounding and truncation error that we discussed earlier.

Third, *Derive* uses different levels of accuracy for plotting, which are selected using the menu options Options, Accuracy. If we select a level other than 9, the program does not compute every y value for each possible x value. Instead, it computes fewer (x, y) pairs, and connects them with line segments. Exactly how many points *Derive* needs to compute is determined by the accuracy level setting. This common scheme allows the CAS to save time when plotting points of smooth graphs, but can lead to disastrous error when it smoothes over important details actually present in curves whose surfaces vary rapidly and often.

The point to remember is that a graph on a computer screen is an approximation of the true graph of an expression. As mentioned earlier, the monitor screen is limited by both the resolution of the monitor and the accuracy of the algorithms used in the CAS. For most exploration purposes, we need not be concerned over these issues. Occasionally, however, we have to question whether we are pushing the limits of our machine capacity, and if we believe the picture we are seeing on the display. Fortunately, this situation does not arise frequently.

2.2.3 Limitations of CASs

Like any other computer program, a CAS will do only what we tell it to do. It will graph an equation; it won't tell us which equation to graph, what the graph means, or why it is important. It will find the root of an equation to a specified level of precision, but it is unable to communicate the significance of finding that root. It yields approximate values where appropriate, but won't tell us if the approximation is good enough for our purposes.

Additionally, each CAS possesses technical limitations that will occasionally concern us. We have already seen one example of a limitation of *Derive*; we will see more.

Computer algebra systems are wonderful tools that we can use to assist us in solving problems and visualizing new ideas. Once we determine that we should attack a problem with mathematics, we still must create expressions that describe the problem before we can use a CAS to explore possible solutions. This *modeling* process is the focus of the next chapter.

Derive can help us analyze the expressions we develop numerically, symbolically, and graphically. However, we are still left with the task of checking to see if our answers make sense. Moreover, we are very sensitive to making and checking assumptions that we make to create the expressions. Finally, we must effectively communicate our results to others, or all of our work may go down the drain.

The modeling process naturally highlights the abilities that a human brings to problem solving within our technologically changing environment. The modeling process is very much a human process. We translate observed real-world events into mathematical terms. We apply creativity in problem solving when choosing to use nonstandard techniques to analyze a problem. And, we must interpret and communicate the model's results in the end.

It is not difficult to invent examples where human insight has an advantage over raw computing power. We can imagine what the graph of $\sin(1/x)$ must look like in the vicinity of the origin, even if *Derive* can not plot it. We can notice patterns, make conjectures, and find rules of thumb that support further analysis; a CAS cannot. We possess imagination; even the best CAS does not. But, the combination of a human modeler and a CAS is an effective problem solving team.

2.3   SPREADSHEETS

Spreadsheets are another useful exploration tool. They are so commonly used in business today that being good at using a spreadsheet can actually help you find a job.

Like the CAS environment, most spreadsheets offer a similar set of capabilities. For reasons of economy and style, we used a combination of QuattroPro for Windows (QPW) and Excel in this book. However, any commercial software package such as Lotus 1-2-3, VisiCalc, or Symphony can easily be used to explore exactly the same ideas.

2.3.1   Overview

A spreadsheet is a tool designed for managing tables of data. Each worksheet is divided into boxes called *cells* that can contain data, formulas, or graphics. We can easily link calculations by referencing entries contained in other cells of the spreadsheet. We can also use either preset or custom designed formulas to create other table entries. Spreadsheets are very useful for organizing and analyzing large amounts of data, which explains their popularity in the business world.

Although CAS and spreadsheets complement each other for analysis purposes, they are two separate products for good reasons. A CAS is designed to be as fast and accurate as possible. Consequently, the user interface, or the input screen that we see while working in a CAS, is designed to accommodate computational routines in the best way possible.

Spreadsheets, on the other hand, have good subroutines for basic numerical calculations, but are primarily designed for excellent data handling. As a result, data entry is generally easier in a spreadsheet than in a CAS such as *Derive*, but we may sacrifice some power in the process.

Perhaps the most significant limitation of a spreadsheet is that it cannot perform symbolic manipulation of expressions. It performs numerical calculations well, and graphs these numerical results, but it is not designed to manipulate a symbolic formula. Consequently, if you needed to identify the general solution to a particular problem, you would either need to perform the calculation by hand or use a CAS such as *Derive*.

As we illustrate, spreadsheets have an advantage over *Derive* for multiple interrelated calculations because the manner in which formulas are specified allows for linking between cells. Because of these basic differences, the two software packages complement each other nicely.

Last, although spreadsheets have excellent graphing capabilities, they are designed around the philosophy of organizing and presenting data, and not with a focus on plotting accurate symbolic expressions, as is *Derive*. Spreadsheets and CASs are fundamentally different tools with different capabilities, and we exploit each for what it does best.

2.3.2   Tables

Let us revisit the example profit example used earlier in this chapter. Recall that the profit equation was given by

$$P = 5x - \frac{x^2}{200} - 1000$$

To illustrate how nicely a spreadsheet works, we'll use this equation to create a table of x values and P values for Excel to use as data points for the next example. QuattroPro has a similar feature called `Speedfill`.

Example 2.13. To generate values of x for use in the spreadsheet, let's generate x values between 0 and 1000 inclusively, using increments of 20. We could simply type a column of entries 0, 20, 40, 60, and so on, ending with the entry 1000. However, a labor saving feature of Excel is to use the menu options `Edit, Fill, Series` to do this automatically. We first enter the starting value of 0 in cell A2. Then, by selecting `Edit, Fill`, and entering the appropriate values in the dialog window, Excel automatically fills the data we need in the first column of the spreadsheet. This operation is illustrated in Figure 2.11.

We next enter the formula for P once only in a single cell, in this case the cell B2, in the second column.

By then selecting all of the cells in the second column that need this formula, starting with B2, we select the Excel option `Edit, Fill, Down`. Excel automatically copies the formula for the profit expression that we wrote to every cell in the second column that is highlighted. However, it does so with a cute twist that highlights its excellent data handling design.

The formula we typed into cell B2 is called a *relational* formula. This means it will apply the formula we entered relative to the cells that it is pointed at. In this case, we have the formula entered so that it is automatically pointing at the cell A2, which contains the x value it needs to compute a numerical result for P. We can see this in the formula for the highlighted cell that appears in the

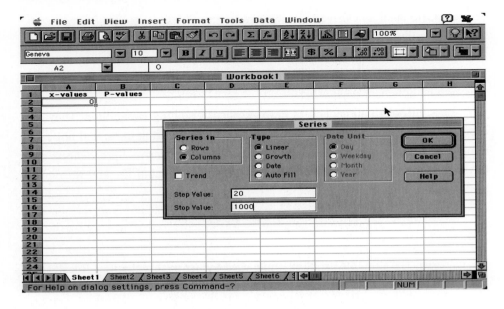

FIGURE 2.11
Spreadsheet Edit, fill menu option. Different versions of Excel will vary in appearance. However, the features remain the same.

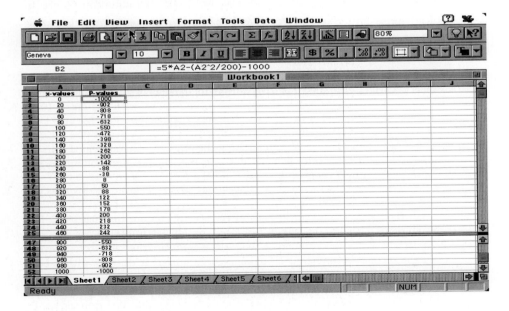

FIGURE 2.12
Relative linking of formula between cells.

formula bar at the top of the worksheet in Figure 2.12:

$$= 5 * A2 - \frac{A2^2}{200} - 1000$$

If we had highlighted the cell B3, the formula that would appear would be

$$= 5 * A3 - \frac{A3^2}{200} - 1000$$

And so on down to cell B52.

At this point, we have generated a table of (x, P) values. Since the screen was not large enough to show the entire data table, we split the screen using the scrollbar on the right. The profit P for a given x value is located immediately to its right. Maintaining data in a table such as this has advantages over the approach used in *Derive*, where it is necessary to input each separate x value to see the corresponding P value.

The relational ability of a spreadsheet to link cells is very powerful. It allows us to answer "what if" questions very quickly by simply changing a single cell's value, causing every cell that uses that location's value to subsequently change. The change ripples throughout the spreadsheet, allowing us to see how the change affects all the other quantities of interest that are linked to its value.

For precalculus and calculus, spreadsheets contain larger formulas known as *macros* representing a good deal of the standard calculations introduced in these courses. *Derive* adds the ability to symbolically manipulate the expressions defining these formulas.

2.3.3   Graphing

After we generate a table of values, such as the x and P values in Figure 2.12, we can use the spreadsheet to graphically display these points. Like *Derive*, Excel graphs expressions by plotting coordinate points and connecting these points using straight line segments. Unlike *Derive*, Excel does not automatically adjust the spacing of the points on the x-axis. It uses coordinate values, or tick GRAPHING marks, corresponding to those included in the table. If the x values that you are using are equally spaced, such as in the example we are using, this is not really a problem. Figure 2.13 shows a spreadsheet graph of the profit expression of Example 2.9, which we are approximating using the tabular values of x and P that we generated. Notice that it is a graph of 50 line segments, corresponding to 51 evenly spaced connected points.

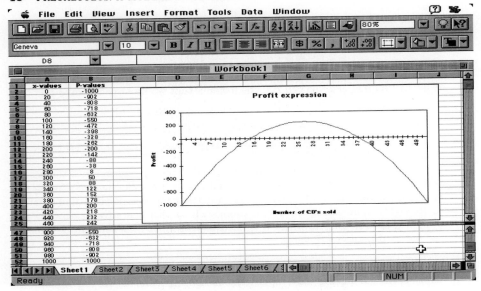

FIGURE 2.13
Graphing the profit expression.

If the x-value spacing varies, you could get an erroneous representation. To improve the representation of the data on a spreadsheet graph, we would have to adjust the points being used for the x-axis to be closer together.

Excel has many other useful automatic graphing capabilities that we mention in passing. It can combine several different sets of y values against the same x values on a single image. It can generate pie charts and histograms. It can also create 3-D graphs for effect. We may not make direct use of all of these capabilities in precalculus, but they are nice to have available if the need arises, such as for making presentations in other courses.

2.4 ADVANCED SCIENTIFIC CALCULATORS

An advanced scientific calculator (ASC) is a calculator that offers graphing, symbolic manipulation, and a wide range of preprogrammed formulas for performing numerical calculations. Many ASCs have customized menus for different applications, and are capable of being programmed by a user to perform more complicated mathematical operations.

2.4.1 Overview

There are far too many ASCs to list, but we will mention a few of the more popular manufacturers. The HP48 and HP28 series of calculators offered by Hewlett-Packard are indicative of the current generation of ASCs. They offer graphing capabilities, extensive menus, and sophisticated programming abilities. The TI-92, which resembles a miniature computer display, has *Derive* for Windows programmed onto it, and is very powerful. Casio also makes an excellent line of powerful ASCs.

ASCs are compact, very portable, relatively inexpensive, and powerful. Largely because of their compactness, most ASCs require training in order to master their capabilities. Their viewing windows for graphics and expressions are limited. Whereas the typical number of pixels on a computer monitor might be 640×480, the older HP28S has 32×137 pixels. The new HP48SX has an improved resolution at 64×131. Technological advances in liquid crystal displays since the writing of this book may have increased ASC graphical resolution even further.

Many schools find these calculators a good choice because of their power and low cost. They have a high "bang-for-the-buck." It's reasonable to ask students to purchase a calculator for \$80–\$150, whereas it may be unrealistic to expect every student to purchase a computer. For this reason, schools usually create computer laboratories for complicated graphical exploration and rely on calculators for the bulk of scientific calculation.

2.4.2 Graphing and symbolic calculations

Graphing calculators offer most of the advantages of graphing found in *Derive*, subject to the limitations of screen size, screen resolution, and processing time. They can plot multiple expressions at the same time, and can perform changes of scale and translations to support a "best" view for a particular graph of an expression.

The ability to perform symbolic calculations varies among ASCs, with the TI-92 being comparable to the computer version of *Derive*, whereas others are slightly less capable. The older HP28S, for example, will perform symbolic operations, but cannot easily simplify its answer into a standard format that is customary in mathematics.

Example 2.14. The symbolic expression

$$(x + 2) * (x + 3) * x$$

returns the result

$$x * x * x + 2 * x * x + (x * 3 * x + 2 * 3 * x)$$

after 4 iterations of the EXPAN (expand) command, and

$$x^3 + 5 * x^2 + 6 * x$$

after one iteration of the COLCT (collect) command.

Symbolic division on the HP28S is also limited. The same expression divided by $(x - 1)$ yields

$$\text{INV}(\text{INV}(5 * x^2 + x^3 + 6 * x) * x - \text{INV}(5 * x^2 + x^3 + 6 * x))$$

instead of the more customary expression

$$x^2 + 6x + 12 + \frac{12}{x - 1}$$

Nevertheless, ASCs possess the requisite capability for symbolic manipulation, and their resulting expressions, albeit awkward, can still be subsequently plotted and manipulated.

2.5   SUMMARY

The tools that are available to support exploration in precalculus are very powerful, and who knows what the future brings. They currently offer us the means to discover mathematics in a much more interesting and intellectually appealing context. Fifty years ago, these tools were beyond the imagination of most mathematicians. Today's challenge to students and teachers is to use these tools to work efficiently, and to focus more on developing tasks best performed by humans. CASs, spreadsheets, and ASCs go a long way to removing the drudgery of computation from mathematics, freeing us to explore and discover.

Exploration Exercises

2.1. In Example 2.4, we derived the quadratic formula to find the symbolic roots of $ax^2 + bx + c = 0$. Use *Derive* to find the symbolic roots of $ax^3 + bx^2 + cx + d = 0$.‖

‖This expression is complicated, as we will see, which is why we have not encountered a

2.6 COMPLEMENTS

The resources listed are inexpensive, comprehensive sources for the history of mathematics. They are accessible to a student of precalculus, and are quite detailed in their treatments of the subjects. In addition, they provide numerous references for each of the topics that they address.

1. This book provides a decent coverage of the development of mathematics from its earliest years, and includes many of the contributions made by mathematicians of the 18th and 19th centuries.

   * *History of Mathematics*, 2 vols, by David E. Smith. Dover Publications, Inc., New York, New York, 1958.

2. This reference provides a very detailed coverage of the development of early mathematics in Babylonia and Egypt.

   * *A Concise History of Mathematics*, 4th edition, by Dirk J. Struik. Dover Publications, Inc., New York, New York, 1987.

3. An excellent book on the history of the concept of numbers and how it has changed with society, which is both facinating and easy to read is

   * *Number: The Language of Science*, by Tobias Dantzig. The Free Press, New York, New York, 1954.

4. A good reference book to keep available for classroom use is

   * *The VNR Concise Encyclopedia of Mathematics*, by Gellert, Küstner, Hellwich, and Kästner, eds. Van Nostrand Reinhold, New York, New York, 1975.

---

cubic formula in algebra, as we have the quadratic formula. The original discovery of methods of solving for the roots of a general cubic equations is attributed to mathematicians at the University of Bologna in Italy, and Professor Scipio del Ferro (died 1526) in particular. Their method was kept secret until 1545 when a Milanese doctor named Hieronimo Cardano, privy to the secret, improved the method and published his results, much to the disgust of the Bolognese. With *Derive*, we can replicate one of the celebrated achievements of medieval mathematics!

CHAPTER 3

MODELING CONCEPTS

It is here (in mathematics) that the artist has
the fullest scope of his imagination.

Havelock Ellis

Chapter Goals

⇒ Understand the origins of math models.

⇒ Understand the mathematical modeling process.

⇒ Identify dependent and independent variables from a problem description.

Although there are a number of different ways of interpreting what models are, all models serve as a means of organizing information in a useful form. This is true regardless of whether the model is a flowchart, a poem, a reduced-scale model of an aircraft, or some mathematical expression. Our brains seek order, and models provide it.

A language, such as English, is a model that represents and expresses what we experience, what we are thinking, and what we observe in the world around us. The English language, for example, has its own symbols (the alphabet), and grammar rules for constructing sentences (expressions) in a logical fashion.

Mathematics is also a language. It has its own symbols, rules for building expressions, and logic structure that we use to describe, predict, and/or control the world around us. Mathematical models are an organized representation of something that we want to analyze using the tools of mathematics.

In this chapter, we begin our study of a natural way of creating mathematical models called the *modeling process*, which provides a framework we will use MODELING to examine the mathematical ideas in later chapters. We use a five-stage pro- PROCESS cess based on what we see in the real world: the evolution through *mess, model, solution, analysis*, and *report*. Faced with a mess, we identify and focus on a particular problem, build a math model, solve the model, analyze our results, and communicate our our interpretation of the results in the most effective means possible.

Mathematical models consist of a set of variables together with relation- MATH MOD-ships that bind the variables together. Taken as a whole, a model attempts to ELS accurately represent something in the real world. The relationship between the variables doesn't have to be a cause-and-effect relationship, although many that we will examine will make this assumption.

In this chapter, we focus on identifying and classifying variables that influence our models. The next chapter introduces a very special type of relationship between variables that will carry us through the remainder of the book, called a *functional relationship*. The remainder of the chapters of the book explore various types of functional relationships used in mathematical modeling. This sets the stage nicely for the study of calculus.

3.1   MESSES AND MODELS

Problem solving begins when we are confronted by a *mess*. This mess is typically a mish-mash of confusing information, poorly gathered facts and data, and conflicting opinions. We need to convert this mess into a properly formed problem statement. A problem, in the form that you are accustomed to seeing, is a mess that has been analyzed, filtered, and organized into something that makes sense. These problems are what we find in a typical mathematics book, where all the information we need, and the only information that we need, is presented neatly

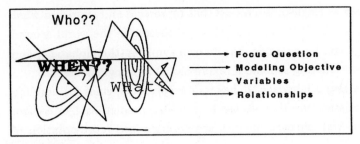

FIGURE 3.1
A modeler is confronted by a *mess*. From this mess, the modeler extracts a focus question, modeling objective, variables, and mathematical relationships.

and in order. More important, the question that we need to solve is identified for us.

How do we become aware of messes? Sometimes, it's subtle. We gradually get the feeling that things are not going well. Our manufacturing facility may not be making money, workers may be starting to go off to other jobs, the quality of our products may be decreasing in some way, our grade point average (GPA) may be slipping, or our customers may not be as enthusiastic as they once were.

Other times, the signs of a mess are more dramatic: Our airplanes start crashing, stock prices plummet, employees go on strike, our laboratory burns.

In each case, our challenge is to wade through the mess and identify a problem. And, the problem may not be obvious from the symptoms that we observe. What is at the heart of the mess? What is the precise thing that concerns us? Quality? GPA? Money loss?

RESPONSE   In mathematical terms, this central item is called a *response*. The factors that influence this response, either directly or indirectly, are commonly called PREDICTORS *predictors*. The predictors act as input factors for the response, influencing the observed value of the response. As the values of the predictors change, the response changes as a result.

> **Example 3.1.** As you undoubtedly know, fast food is considered a staple of the American lunch diet for students. We could argue that a meal of hamburgers, chicken nuggets, french fries, milk, and sodas does provide a certain amount of nutritional benefit while adding to our intake of not-so-good food components. The question is: what's the trade off? Is there some amount of fast food that we can munch without significantly risking our health, following the recommendation of "everything in moderation"?
>
> We should be able to create a mathematical model that will help us find reasonable answers to these questions. We first have to figure out what information we need to identify, and then build a model that will allow us to get at

it. It appears that we could pick any one of several different quantities to use as a response: the total amount of calories, the total amount of cholesterol, the percent of saturated fats, or the total amount of specific vitamins provided. Each of these quantities is recognized as representative of our physical well-being and is measurable.

The appropriate predictor(s) we pick will depend upon our choice of response. If we used the total amount of calories as the response, we could construct various combinations of the foods noted, and use the information on how many calories each food type contributed to the specific lunch as the predictors of the model. If we chose the total amount of saturated fats as the response, we could let our predictors represent the amount of saturated fats each food type contributed to the lunch meal.

Both the response and the set of predictors we pick become variables in our math model. The value that the response takes on depends on the values of the predictors. This is why it is also called a *dependent variable.* Since we can pick the value of the predictors individually, without relying on the value of the other predictors, they are referred to as *independent variables.*

DEPENDENT VARIABLE

INDEPENDENT VARIABLE

For the discussion of this chapter and most of this book, we limit our attention to identifying a single response. This will allow us to focus on a straightforward relationship between the predictors and the response. As you will see in Chapter 6, multiple responses are possible when we build models of systems.

Example 3.2. If the response that we were interested in was, say, a good cup of mocha java, some of the predictors we might use in a mathematical model of this beverage would be type of coffee bean, time of brewing, amount of sugar, type of milk, and temperature of the water. These predictors interact to affect the response we are tasting. They are linked to the response in a way such that changes in these predictors will change the response. Since we can control these predictors, they would become independent variables in our model, whereas the "good cup of mocha java" would be the response.

The art in modeling comes in defining a useful set of variables, and then expressing relationships between them. Very simply put, when the relationship between the variables is mathematical, our model is a mathematical model.

3.1.1   The effect of assumptions

All models are simplifications of the real world. With mathematical models, simplification results from having to make various assumptions to create the model. Sometimes, these assumptions are necessary if we hope to ever solve the model. This is known as keeping the model formulation mathematically *tractable.*

There is a good chance that these kinds of assumptions, once made, will stay with the model permanently.

In other situations, we make simplifying assumptions to just get an initial working model. Later, we hope to discard these assumptions, as we refine our initial model into a more complete representation of the problem we are interested in.

> **Example 3.3.** Suppose that we were assisting an automobile manufacturer who is deciding how many of each type of automobile to make to obtain the greatest amount of profit from sales. We might initially assume that the number of automobiles can be fractional in our model, even though this simplifying assumption doesn't match reality (What exactly is three-fourths of a car?). This assumption simplifies the problem because it allows us to use a model with continuous variables, as opposed to integer ones. Later, after verifying that our initial model works, we can discard or revise this assumption to more accurately represent the real world production process.

Assumptions have an interesting impact on how we interpret model results. Each assumption adds another layer of abstraction between reality and the model. This means that, with each new assumption we make, the model results move farther away from reality. We must interpret any results we obtain from a model with our assumptions in mind.

Assumptions cause us to make statements such as: "Given that assumption A is true, our model indicates . . ." They also cause us to investigate the possibility that the assumptions do not hold. This is one of the motivations for our actions during the analysis stage of the problem solving process.

> **Example 3.4.** Suppose that we were to try to build the fast food nutritional model for eating hamburgers, chicken nuggets, french fries, and a soda or milk using the the total amount of saturated fats as the response. We would have to make several assumptions for the model's results to make sense.
>
> First, we would probably assume that the meal we were constructing was a lunch meal, because it is the most likely meal to be consumed by students at a fast-food restaurant. Ok, we also know some folks who like chicken nuggets for breakfast, but let's go with the vast majority here.
>
> Second, if we were going to use the "per serving" nutritional information provided by the restaurant, we would have to assume that each individual food (e.g., each hamburger) possessed the specified amount of saturated fat regardless of the location of the restaurant or the time of day that the food was made; no more, no less. This assumption might be a source of error if we were actually going to measure the amount of saturated fats in a person's blood stream as a result of eating these foods, since, in reality, no two hamburgers will be exactly alike. However, since we are not, we are probably safe using this assumption.

FIGURE 3.2
Good models are valid, credible, and adaptable.

Last, we would probably assume that each food added to the total amount of saturated fats for the meal in an additive manner. That is to say, two individual meal components (e.g., a hamburger and a medium french fries) do not experience some chemical reaction when digested that causes their saturated fats to combine in such a way that the sum of the two individual totals is more or less than the combined amount in a person's system.

The degree to which the results obtained from a mathematical model are sensitive to changes in assumptions is called the *robustness* of the model. A very robust model allows us to discard or alter several assumptions without significantly affecting the results.

3.1.2 Model characteristics

Models can be evaluated in terms of several general characteristics that help to define their usefulness. The three most common are:

1. VALIDITY. Does what the model predicts or describes agree with what actually happens in the real world?
2. CREDIBILITY. How believable are the model's results?
3. ADAPTABILITY. Can the model be applied and extended to new situations, both similar and dissimilar?

A model can be valid without being precise. Many simple models attempt to capture trends, and it may be enough to know, for example, that more money spent on advertising does or does not increase sales. Or, that the stock market will or will not go up on a certain day. In both these cases, it is not necessary to know precisely how much sales will increase or the market will go up to make use of the model, knowledge of the trend is sufficient.

A credible model, whose results are believable, has a higher likelihood of actually being used. Unfortunately, models can be credible without being valid. This usually results in bad decisions being made. One rather unfortunate example

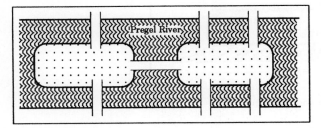

FIGURE 3.3
The bridges of Könisberg.

credible
models

of this was the treatment model from the Middle Ages that called for bleeding people who were suffering from disease: Weakening due to loss of blood did little to fight the disease, and frequently resulted in the early dispatch of the person. A second, less threatening example was the once widely believed geocentric model of the universe, which said that the sun, other planets, and stars all revolved around the earth.

The credibility of a model often depends on the reputation of the modeler and the quality of the way that its results are presented—the fifth stage of our process for solving problems.

Sometimes, the usefulness of a model is limited to a very small number of problems. Such a model would not be very adaptable, since adaptable models find wide use outside of their original settings. Here is an example of a model that has proven to be very adaptable.

> **Example 3.5.** In 1736, Euler was asked if it were possible to cross each of the seven bridges of Könisberg once and only once during a walk through the town. Figure 3.3 shows a simplification of the layout of the bridges and the surrounding town of Könisberg. After creating a mathematical model of the problem, Euler proved that the required solution was impossible. (Give it a try!)

The model that Euler originally developed was adapted to describe the best routing for a salesman to take to cover his territory, and has come to be known as the *traveling salesman problem*. This model has been applied to many routing problems from computer network design, to telephone networks, to emergency search problems.

Adaptable models can save us a lot of work if we recognize that the problem we are faced with can be solved using an existing model that we can change to meet our needs.

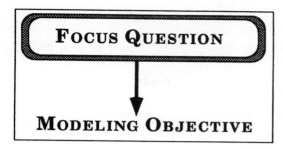

FIGURE 3.4
The focus question produces the modeling objective.

> **Example 3.6.** If we were to actually build the model of fast-food nutrition mentioned earlier, we could use the same model to analyze the nutritional benefits of eating pizza, dining at some great restaurant, or any other situation involving one of the responses noted. We could probably even use this model to examine the nutritional benefits of the food that we serve our cats and dogs, although we hope the food types would be different!
>
> This particular model would be very adaptable because it can be applied to a lot of different situations. If we based our model on the nutritional content information provided by the food manufacturers, we would consider it to be a credible model. Finally, if we used the proper nutritional data, and actually ate food in the combinations that we selected (and not, say, 1000 hamburgers for lunch), the model would be valid, since it would represent what actually occurs in the real world.

3.2 FOCUS QUESTIONS AND MODELING OBJECTIVES

We sort of took a short cut in the previous sections by introducing the idea of a response and predictors straight away. We did this because it sets the stage for us to now take a step backward to the actual first step in the modeling process and introduce it in a setting where you already have seen its impact.

The mathematical modeling process actually begins with a simple observation of something that demands our attention. Usually, this attention-getter takes the form of a question such as "I wonder why that happened?" or "Is there a better way of doing this?" or "Can I make more money doing this?" This FOCUS question forms the basis for our investigation. It the first step taken to turn a QUESTION mess into a model. We call this question a *focus question*.

> **Example 3.7.** For the fast-food nutritional model, the focus question was posed as: Is there some amount of fast-food that we can munch without significantly risking our health, following the recommendation of "everything in moderation"?

Of all the possible models that we could build concerning hamburgers, chicken nuggets, french fries, and soda or milk, this question points us in the direction of creating a model that looks at the nutrition of the food. Trying to answer this focus question lets us identify the type of information that our model must provide, thus guiding the identification of a response and associated predictors.

As an aside to illustrate how the focus question effects the rest of the modeling process, consider if we were to have asked the question: "I wonder how many hamburgers, chicken nuggets, and french fries a person can physically eat in a single lunch meal?"

For a really big mess, we might develop a long list of possible focus questions. From this list, we select one to work with. In some books, this step is also known as *identifying the problem*. But, regardless of its label, this focus question

MODELING
OBJECTIVE

allows us to form a *modeling objective*, which is a clear statement of what we want our model to do.

We develop all models with some objective in mind. Whether this modeling objective is to develop a tool to describe an earthquake, predict the behavior of some investment company to make a billion dollars in the stock market, assign students to class schedules, or simply to answer a question of curiosity, it provides a guide for our modeling effort.

Modeling objectives usually include one of the following verbs: *describe*, *predict*, *control*, or *optimize*.

Example 3.8. We are observing an ant colony building a nest, and we decide to model this activity. What are some of the focus questions and modeling objectives associated with this mess?

One focus question might be: "What factors affect how long it takes the ants to build the nest?" The modeling objective would then be to identify the main predictors (variables) that affect the time to build a nest (response), and to *describe* the relationship between the predictors and response.

A second focus question might be: "How many times, on average, does one ant interact with the rest of the colony during the construction of the nest?" Again, we identify a response (what do we mean by interaction?), and the appropriate predictors to *describe* the interaction of ants.

A third focus question might be: "Why are they building a nest in my closet?" From this question, we might want our model to be able to *predict* the likelihood that the ants will build their nest in a certain spot, based on the predictors that we identify and the relationship between the predictors and response. We might even be able to *control* the ant's activities by changing the values of the predictors.

Each of the focus questions in the previous example helps us to begin to identify responses and predictor variables. Exactly which factors we identify is

FIGURE 3.5
Ants building a nest. Different observers would have different focus questions, which would lead to different modeling objectives.

very dependent upon the focus question asked, and results in different modeling objectives.

> **Example 3.9.** Suppose that we are watching an assembly line on a factory floor of a manufacturing plant. This particular assembly line takes electronic printed circuit boards (PCBs) and installs different electronic devices on the board such as microprocessors, memory chips, capacitors and resistors. The finished product is called a *motherboard*.
>
> At the end of the assembly line is a machine that samples and tests each of the completely assembled motherboards.
>
> Examining the rejection bins, we notice that there are quite a few defective boards being produced. Out on the plant floor, we further notice that most of the people working on the line seem rushed to perform the tasks they need to accomplish to meet the company's production goals.
>
> One focus question that our observation generates could be: "Is it possible to improve the quality of the assembly process so that the number of defective motherboards decreases?" Another might be "Is it possible to distribute the tasks in a different manner, use automation, or reengineer the entire process to allow the assembly line workers more time for specific tasks?"
>
> Using the first focus question, our attention would focus on aspects of the assembly line that contribute to defects. The response would be a measure of quality, and the predictors would be the factors that we speculate are affecting the number of defective motherboards. We could save other aspects of the assembly line operations for later consideration. Our modeling objective would be to *control*

the number of defective motherboards.

The second focus question is much broader in scope. It might lead us to examine several larger aspects of assembly line operations, such as job satisfaction. In this case, the amount of job satisfaction would be the response, and the factors that contribute to job satisfaction would be the predictors. Our modeling objective might be to *maximize* the amount of time available to a worker.

Discussion Ideas

Consider the following situations:

1. A car passes by with huge boom speakers blaring

2. The best wine produced in Napa Valley, California

3. A deep pothole in the road

4. A chicken on the other side of the road from the chicken coup

5. A collapsed automobile bridge over a river

6. A melted stick of butter on a kitchen counter

7. A coronary heart attack in a person

8. A good cup of tea

9. A pimple that appears on the end of your nose

10. A cat that runs in a circle exactly twice then jumps straight up into the air

11. A well-thrown football

12. An epidemic of tuberculosis

13. A curve ball thrown in a baseball game

14. A sonic boom from an aircraft is heard

15. SAT scores improve by 22% at your local high school

16. Tires lose traction on the road during a heavy rainfall

17. A ski jump competition during the Olympics

For each situation,

⇒ Identify a focus question that could be used to start building a mathematical model of the observation.

⇒ What modeling objective would most likely follow from the focus questions you identified?

⇒ What would you select as the response for your model? Can you assign a numerical value to the response? Is it measurable already, or are you going to have to come up with some creative way of measuring the response?

⇒ What would you select as the predictor(s) for your model? Check to make sure that, for each of the predictors you identify, the response will change if the value of a predictor changes.

⇒ Discuss how you might measure the validity, credibility and adaptability of a model that met your modeling objective.

⇒ Assume that your model was successful in achieving your modeling objective. What difficulties would you anticipate if you had to convince someone to use your model? Do you think that your education and background would have an influence on the credibility of your model? Should it?

3.3 MORE ON SELECTING VARIABLES

For any given mess that we are faced with at the start of our modeling process, there are far too many things capable of being measured than we can ever practically consider for use in our model. Thankfully, the focus question we pose helps to narrow the possibilities somewhat, and the modeling objective further refines the scope of our model. Out of all the remaining factors to pick as variables, we want to select a manageable set to initially work with.

As stated earlier, our first goal is to select a response variable, which is the problem characteristic we wish to describe with our model. Following that, we select a set of predictor variables that we think are influencing the response. This is the pattern that we followed in the fast-food nutritional example earlier.

3.3.1 Responses

Identifying a response to use as the dependent variable of a model is typically not difficult once we gain a basic understanding of the initial mess we are faced with. The focus question we pick and modeling objective that we derive from it both drive the selection of the response for our model.

In Example 3.8, we listed three possible focus questions stemming from observing a colony of ants building a nest. What are the possible response variables for each focus question?

> **Example 3.10.** The first focus question asks about how long it takes the ants to build the nest. Here the response is pretty clearly measured in units of time. However, what period do we wish to address? Do ants ever finish building a nest? If so, how will we identify the finish point? When do they start? Once we answer these questions, we can define our response variable precisely as the time between the start of the nest building and its completion.

> **Example 3.11.** The second focus question asks about the number of interactions between one ant and the rest of the colony during the construction period. Here we need to define what we mean by an "interaction." Does it mean physical contact? Does it mean communicating by scents and markings (pheromones)? Do we mean working together? Also, how can we measure if an interaction occurs, especially within the nest?
>
> This response may be harder to define, and it may be difficult to collect the data that we would need. Without measured data, we may never be able to know the validity or adaptability of a model based on this response.
>
> These concerns may cause us to refine our modeling objective, and to focus on the number of occurrences of some specific *observable* ant behavior for a response. One possibility might be the number of times a randomly chosen ant touches another ant while on the surface of the nest.

> **Example 3.12.** The third focus question asks why the nest was built in my closet. Here, there seems to be an element of chance involved. One possible response might be the probability that an ant colony is built in a given location. Of course, determining probabilities presents its own challenge, as they require long-term averages to properly measure. If we had lots of data, defining this response might be easier.

These examples are meant to illustrate that some care is needed in selecting a response. Although the characteristic or behavior that we want to select seems to best answer the focus question and achieve the modeling objective, it may not be observable as a response. Our intention is to build a mathematical model that we can use as a workbench, changing the value of the predictors and watching how the response behaves. If the response can't be observed, it is very difficult to compare the model's results with the real-world event, a necessity for validating the model. Worse yet, those factors or behaviors that are observable may not be helpful for answering the focus question. A certain amount of art, skill, and experience are required; compromises may need to be made.

3.3.2 Predictors

As was illustrated in the previous examples, we next attempt to identify all the factors that might be influencing the response variable. We can accomplish this task either by brainstorming, by considering another model that may be transferable to our problem, or by analyzing historical data. In the fast-food example, we presumably had enough experience with food and nutrition to be able to identify some predictors immediately. This will not always be the case. In any event, our goal is to develop as complete a list as possible, recognizing the limits of our understanding of the event.

There is a potentially huge number of predictors we could include in any model. Some judgement is initially required to select a starting set that is broad enough to capture all the possibly useful predictors, but small enough to be manageable. We know that by saying this we're highlighting a downside of being a neophyte modeler: Judgement comes from experience and from knowledge of the event that we are attempting to model. So, if you have a limited amount of either quality, then the creating a math model is a little more challenging. But, we all have to start somewhere, so let's continue.

Once we have an initial list of possible predictors, we select those we will include in the first cut for our model, setting aside other possible predictors for later consideration. Often, we'll start with a single predictor that we either suspect is the most influential or important, or that will be the easiest to gather information about.

The influence of our past education and experience in identifying predictors is best illustrated by the next example.

Example 3.13. Suppose that we visit a local hospital accompanied by a physician and an engineer. Suppose that both the physician and the engineer were to observe the same patient who is ill. They could both form the same focus question: "What is causing the patient's illness?"

Although the engineer may have a good degree of practical experience in coping with illness, she may not have been trained to observe the type of characteristics effecting the illness that the physician has. The physician and the engineer would probably select different sets of predictors.

This is not to say that either person's experience is better than the others. It's just that the usefulness of a person's education and experience depends upon the situation they find themselves in. To make the point, the physician's list of predictors might not be as comprehensive as the engineer's if they were both observing the same cracking in a large office structure's foundation, or deformation of a bridge's steel infrastructure.

As math modelers, when we are not familiar with the details and workings of the original mess we are faced with, we find ourselves performing a good deal of background research to better understand the problem's environment.

Discussion Ideas

⇒ The manner in which we go about selecting our list of predictors for a given situation has the potential to vary dramatically between individuals. Should we attempt to create a standard approach for everyone? What would we gain or lose by doing so?

⇒ Consider yourself to be a mathematician. If you were given the opportunity to form a team of three people (including you) to model each of the situations that follow, what other experts would you pick to have on your team? Why? What type of background would they need to have? How might their background experience and education bias the way they perceive each situation? Could you use this bias to your team's advantage?

1. Designing the national Advanced Placement Calculus test
2. Determining how much time a person would have to wait after consuming alcoholic beverages to be sure that they were operating a motor vehicle within the limits of the law
3. Building a World Wide Web site to help diabetics plan their daily diets
4. Tracking the migration of sea lions along the western coast of the United States
5. Identifying remote villages in the Amazon jungle using satellite imagery
6. Building small robots capable of going over very rough terrain
7. Determining where to pre-position police officers to respond to crime in neighborhoods
8. Assessing the amount of environmental damage an oil spill caused in Valdez, Alaska
9. Tracking the amount of drug traffic across the U.S.–Mexico border
10. Determining which telephone long-distance carrier to use
11. Containing an outbreak of the virus Ebola Zaire in Reston, Virginia
12. Setting up a small business in your house
13. Designing the traffic flow controls for the city hosting the 2000 Summer Olympic Games
14. Designing a national health care plan (If you figure this one out, you might want to send your thoughts to someone in Congress.)

⇒ How do the classes you have taken to date influence your selection of predictors? What are the sources of your individual biases?

⇒ In order to identify predictors, they have to be able to be detectable by our senses. Pick one of the modeling situations listed above, an consider each of the five human senses. For each sense, identify at least one example or reason supporting the claim that there exist predictors we cannot detect in any given modeling situation. As an example, if we did not have specialized instruments, we would not have the ability to detect the amount of radon gas or carbon monoxide gathering in the basement of an old home. In the case of carbon monoxide, the first evidence that an accumulation has occured is unconciousness and death.

⇒ What technological advances do you know about that have either extended the sensory range of humans, or have made predictors available that previously were not possible? (*Hint:* the instrumentation mentioned in the previous exercise is one illustration of this idea.)

3.3.2.1 BRAINSTORMING.

One technique for identifying possible predictors is called *brainstorming*. It is not complicated, and it will definitely help you get off to a good start in any modeling effort. The overall idea is to systematically identify important factors or characteristics that might contribute to the response we are interested in.

Brainstorming is most effective when accomplished by including persons on the brainstorming team who have knowledge of the original mess. However, you want to include folks with different backgrounds also, if possible. Their different education and experience influences them to see the problem differently from other team members, like the physician and the engineer viewing the ill patient. In this way, we're hoping that what is viewed as an unusual and difficult problem by one member of the team may not be a problem for one of the other members. Someone in the group may have the previous knowledge and/or experience to be able to recommend exactly the predictors needed.

BRAINSTORMING

To brainstorm, we record all the possible predictors as they come to mind. DO NOT try to judge the merits of these predictors during this process because one listed predictor may spark an idea in someone else's mind. If done as a team effort, the predictors that one person suggests usually prompt another person to suggest others. We continue to record possible predictors until the team agrees that they have exhausted the topic (or themselves!).

Let's go back to the ants.

Example 3.14. Recall the third focus question that asked why the ants chose to build a nest in my closet. How would brainstorming work to help identify a response we could work with?

First, we would want to assemble a team with the appropriate knowledge. This team might include other residents (spouse, significant other, parents), neighbors, and pest control professionals.

Next, we would attempt to identify a response that was observable using the suggestions of the team. One possibility might be to use a variable whose value is 1 if there are ants in my closet, and 0 otherwise. Such a variable is called an *indicator variable*, because it indicates whether an event has occurred. The response variable is limited to one of two values: 0 or 1.

A second response variable might be one that measured the probability that an ant nest was built in my closet over some time period we decide upon. Since all probabilities must be between 0 and 100%, (or 0.0 and 1.0), this response variable is also limited to between 0 and 1.

A third response might be a number that indicated how attractive the closet was to ants, on a scale of 1 to 100, with 100 being the most attractive. This might be set up to be observable by creating selection options for the ants in other locations. Perhaps we allow them to roam into other areas of the house to see which they prefer the most.

From this example, you see that modeling is as much an art as a science. Each of these choices for the response variable seems reasonable. You, as the modeler, would choose one that was most comfortable for you or that best suits your needs. As we suggest the three mentioned, others might come to mind that better meet your modeling needs.

Here's a little more complicated example of identifying a response and predictors. It comes from astronomy.

Example 3.15. Suppose that we are interested in developing a model of the solar system to answer the focus question: "Is it possible to predict the location of planets relative to the sun based on the day of the year?" Clearly, even if we are able to identify the exact predictors that affect the orbits of the planets, it is doubtful that we could do much to control them. Consequently, any model we develop will be a descriptive model that we hope will be able to at least predict the location of the planets as time goes on. An initial listing of predictors influencing the relative location of planets could be:

- The average distance from the sun to any planet
- The gravitational constant of one planet (for reference)
- The mass of each of the nine planets and the sun
- The angular velocity of each planet on its orbit
- The specific shape and direction of each planet's orbit
- Whether any orbits cross
- The sidereal period for all planets (time to make a complete revolution around the sun

- The inertial reference system we will be using
- The time reference system we will be using
- The angular acceleration of each planet
- The specific physical laws that our system will follow, both on a macroscopic and a microscopic level
- The medium, if any, that our planets will be traveling through during their orbits
- If the medium our planets travel through is homogeneous (made up of a single substance), then the properties of the medium (light propagation, sound propagation, drag factors, etc.)

For this rather complicated situation of modeling a planetary system, there are several useful definitions and assumptions about the planetary system we would include in our model:

- A *planet* is a body of mass that revolves around a star.
- The sun in our system is a *star*.
- Eight of the nine planets are in eccentric, co-planar orbit around the sun; Pluto is out of plane.
- The mass of each of our objects, the sun and nine planets, can be represented by a point mass centered in the core of the objects.
- The sun's mass is many times greater than that of the planets.
- Newton's law of gravitational attraction, $F = gm_1m_2/r^2$, holds for any two masses.

Notice again, that one of the assumptions mentioned greatly simplifies what is actually the situation observed in the real-world: planets are not point masses. However, building this assumption into the model makes the resulting mathematics manageable. At the same time, it weakens the model's ability to have its results directly apply to the real-world situation. It's a necessary trade off to be aware of.

3.3.2.2 ADAPTING EXISTING MODELS.

Another way to identify our set of predictors is to examine existing models that address the response we picked. What general category or field of study does our response and focus question fall into? Physics? Fluid flow? Entomology? Psychology? Nursing? What have other modelers done when faced with a similar situation? How successful were they? What assumptions did they rely on to build their model? Is their model adaptable to our situation? Can we include or modify the predictors they used for our model? If we make changes to their model, will it still be valid? Many areas of science have widely accepted models that are used over and over again.

Example 3.16. The speed of a box falling in a vacuum under the influence of gravity is typically modeled using only a single predictor—the time that the box has been falling. The math model that describes this behavior is

$$\text{Speed} = -32t + \text{Speed at start} \tag{3.1}$$

where t is the time elapsed since the beginning of the box's fall. If our response were the same as the one this model uses, we could use the same predictor t.

Suppose that our response was different, say, the speed of a box falling in the actual atmosphere, and not a vacuum. We might include the predictor t from the simpler model, and look for other predictors in other models, or by brainstorming. Our resulting model might then include such additional predictors as air density, air friction, and the drag coefficient of the box.

For the ant nest problem, we might look to the fields of entomology (the study of insects) or pesticides to find existing models. By the way, models of ant colony growth have been used to solve the traveling salesman problem and other very difficult problems. See the references at the end of this chapter!

Exploration Exercises

3.1. For each of the observations listed below, try to identify a known mathematical model that is commonly used to model an aspect of the observation. Identify any assumptions that the original model uses. If you were to use the model that you identified for this particular situation, list some of the information that the output of the model would give you.

1. The position of a ball thrown upward through the air
2. The position of the same ball thrown upward on the moon
3. How far a spring stretches when a weight is attached to it
4. How long it takes to travel between cities in an automobile
5. How long is takes for a chunk of radioactive material to decay
6. The height of a distant tree, knowing the height of a friend who is with you
7. The temperature in degrees Celsius, knowing the temperature in degrees Fahrenheit

3.2. Consider each of the situations that follow. For each situation, formulate a focus question. Identify both a response and those predictors that might be contributing to the behavior. Did you use brainstorming or existing models to guide your selection of predictors? Explain whether each of the predictors will be easy or difficult to measure.

1. While sitting in the school cafeteria reading, you become aware of the noise of the conversations of your classmates. Glancing around, you decide to investigate some aspect of human communication.
2. While standing on the corner waiting for a local bus, you notice the amount of traffic passing through the intersection. One direction seems to have a longer line than any of the others.
3. At the food court in the local mall, you are standing in line to order your favorite fast food. You notice that the establishments seem to have two common ways that they serve their customers. At four of the ten establishments,

there is only a single waiting line that then feeds into several cashiers. The remaining six establishments have a waiting line for each of the several cashiers working.

4. While flying to some other city on vacation, you get involved in a conversation with another passenger. You find out that, although you are seated next to each other, your new acquaintance paid about $100 less than you. In fact, it may surprise you that only about 17 of the 100 passengers on board paid the same airfare as you did.

5. Frustrated with trying to get the disaster that you call a garden to grow, you notice that some of the plants respond to watering and fertilizing better than others.

6. After thinking that you lost your favorite mug, you discover it in the bottom of your desk drawer. It seems to contain a small amount of old beverage, and a large amount of some blue-green fuzzy growth that seemed to grow only where there was old beverage present.

7. While watching a baseball game, you see a player hit a long fly ball to the outfield. The ball seems to dance around in the air a bit because of the wind in the stadium, but somehow the outfielder is able to position himself directly in the path of the ball and catch it.

8. While crossing the street, you notice several sets of tire skid marks on the street. All seem to be of different lengths, leading you to wonder what the weather was like on the day each was made, and whether different weather conditions would make a difference.

3.3. For each of the response-predictors sets that you identified in the exercises above, compare the factors you identified with the original situation. Identify any assumptions that you made by selecting these factors. Did you find it necessary to make any of the assumptions because of lack of information about the problem? How might you eliminate any of these assumptions later in the modeling process?

3.4. Here is something to think about: When you are trying to identify predictors that are associated with a response, you are typically going to be focusing on the characteristic of change. In the previous exercise situations, can you identify a characteristic of the modeling situation that is *not* changing? What is not varying? For example, in the last situation involving tire skid marks, the speed limit on the street is a characteristic that is constant. This is important, because if all the vehicles were traveling at the same speed, something else must be influencing the length of the skid marks that they made.

3.4 PREDICTORS FROM DATA

As we search for models previously built to model the response that we are interested in, there is a good chance that we may come across historical data from previous experiments involving some combination of our response and predictors. We often directly use this data to create a model, mainly because gathering new data can be costly in terms of time, money or effort.

empirical
model

This *empirical* model based solely on a data set uses statistical techniques to select an appropriate subset of predictors for those available in the data. This approach works well if the data already exists. If we have to devise a plan to collect new data, then we are back to our previous approach. We need to identify our predictors before deciding on a data collection plan, which may involve surveys, samples, or experiments.

> **Example 3.17.** Suppose that we observed ants building a nest in our backyard, and we again ask the focus question "Why are they picking our yard for their nest?" We might sample some of the houses around ours to see if they also had ants in their yard, how many they had, what type they had, and so on. We would be hoping to find some predictor that was present in yards that had ants and missing in yards without ants, and vice versa.
>
> We might also conduct an experiment to gather data using the pest control professional in our brainstorming team whose expertise in the area would help.

At times, the data sets that we find simply have tables of values for various variables without identifying which represent predictors and which represent responses. Since we went looking for the data with a particular response in mind, it is generally not difficult to specify which variables should represent the dependent and independent variables by thinking of an input-output relationship of the form

$$\text{response} = f(\text{predictor}_1, \text{predictor}_2, \text{etc.}) \tag{3.2}$$

as saying: the value of the variable *response* depends upon the values selected for *predictor*$_1$, *predictor*$_2$, etc.

> **Example 3.18.** You may have noticed in your experience that as people get older, it seems as if they tend to get a little chunkier. Suppose that we were interested in building a model to answer the focus question: "Do people get fatter as they get older?"
>
> Well, in a study[†] that investigated a new method of measuring body composition, the data in the following table were collected: the age, body fat percentage (%fat), and gender for 18 normal adults between the ages of 23 and 61.

[†]Mazess, R.B., W.W. Peppler, and M. Gibbons. (1984) Total body composition by dual-photon (^{153}Gd) absorptiometry. *Amer. J. of Clinical Nutrition*, **40**, 834–839.

age	% fat	gender	age	% fat	gender
23	9.5	M	23	27.9	F
27	7.8	M	27	17.8	M
39	31.4	F	41	25.9	F
45	27.4	M	49	25.2	F
50	31.1	F	53	34.7	F
53	42.0	F	54	29.1	F
56	32.5	F	57	30.3	F
58	33.0	F	58	33.8	F
60	41.1	F	61	34.5	F

We would not speculate the relationship

$$\text{age} = f(\%\text{fat}, \text{gender}) \tag{3.3}$$

holds, because this would mean that changing either the percent fat or the gender of an individual would alter his/her age. Similarly, we probably wouldn't buy off on the speculation that the relationship between these variables should be expressed as

$$\text{gender} = f(\%\text{fat}, \text{age}) \tag{3.4}$$

This particular relationship would suggest that, as folks get older, they might have a more pressing reason to update their clothing wardrobe than simply for fashion.

Consequently, given the variable quantities listed along with our knowledge of what they represent, we could hypothesize the relationship

$$\%\text{fat} = f(\text{age}, \text{gender}) \tag{3.5}$$

exists. This would make the quantity %fat the response of our model, and age and gender the predictors upon which %fat depends.

In the exercise set that follows, try this way of picking out a response and predictors from a data set. In the cases where you have no idea what a reasonable relationship ought to be, you can check with one of the other instructors at your school, or read about the topic in some reference source to get a basic understanding of the topic rather than guessing. This is research.

Exploration Exercises

For each data set that follows, read the general setting of the problem and identify which of the data categories correspond to predictors and which are responses. Next, speculate an input-output relationship between the predictors and the response in the form

$$\text{response} = f(\text{predictor}_1, \text{predictor}_2, \text{etc.}) \tag{3.6}$$

which can be read "the response is dependent upon the predictors in the factor list f." Plot the data and describe any patterns that you see.

3.1. Lowering blood pressure during surgery.[‡]

It is sometimes necessary to lower a patient's blood pressure during surgery, using a hypotensive drug. The total amount of drug administered to a patient varies because it is given continuously throughout the surgery, and the total time of surgery for each patient also varies. The effectiveness of the drug in lowering a patient's blood pressure also varies. However, in all patients, the sooner the blood pressure rises again to normal after the drug is discontinued, the better. The data in Table 3.1 relate to one particular hypotensive drug, and give the time in minutes before the patient's systolic blood pressure returned to 100mm of mercury (the *recovery* time) (RT), the logarithm (base 10) of the dose of the drug in milligrams (DOSE), and the average systolic blood pressure achieved while the drug was being administered (BP).

3.2. Blood alcohol.[§] A majority of state legislatures have adopted a legal blood alcohol concentration limit of 0.08 grams per deciliter (g/dl) (80 mg/dl) for legally operating an automobile. In the course of upholding the law, police must sometimes estimate a person's peak blood alcohol concentration (BAC) from their BAC level determined some time later than when the person was stopped. The delay occurs because of the time it takes to transport the suspect to a location where a breath test can be applied or blood can be drawn. Making such a back estimation of the BAC requires an experimental average rate of elimination of alcohol from blood be determined (the topic of one of the projects at the end of this chapter) from the BAC profiles of large sample of people. A BAC profile tracks the concentration of alcohol in a person's blood from ingestion to nearly complete elimination. The data in Table 3.2 gives two examples of BAC profiles for two subjects, SP and JS, for two experimental situations in which they ingested 0.8 g/kg of alcohol on an empty stomach, and one week later immediately after breakfast.

3.3. Chemical process.[¶]

In a chemical process, batches of liquid are passed through a bed containing an ingredient which is absorbed by the liquid. Normally, about 6% to 6.5% (by weight) of the ingredient is absorbed by the liquid. However, to be sure

---

[‡]Robertson, J.D., and P. Armitage. (1959) "Comparison of two hypotensive agents," *Anaesthesia*, **14**, 53–64.

[§]Jones, A.W. (1993) "Disappearance rate of ethanol from the blood of human subjects: Implications in forensic toxicology." *J. of Forensic Sciences*, **38** (1), 104–118.

[¶]Bissel, A.F. (1992) "Lines through the origin – is NO INT the answer?" *J. of Appl. Stat.*, **19**, 193–210.

TABLE 3.1

Blood pressure data.

DOSE	BP	RT	DOSE	BP	RT
2.26	66	7	2.70	73	39
1.81	52	10	1.90	56	28
1.78	72	18	2.78	83	12
1.54	67	4	2.27	67	60
2.06	69	10	1.74	84	10
1.74	71	13	2.62	68	60
2.56	88	21	1.80	64	22
2.29	68	12	1.81	60	21
1.80	59	9	1.58	62	14
2.32	73	65	2.41	76	4
2.04	68	20	1.65	60	27
1.88	58	31	2.24	60	26
1.18	61	23	1.70	59	28
2.08	68	22	2.45	84	15
1.70	69	13	1.72	66	8
1.74	55	9	2.37	68	46
1.90	67	50	2.23	65	24
1.79	67	12	1.92	69	12
2.11	68	11	1.99	72	25
1.72	59	8	1.99	63	45
1.74	68	26	2.35	56	72
1.60	63	16	1.80	70	25
2.15	65	23	2.36	69	28
2.26	72	7	1.59	60	10
1.65	58	11	2.10	51	25
1.63	69	8	1.80	61	44
2.40	70	14			

TABLE 3.2

Blood alcohol concentration (BAC) profiles.

Time minutes	Subject SP, 24 yrs, 73 kg		Subject JS, 23 yrs, 73 kg	
	Empty mg/dl	Full mg/dl	Empty mg/dl	Full mg/dl
10	13	7	13	3
20	20	25	42	11
30	64	26	64	37
45	93	43	110	42
60	88	41	100	52
90	82	57	97	76
120	80	55	87	70
150	76	52	81	61
180	70	40	71	53
240	60	25	60	32
300	42	9	42	10
360	30	2	20	2

TABLE 3.3

Chemical process data.

Liquid (kg)	Take-up (kg)	Take-up (%)	Liquid (kg)	Take-up (kg)	Take-up (%)	Liquid (kg)	Take-up (kg)	Take-up (%)
310	14.0	4.52	330	17.1	5.18	370	21.3	5.76
490	27.2	5.55	400	20.4	5.10	450	27.4	6.09
580	31.9	5.50	560	32.5	5.80	520	28.4	5.46
650	34.1	5.25	650	39.8	6.12	650	38.5	5.92
810	50.4	6.22	800	43.8	5.48	760	50.4	6.63
1020	71.3	6.99	1020	64.3	6.30	910	53.5	5.88
1230	78.5	6.38	1200	80.8	6.73	1160	79.6	6.86
1490	98.6	6.62	1460	105.6	7.23	1380	98.9	7.17

that enough liquid is available to be absorbed, about 7.5% is supplied to the bed prior to passing the liquid over the bed. Since excess ingredient cannot be reused, there is desire to minimize waste and variation. The data in Table 3.3 shows data for 24 different quantities of liquid passed over the bed, along with the amount(in kilograms and as a percentage) absorbed by the liquid.

3.4. Temperatures in America[||]

Table 3.4 gives the normal average January minimum temperatures in degrees Fahrenheit along with the latitude and longitude for 56 cities in the United States. Average minimum temperature for January is calculated by adding the daily minimum temperatures and dividing by 31. For this table, the January average minima for the years 1931 to 1960 were averaged over the 30 years.

3.4.1   Collecting data

If we first start out by identifying a response and predictors without the benefit of existing data, more than likely we will have to gather the necessary data on our own. For each response and predictor, we would need to have a data collection plan that specified what, how, when, where, and why we are gathering the information that we want. This plan could include performing measurements, controlled experiments, mailing out surveys, or doing more historical research.

In some modeling situations, collecting data may demand a great deal of ingenuity and creativity, as in the case of a marine biologist modeling the

---

[||] Peixoto, J.L. (1990) "A property of well-formulated polynomial regression models." *Amer. Statistician*, **44**, 26–30.

TABLE 3.4

Average temperature data.

city	temp	latitude	longitude	city	temp	latitude	longitude
Mobile, AL	44	31.2	88.5	Baltimore, MD	25	39.7	77.3
Montgomery, AL	38	32.9	86.8	San Francisco, CA	42	38.4	123.0
Phoenix, AZ	35	33.6	112.5	Los Angeles, CA	47	34.3	118.7
Denver, CO	15	40.7	105.3	St Louis, MO	24	39.3	90.5
New Haven, CT	22	41.7	73.4	Helena, MT	8	47.1	112.4
Wilmington, DE	26	40.5	76.3	Omaha, NB	13	41.9	96.1
Washington, DC	30	39.7	77.5	Concord, NH	11	43.5	71.9
Jacksonville, FL	45	31.0	82.3	Atlantic City, NJ	27	39.8	75.3
Key West, FL	65	25.0	82.0	Albuqurque, NM	24	35.1	106.7
Miami, FL	58	26.3	80.7	Cleveland, OH	21	42.3	82.5
Atlanta, GA	37	33.9	85.0	Cincinnati, OH	26	39.2	85.0
Boise, ID	22	43.7	117.1	Bismarck, ND	0	47.1	101.0
Chicago, IL	19	42.3	88.0	Raleigh, NC	31	36.4	78.9
Indianapolis, IN	21	39.8	86.9	Charlotte, NC	34	35.9	81.5
Des Moines, IA	11	41.8	93.6	New York, NY	27	40.8	74.6
Wichita, KS	22	38.1	97.6	Albany, NY	14	42.6	73.7
Louisville, KY	27	39.0	86.5	Minneapolis, MN	2	45.9	93.9
New Orleans, LA	45	30.8	90.2	Detroit, MI	21	43.1	83.9
Portland, ME	12	44.2	70.5	Boston, MA	23	42.7	71.4
Little Rock, AR	31	35.4	92.8				

mating practices of moray eels, or in our earlier ant example. In other cases, we may simply have to dig more to find what we need. For the planetary system mentioned earlier, most of the information that was listed as predictors can be obtained from reference sources. Whenever possible, try not to reinvent the wheel. That is, use the work that has been done before.

For the ant example, there is an elementary data collection scheme for insects available on the World Wide Web from the Minnetonka, Minnesota schools. (See http://www.minnetonka.k12.mn.us/groveland/insect.proj/describe.html)

Exploration Exercise

3.1. Identify a response and at least one predictor for each of the modeling situations below. Using the format "what, how, when, where, and why," specify a data collection plan for one predictor that you hope to use.

3.1. Identify a response and at least one predictor for each of the modeling situations below. Using the format "what, how, when, where, and why," specify a data collection plan for one predictor that you hope to use.

1. Designing the national Advanced Placement Calculus test
2. Tracking the migration of sea lions along the western coast of the United States
3. Identifying remote villages in the Amazon Jungle using satellite imagery
4. Building small robots capable of going over very rough terrain
5. Assessing the amount of environmental damage an oil spill caused in Valdez, Alaska
6. Tracking the amount of drug traffic across the U.S.–Mexico border
7. Containing an outbreak of ebola Zaire in Reston, Virginia
8. Setting up a small business in your house
9. Designing the traffic flow controls for Atlanta, Georgia for the 1996 Olympic Games
10. Designing a national health care plan

3.5   FINISHING THE MODEL

Once we have our data inhand, we attempt to identify any specific relationships that exist between the predictors, which will now become the independent variables in our model, and the response, which is now the dependent variable in our model. The techniques introduced in this book in the later chapters focus on both *functional* and *statistical* relationships, what they are, how to identify them, and what you can do with the relationship information once you have it.

A functional relationship shows how the response depends upon the predictors used in a model. This is based on the all-important function concept in mathematics. We examine statistical relationships for a slightly different reason. They are useful for identifying the *degree of dependence* that exists between the predictors. When two predictors are very dependent on each other, they are linked in a way that causes mathematical problems if both predictors are used in the same model. Simply put, they end up representing the same information.

We use the statistical relationship to justify dropping one or more of these dependent predictors. This type of data analysis has the potential of further simplifying our model by reducing the number of variables without losing information.

values, there are some values that they will never be allowed to take on. These CONSTRAINTS conditions cause us to include additional mathematical equalities or inequalities in our model, which are called *constraints*.

> **Definition 3.1. Constraint.** A *constraint* is a mathematical expression that restricts the values that a variable can assume.

Example 3.19. If we were to develop a model of the ant colony developing in our back yard, we would have to include constraints on the predictors used. The number of ants, the amount of dead wood present, and the amount of pesticide present would all have to be nonnegative. Letting these predictors be represented by a, dw, and p, we would specify the constraints $a \geq 0$, $dw \geq 0$, and $p \geq 0$ in our model, in addition to the relationship between these predictors and the response variable we were working with.

Example 3.20. Suppose we were attempting to model a manufacturing facility and we identified the factor "number of cat collars produced" as a predictor, and represented it with the variable c in our model. Because of the type of equipment the company uses, the facility might be capable of producing only 1000 cat collars per month. The predictor is constrained to be between 0 and 1000 cat collars per month, since the facility can't make a negative number of cat collars. So, somewhere in the mathematical model, we would include the expression $c \geq 0$. We would also include the upper limit, or bound, on the value of c due to the factory's production limitation: $1000 \geq c$. For convenience, we could combine these both into a single constraint

$$1000 \geq c \geq 0$$

If the focus question we selected required the facility to keep costs low while maintaining a certain level of output of cat collars, the facility's output may be constrained to be *exactly*, say, 1000 cat collars per month. We would then include the constraint $c = 1000$ in our model. If the requirement was to maintain an output level of *at least* 500 cat collars, we would use include the constraint $c \geq 500$. Notice that if this last condition were the case, we would not include both constraints $c \geq 500$ and $c \geq 0$. Can you see why?

Both of the previous examples show how inequality constraints enter into models. The following example shows how an equality constraint can be needed.

Example 3.21. Suppose that the manufacturing facility makes 3 different types of pens, w_1, w_2, and w_3. It costs \$2 to make each w_1 pen, \$3 to make each w_2 pen, and \$5 to make each w_3 pen. The total number of pens that the manufacturing facility decides to produce must guarantee that the company's budget is

pen, and \$5 to make each w_3 pen. The total number of pens that the manufacturing facility decides to produce must guarantee that the company's budget is completely spent.[tt] If the budget was, say, \$50,000, then we would include an equality expression:

$$2w_1 + 3w_2 + 5w_3 = 50,000 \qquad (3.7)$$

in addition to the mathematical relationship between the response and predictors in our model.

The effect of including constraints in a model is significant. By restricting the values of the predictor variables, the response variable, which depends upon these values, is also restricted in the values that it can possibly take on. This is the heart of the section on linear programming that we will introduce you to in a later chapter.

3.5.2 The response-predictor relationship

So far, we've left out a very important aspect of the modeling process: how to determine the mathematical relationship between the response we select and its predictors. This topic forms the core of the important concepts that you need to understand prior to calculus.

The next chapter begins our study of mathematical expressions known as *functions*. Functions are used to describe a functional relationship between the response and its predictors. So, what's the difference between a regular expression and a functional relationship? (If this question just popped into your head, give yourself a big pat on the back.) Once you understand the answer to this question, you know a fundamental idea supporting calculus. After we discuss this key idea, we'll launch on an exploration of the many different kinds of functions that are used both in modeling and calculus.

When we have found a function that describes our response in terms of the predictors, and include any constraints we need to also consider, we have completed the construction of our mathematical model.

[tt] This situation happens frequently in government organizations whose budget allocation for the next year depends upon how much of the current year's budget is spent. By not spending money in the current year, a government organization typically gets their budget reduced for the following year. Because of this penalty logic, there is usually no incentive to curb spending, as illogical as this seems.

3.6 SUMMARY

The modeling process is a framework for systematically analyzing problems. It follows the five stages: mess, model, solution, analysis, report.

In the real world, we are presented with messes, not problems, and our challenge is to convert a mess into a problem, and the problem into a model. This requires us to identify a response and its predictors, and the relationships between them.

To find the response and predictors, we start with a focus question. A focus question helps us determine what we want our model to do: describe, predict, control, or optimize. It also guides our selection of our response variable.

To find our predictors, we can brainstorm, use other models, or examine the available data. Predictors can be constrained to only have certain values.

Once we have finished our model, we can solve it, analyze the solution, and report our results.

Functions will allows us to represent our response mathematically in terms of our predictor, and form the core of the rest of the book.

3.7 PROJECT: COLLEGE ADMISSION

How does a college decide whether to admit a student?

For this project, you need to examine the admissions mess for a college of your choice. Pick one in your local area, since you may have to contact their admissions office for some information you may need.

Determine a focus question, and your response variable. Then find your own list of predictors. Don't restrict yourself to numerical predictors, since there may be very important predictors to the admissions process that are not easily measured.

Next, contact the admissions office of your chosen college, and ask what predictors or factors they use to determine whether to admit a prospective student. Do they have an explicit model? Can they send you information on this model? Do they have data from past years that they can provide to you? You may be able to gather some of this data from your guidance counselor.

Do you think students should be admitted to a college on the basis of their past accomplishments or on the basis of their future potential? Do your predictors reflect this belief? Does a student's past accomplishment predict future performance? If not, what kind of predictor would you recommend to better predict a student's college performance?

To present the results of what you discover and conclude, write a short paper on the actual admissions process and an ideal admissions process for the college you chose. Be sure to address and explain the predictors actually used to admit students, and what predictors you think they should use. Do the predictors change from year to year? Or does the way the predictors are used change? What assumptions is a college making by using their predictors?

3.8   PROJECT: WE ARE WHAT WE EAT

Is it possible to consume fast food in moderation so that we benefit from the good things it brings and keep the bad effects as small as possible?

Now would be a good time to examine this focus question. First, select a fast-food restaurant to use for this project. Next, using one of the responses proposed earlier in the fast-food examples of this chapter, specify the modeling relationship that you think will exist between the response and the predictors using the form

$$\text{response} = f(\text{predictor}_1, \text{predictor}_2, \text{etc.}) \tag{3.8}$$

where each predictor that you use in your model represents a single serving of one of the fast food items that you are including in the composition of one lunch. Explain any assumptions that you need to build into your proposed model.

You will undoubtedly have to visit your local fast food establishments to get the data on each one of the predictors that you will need for this modeling project. So-o-o, you might as well sample the delicacies offered! (Just a little marketing plug for local businesses!)

Since you will want to develop an actual working mathematical model and we haven't discussed how to identify relationships between predictors from data yet, assume that the various predictor values combine in an additive relationship. That is, each predictor contributes to the overall total quantity of the response independent of the other food items: Hamburgers don't interact with chicken nuggets, etc.

3.9   COMPLEMENTS

We recommend the following readings as either supplements to the ideas presented in this chapter, or as resources for classroom discussion. Most are written in a readable manner, even though some of the mathematics contained in a few of the books may be beyond the capabilities of a precalculus student. The ideas, however, are not. We trust that the instructor can pick and choose to fit the class' needs.

1. An excellent reference on the limitations of the senses with regards to mathematics and modeling is

   - *Mathematics and the Search for Knowledge*, by Morris Kline. Oxford University Press, New York, New York, 1985.

2. The next two books are tremendous resources that manage to capture a multitude of the mathematical ideas involved with developing models. Several portions of each book are beyond the level of an average student in precalculus. However, we include them here more as sources of concepts for classroom discussion than as casual reading.

   - *Reality Rules I: Picturing the World in Mathematics—The Fundamentals*, by John Casti. John Wiley and Sons, New York, New York, 1992.
   - *Reality Rules II: Picturing the World in Mathematics—The Frontier*, by John Casti. John Wiley and Sons, New York, New York, 1992.

3. A book that presents the entire modeling process from a mathematical perspective, and is written for students who are involved with calculus, is

   - *A First Course in Mathematical Modeling*, 2nd Edition, by Frank Giordano, Maurice Weir and Bill Fox. Brooks/Cole Publishing, Pacific Grove, California, 1997.

4. Many modern day concerns regarding the interpretation of reality, without overemphasizing aspects of physics involved in these interpretations, are presented in the book

   - *Quantum Reality: Beyond the New Physics*, by Nick Herbert. Anchor Books, Doubleday, New York, New York, 1987.

5. Brainstorming is discussed in many texts. Here are one text and one Web site with information.

   - *Serious Creativity*, by Edward de Bono, Harper Business, New York, 1992.

- http://www.demon.co.uk/mindtool/brainstm.html

6. If you are interested in ants, try the following link:

- http://crux4.cit.cornell.edu/ aca1/ants.html

7. Ant colony models offer a new way to conceptualize and solve problems. Some references:

- "The ant system: optimization by a colony of cooperating agents," by M. Dorigo, V. Maniezzo, and A. Colorni. *IEEE Transactions on Systems, Man and Cybernetics, part B*, Vol 26, Number 1, pp. 29-41. (1996)

- "Heuristics from nature for hard combinatorial problems," by A. Colorni, M. Dorigo, F. Maffioli, V. Mariezzo, G. Righini, and M. Tribian. *International Transactions in Operational Research*, in press.

- http://iridia.ulb.ac.be/dorigo/ACO/ACO.html — Marco Dorigo's web site for ant colony optimization.

CHAPTER
4

MESS TO MODEL: FUNCTIONS

Most of the fundamental ideas of science are essentially simple, and may, as a rule, be expressed in language comprehensible to everyone.

Albert Einstein

Chapter Goals

⇒ Understand the concept of a functional relationship.

⇒ Understand the mathematical definition of a function, its elementary properties, and how to test an expression to see if it satisfies the requirements of the definition.

⇒ Understand and apply functional notation to functional relationships.

⇒ Understand and apply the ideas of domain and range.

⇒ Understand and apply algebraic manipulations of functions.

In this chapter, we finish the process of converting the MESS we began with into a MODEL. We have already chosen a focus question, posed a modeling objective, and identified our response and predictors, which have become variables for our math model. Some of the conditions on the variables that we selected may have caused us to specify constraints that will limit the values of these variables.

Our remaining task is to identify and specify the mathematical relationships that exist between the variables we select. This task requires us to consider two different locations where relationships exist: between the response and the predictors, and between the predictor variables alone.

For the relationship between the response and predictors, we will concentrate on one special type of relationship called a *functional* relationship. The math expression that represents this type of relationship is called a *function*.

Both the idea of a functional relationship and the mathematics associated with functions are central topics in collegiate mathematics and modeling. We encounter them time and time again. Since they are so important, we're devoting this entire chapter to an examination of functions from several different perspectives.

In the chapters that follow, we build on our understanding, examining various classes of functions, such as linear functions, polynomial functions, exponential functions, and so on. At that time, we will use the skills and knowledge we develop in this chapter to describe and classify these very special mathematical relationships.

4.1   THE FUNCTION CONCEPT

The idea of a function is more general than its use in mathematics might convey. It's a way of viewing how components of some behavior interact to produce a response we can observe. It shows how this real-world behavior "functions." If we provide the object displaying the behavior with some kind of allowable input (a question, a value, a chemical stimulus, an electric pulse), it responds with an answer, a value, an explosion, light.

When we identify the response and predictors in the modeling process, we are seeking an answer to the question "What input is influencing the output that we are observing?"

Example 4.1. Suppose that you have a trained dog named Einstein. Einstein

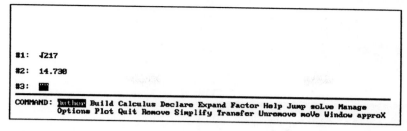

FIGURE 4.1
Function call to the *Derive* square root function.

can perform a most amazing feat; one that you are hoping will bring you fame and riches in the years to come. You can tell Einstein any number, and, for a small treat, Einstein will scratch out the square root of the number in the dirt. Exactly. He even puts a bar over repeating decimal numbers, such as in $2.3\bar{3}$. Amazing. No one, even you, knows how he does it.

Mathematically, we can think of Einstein as a "square root function"; it is what he does, it is how he functions. Granted, we don't know why he can do this, but we can save that for later investigation. The response is the "square root of a number." The allowable input to this "Einstein function" are two predictors that we can control: a number and a treat. In functional notation:

$$\text{square root of number} = \text{Einstein}(\text{number, treat}) \tag{4.1}$$

Computer programming languages and computer algebraic systems (CAS) such as *Derive* have mathematical "functions" already pre-programmed into them. Using one of these functions, such as in computing a square root, is known as a *function call.* You type in and send an allowable input value, and it returns a result based on what its function is.

In *Derive*, a square root function call is done by authoring the expression `sqrt(x)`, where x is an allowable input. Selecting the `approX` option sends the value of x to the square root function, which returns the approximate value of the square root of x. Figure 4.1 shows this particular function call sequence for the square root of 217.

Derive returns the square root of a number passed to it, as long as the input is allowable. Does it make any sense to call to the square root function in *Derive* for the square root of a negative number? Not if we are expecting a real number for a response.

The next example shows how we can translate a real-world mess into a mathematical function.

Example 4.2. Suppose that we're observing four gasoline stations located at an intersection, one on each corner, as in Figure 4.2. We notice that there are always

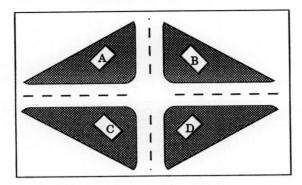

FIGURE 4.2
Gasoline station example.

lines for gasoline at gas station A between 11:00 am and 1:00pm, but the other stations seem to have only a modest number of customers during this period. The focus question we choose is "Why is gas station A receiving the majority of customers?" Our modeling objective would be to predict the number of customers through our knowledge of certain predictor variable values. We pick number of customers as the response. Three predictors that we start with might be time of day, traffic patterns, and fuel price. We are hypothesizing that the number of customers depends, or is dependent upon, the predictors we identified.

We can express this relationship in the form:

$$\text{number of customers } = f(\text{ traffic pattern, price}) \qquad (4.2)$$

Or, letting $c =$ number of customers, $TP =$ traffic pattern, and $p =$ fuel price, we have the mathematical equation: $c = f(TP, p)$.

By using this notation, we are saying that as the factors change (traffic is rerouted, or the price of gasoline rises), the business level of the gas station will respond to these changes.

Once we determine how to combine the variables TP and p into a mathematical expression, the finished model might look something like:

$$c = 1.1TP - 0.5p \qquad (4.3)$$

for example. Knowing the values of the predictors TP and p allows us to calculate the value of the response, c.

This input-output way of viewing a functional relationship fits nicely with our predictor-response modeling approach (Figure 4.3). The notation

$$\text{response} = f(\text{predictors})$$

is equivalent to writing

$$\text{output} = f(\text{input})$$

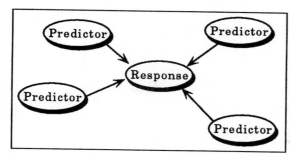

FIGURE 4.3
Predictor-response relationship.

It identifies how the predictor variables values act to produce the response value. It also shows that the response is dependent upon the predictors, or that "the response is a function of the predictors."

Our interests lie in the ideas and details of mathematical functional relationships, which mimic the general concept used across all modeling.

4.2 RELATIONS

If you look at the equation in the last example $b = 1.1TP - 0.5p$, it looks a lot like expressions that you have worked with in the past. Why is it a function, and not just an expression? A function is an expression, but an expression is not necessarily a function. The difference is in how the variables are related.

Variables can be related in many ways. Equations are used to describe these relations. For example, consider the three equations shown in Figure 4.4:

$$x + y = 1 \tag{4.4}$$

$$x^2 + y^2 = 1 \tag{4.5}$$

$$\sin(x) + \sin(y) = 1 \tag{4.6}$$

Equation 4.4 represents a line in the (x, y) plane. Equation 4.5 represents a circle centered at the origin. Equation 4.6 is a trigonometric equation that represents an infinite collection of shapes that look like squashed circles that extend parallel to both axes.

Imagine that each of these three equations represented a relationship between the response y and a predictor x. For any given value of the predictor x,

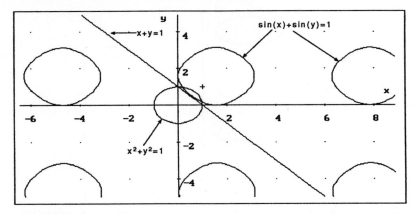

FIGURE 4.4
Three equation relations.

do we know the value of the response y? The answer depends on which equation we use.

For Equation 4.4, the answer is *yes*. Each value of x corresponds to exactly one value of the response y. Substituting a value for the predictor x produces exactly one unique value of y. We can also write an *explicit expression* for y:

EXPLICIT
EXPRESSION

$$y = 1 - x$$

For Equation 4.5 and equation 4.6, the answer is *no*. Each value of x produces either no response value or two response values for either expression. For example, if $x = 0$ in equation 4.5, y can either be 1 or -1. For each input value, we can't tell which output to select. The response is not *uniquely* fixed for each predictor.

Let's try another analogy.

Example 4.3. Imagine that we are playing a game of cards called "I Pay You." x is the value of the card I draw. I pay you the amount y defined by a mathematical expression only if the corresponding value of y is unique. If I can find more than one value for y for the value of x, you pay me \$10.

Suppose I draw a card, $x = 0$, and we are using the expression given by Equation 4.4. I pay you \$1.00.

However, if we are playing the game using the expression in Equation 4.5, you owe me \$10. For $x = 0$, $y = \$1.00$ **and** $y = -\$1.00$. There is not a unique output.

If we are playing the game using the expression given by Equation 4.6, and I draw a card with the value $x = 0$, you have to pay me \$10 again. There is an infinite number of possible y values that satisfy the expression:

$$y = \ldots, \frac{-7\pi}{2}, \frac{-3\pi}{2}, \frac{\pi}{2}, \frac{5\pi}{2}, \frac{9\pi}{2}, \ldots$$

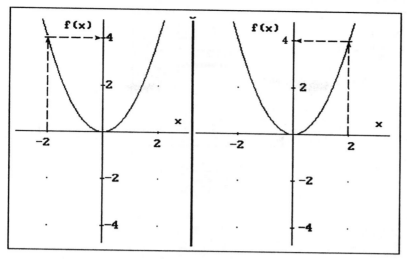

FIGURE 4.5
Unique output function requirement.

Requiring a unique output for each input is *exactly* the condition that distinguishes a function from an expression. Let's use another analogy to make this point a little clearer.

> **Example 4.4.** Suppose that a function was a transportation device. You climb in, push some buttons, and whoosh! Off you go to the location you selected using the buttons. It would be quite unfortunate if the transportation function tried to send you off to two different locations at the same time! However, it is not a problem for you to transport to Paris using this transportation function, and five minutes later, your friend does so also. Two different people going to the same location using the transportation function. No problem. One person going to two different locations, a definite problem.

> **Example 4.5.** The equation $y = x^2$ is a squaring function. Substitute a number for x, and the function returns x^2. We can send two different values to the same output without any problem: $(-2)^2 = 4$ and $(2)^2 = 4$. However, as shown in Figure 4.5, notice that x^2 does not send any single input value off to two different locations.

In Figure 4.4, notice that the graph of the three expressions gives us a quick way to test if an expression assigns more than one y value to any x value. If we can draw a vertical line anywhere on the plot and have it cross the graph more than once, multiple y values are being assigned to a specific x value.

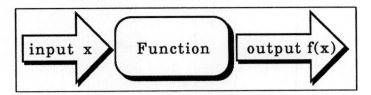

FIGURE 4.6
Input-output function model.

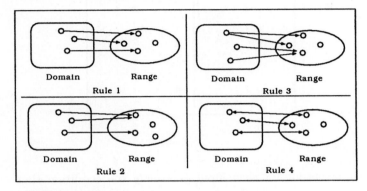

FIGURE 4.7
Four rules for relating inputs to outputs. Which ones are functions?

4.3 FUNCTIONS

We are interested in relations such as the one given by Equation 4.4, where for each value of the predictor, only one value of the response is specified. In other words, for each input into our model, we want a unique output.

Relations that satisfy this property are called **functions**:

> **Definition 4.1. Function.** A *function* is a rule that assigns to each member of one set (called the *domain*) exactly one member of another set (called the *range*).

DOMAIN   The set of all allowable inputs is called the *domain* , and the set of all allowable outputs is called the *range.*

We use the terms input, predictor, and element of the domain as synonyms, conveniently picking one to use depending upon the topic we are examining. We also use the terms output, response, and element of the range as synonyms.

Figure 4.7 shows four possible rules for relating an output to an input. Remember that

$$\text{input} \equiv \text{predictor} \equiv \text{domain element}$$

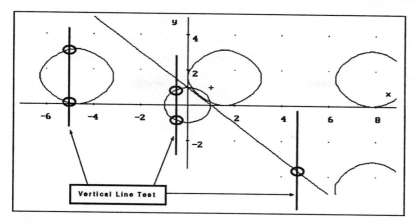

FIGURE 4.8
The vertical line test for a function.

and

$$\text{output} \equiv \text{response} \equiv \text{range element}$$

Rule 1 describes a function. Each predictor in the domain is assigned exactly one element in the output. It doesn't matter that some of the possible outputs are not used—only that every input has only one output assigned to it.

Rule 2 is also a function. Each predictor in the domain is assigned exactly one element in the output. It doesn't matter that some predictors result in the same output—only that no input goes to more than one output.

Rule 3 does not describe a function. One of the predictors is assigned two responses in the range. This is not allowed for a function.

Rule 4 is a function. Each predictor in the domain is assigned exactly one response in the range. In this special case, each element in the range is also assigned exactly one member in the domain. The function requirement is satisfied no matter which direction we examine the rule.

One way to test for a function, given its graph, is to use a *vertical line test*. First, we select an allowable input value x. Then, if we can draw a vertical line on the graph of the expression at this value, and it intersects the graph in more than one place, then the expression is not a function.

VERTICAL
LINE TEST

> **Example 4.6.** Figure 4.8 shows the vertical line test being applied to the three equations of earlier. Since a vertical line cuts across the two circular shapes in more than one point, neither Equation 4.5 nor Equation 4.6 describes y as a function of x.

Using this graphical approach, it is only necessary to find a single place where a vertical line crosses the graph more than once to conclude that an expression is not a function. Conversely, if every vertical line crosses the graph at most once, the corresponding expression is a function.

4.3.1 Notation

We describe functions using a notation that visually captures the input-output/predictor-response relationship. Writing

$$y = f(x)$$

ARGUMENT

means that the output value of y is produced by supplying the function f with input x. The variable x is also called the *argument* of the function. The letter f is the letter-name of the function. We customarily use the letter f, for function, when talking about functions in general.

A subtle point to make is that when we are talking about functions, we are focusing on the underlying rule, or relationship; not the specific variable used for the argument. Since $f(x) = 10x$ is a function, then so is $f(y) = 10y$, $f(3) = 10(3)$, and $f(\$) = 10\$$. The underlying function relationship says "Take whatever the argument is, multiply it by 10, and return the result."

This point might not be obvious using a modeling approach. We typically identify a specific response and predictors first, and then determine the mathematical relationship that exists between them. We would already have picked specific variable names, such as $p =$ profit, $c =$ costs, $r =$ revenue, and so on, by the time we get to the point of determining a relationship between the variables. If the relationship between the response and predictors, say,

$$p = r - c$$

happens to be a function, the functional relationship holds for other variables as well; p, r, and c are merely placeholders that make sense for our problem.

When we need to distinguish among several functions, we use different letters as names, or letters with subscripts:

$$y = f(x)$$

$$y = g(x)$$

$$y = f_1(x)$$

Each of these equations indicates that y is a function of x, but with different names for the functions: f, g, and f_1.

By convention, when we plot a function, we plot the argument on the horizontal axis and the value of the function on the vertical axis. This agrees with our earlier practice of plotting the predictor on the horizontal axis and the response on the vertical axis.

Example 4.7. By setting

$$y = 1 - x$$

we can rewrite Equation 4.4 as a function:

$$y = f(x) = 1 - x$$

This identifies the rule $f(x) = 1 - x$. For each value of x, we get exactly one value of y.

The set of allowable x values (the domain of f) is the set of all real numbers. The set of all outputs (the range of f) is also the set of all real numbers.

What is $f(w)$? Applying the rule to the argument w, we get $f(w) = 1 - w$. This is called *evaluating the function at w*.

The notation $f(x)$ is used to represent the output of f, interchangeably with y, since the two quantities they represent are equal. Instead of writing $y = 1 - x$, we could use $f(x) = 1 - x$ to emphasize the input-output aspect of the function. The function f is the rule; $f(x)$ is a value.

Example 4.8. The relation given by

$$y = \sqrt{1 - x^2}$$

can be written as

$$g(x) = \sqrt{1 - x^2}$$

which emphasizes the rule $g(x) = \sqrt{1 - x^2}$. This is a function, because for each x, we obtain only one output value.

Figure 4.9 shows a plot this function. It is the top half of a circle of radius 1, centered at the origin.

The set of allowable inputs (the domain of g) is all the values for which the output of $g(x)$ is defined. By this we mean that the output has to make sense according to the mathematical system we are using. In this case, we want both the input and output to remain real numbers. To obtain an output from $g(x)$ which is a real number, we must restrict the input to $-1 \leq x \leq 1$. We can also specify this set as $x \in [-1, 1]$. If we were to allow -2 as input, for example, then $g(-2) = \sqrt{-3}$, an operation that is not defined in the real number system. The allowable x values are those under the plot of the upper half circle in Figure 4.9.

The set of outputs (the range of g) is the set $0 \leq g(x) \leq 1$, inclusive (which means 'including the endpoints'). We can also see this from the graph of the upper half circle.

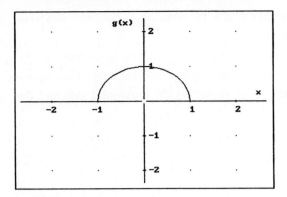

FIGURE 4.9
Function plot for $g(x)$

4.3.2 Domains and ranges

So far, we have said that the domain of a function includes all the arguments for which the function is defined. However, to properly define the mess we start with, we often have to further restrict the domain.

> **Example 4.9.** Suppose that we were modeling the sales of a product as a function of our advertising budget. Let s represent total sales (in thousands of dollars), and a be the amount we spend on advertising (in thousands of dollars). We might obtain the model
>
> $$s = f(a) = 10a \tag{4.7}$$
>
> Although this function is defined for all real values of a, we restrict the domain of a further to match our situation: We cannot spend a negative amount on advertising. We need to restrict the domain of a to $a \geq \$0$ to make sense in our context.

A second way we restrict the domain is by restricting the range. Reducing the range of allowable outputs reduces the set of allowable inputs.

> **Example 4.10.** If the product we were selling in the previous example were only available to a small market, no matter how much we spent on advertising, the total sales of our product would be limited. If $s \leq \$10,000$, then the domain would be further restricted to the interval $0 \leq a \leq 1000$.

4.4 PROPERTIES OF FUNCTIONS

There are two properties of functions help us understand the specific functions we will study later in the book. The first describes a relationship between the domain and the range of a function. The second describes whether a function can be considered increasing or decreasing.

4.4.1 One-to-one functions

In Rule 1 of Figure 4.7, each element of the domain was assigned a different element of the range. There were no elements of the range that had more than one element of the domain assigned to them or *mapped* onto them.

This was not the case with Rule 2, where there was a point in the range with two elements of the domain mapped on it. Rule 4 establishes a one-to-one assignment of the domain *onto* the range, or that there exists a one-to-one correspondence between the elements in the domain and the elements in the range.

We distinguish between these situations with a definition:

Definition 4.2. One-to-One Function. A function is one-to-one (1–1) if, and only if, every element in its range has at most one element of the domain assigned to it.

ONE-TO-ONE FUNCTION

Since f is a function to start, we already know that f assigns only one value in the range to each element in the domain. Our concern is that the reverse is also true: At most one value in the domain is assigned to each element in the range. In other words, if $f(x_1) = f(x_2)$, then it must be true that $x_1 = x_2$.

When this condition doesn't hold, we can algebraically detect a contradiction that causes the function f to fail to meet the requirements of the definition. The function f assigns the value $y = f(x_1) = f(x_2)$ to both x_1 and x_2, but, if $x_1 \neq x_2$, then there are two different points going to the same output value: $f(x)$ cannot be a one-to-one function.

We capture this useful result as a theorem:

Theorem 4.1. A function is one-to-one if and only if $f(x_1) = f(x_2)$ implies that $x_1 = x_2$ for all values x_1 and x_2 in the domain of f.

Definition 4.3. Test for One-to-One. To algebraically test whether a function is one-to-one:

1. Set $f(x_1) = f(x_2)$.
2. Simplify.
3. If the resulting equation implies that $x_1 = x_2$ for all x_1, x_2 in the domain of f, then f is a one-to-one function.
4. Otherwise, f is not one-to-one.

Let's work two quick examples.

Example 4.11. Returning to our sales model, let $s = f(x) = 10a$ as in Equation 4.7. If $f(x_1) = f(x_2)$ then $10x_1 = 10x_2$, by the definition of f. Dividing both sides by 10 shows that this implies that $x_1 = x_2$. As a result, Theorem 4.1 tells us that f is a one-to-one function.

Example 4.12. Suppose that our sales function was given by

$$s = g(a) = 26,000 - 10(a - 50)^2$$

Applying Theorem 4.1 results in the following chain of equations:

$$g(x_1) = g(x_2) \tag{4.8}$$

$$26,000 - 10(x_1 - 50)^2 = 26,000 - 10(x_2 - 50)^2 \tag{4.9}$$

$$(x_1 - 50)^2 = (x_2 - 50)^2 \tag{4.10}$$

$$|x_1 - 50| = |x_2 - 50| \tag{4.11}$$

The condition in Equation 4.11 is satisfied if $x_1 = 51$ and $x_2 = 49$. Since $g(x_1) = g(x_2)$ does not imply that $x_1 = x_2$, As a result, g is not a one-to-one function, by Theorem 4.1.

By its wording, Theorem 4.1 allows us to conclude that a function is a one-to-one function only if we can show that the condition "$f(x_1) = f(x_2)$ implies that $x_1 = x_2$" holds "for all values x_1 and x_2 in the domain of f." If it does not hold, then we can conclude the function is not one-to-one. In other words, it allows us to say something definite about the function we are checking based on the condition stated. This is a special and powerful characteristic of an "if and only if" theorem. In the previous example, we demonstrated that the required condition does not hold, so we can conclude that the function g is not one-to-one.

HORIZONTAL LINE TEST   There is a graphical test called the *horizontal line test* for a one-to-one function. We can think of a one-to-one function as one that allows only one x value for each y value. If we draw a horizontal line on the plot, we are drawing the line $y = k$ for some constant k. That line will intersect our graph at most once if the function is one-to-one. If the horizontal line intersects the plot than once, then the points (x_1, k) and (x_2, k) lie on the graph. Thus, there is more than one value from the domain assigned the value k—so the function can not be one-to-one. This is the same case as Rule 2 in Figure 4.7.

Example 4.13. Figure 4.10 shows plots of the function $y = x^2$ in window #2 and $y = x^3$ in window #3, along with a horizontal line test with $y = 1.5$. Since the horizontal line crosses the plot of $y = x^2$ in two locations, it is not a one-to-one function. However, no matter where on the plot we pick to draw a horizontal line, the function $y = x^3$ will pass the test. It is a one-to-one function.

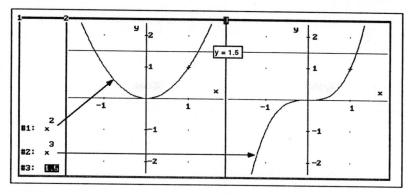

FIGURE 4.10
Horizontal line test.

A one-to-one function must pass both the vertical line test (it must be a function) and the horizontal line test (it must be one-to-one).

4.4.2 Increasing and decreasing functions

We are often interested in whether a response increases or decreases as we vary the values of its predictors. When the relationship between a response and its predictors is a function, we have an intuitive idea of what that means: as we read the graph from left to right, the output of a function either "always goes up," "goes up sometimes and may level out, but never goes down," "always goes down," "goes down sometimes and may level out, but never goes up," or "goes up and down." We will try to clarify these ideas with the following definitions.

> **Definition 4.4.   Increasing Functions.** A function f is increasing if, for every input $x_1 < x_2$ ("going from left to right in order") in the domain of f, it is true that $f(x_1) < f(x_2)$ (the output always goes up).

> **Definition 4.5.   Nondecreasing Functions.** A function f is nondecreasing if, for every $x_1 < x_2$ ("going from left to right in order") in the domain of f, it is true that $f(x_1) \leq f(x_2)$ (the output goes up sometimes and may level out, but never goes down).

> **Definition 4.6.   Decreasing Functions.** A function is decreasing if for every $x_1 < x_2$ ("going from left to right in order") in the domain of f, it is true that $f(x_1) > f(x_2)$ (the output always goes down always).

> **Definition 4.7.   Nonincreasing Functions.** A function f is nonincreasing if, for every $x_1 < x_2$ ("going from left to right in order") in the domain of f, it

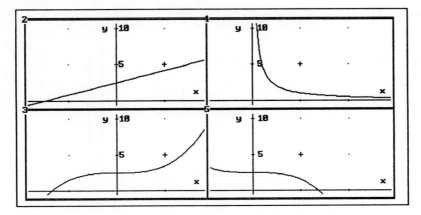

FIGURE 4.11
Increasing, nondecreasing, decreasing, nonincreasing functions.

is true that $f(x_1) \geq f(x_2)$ (the output goes down sometimes and may level out, but never goes up).

The four window displays in Figure 4.11 illustrate these definitions. Window 2 shows an increasing function; window 3 is nondecreasing; window 4 is decreasing; and window 5 is nonincreasing.

Definitions 4.5 and 4.7 allow for the possibility that the output may "flatten out" over some intervals, without decreasing or increasing the output value, respectively. We can also extend Definitions 4.4 and 4.6 to apply only to intervals contained in the domain of f. This allows us to be more precise when describing the behavior of a function. Instead of being limited to drawing a single conclusion for the function, we can say "The function $f(x)$ is increasing between $x = 0$ and $x = 1$," for instance.

Example 4.14. Equation 4.7 modeled sales as

$$s = 10a$$

Is this an increasing function? Algebraically, we can see that

$$a_1 < a_2$$

$$10a_1 < 10a_2 \qquad (4.12)$$

$$f(a_1) < f(a_2) \qquad (4.13)$$

Equation 4.12 is obtained by multiplying the first equation on both sides by 10, which doesn't change the inequality. But $10a_1 = f(a_1)$ and $10a_2 = f(a_2)$, so Equation 4.13 follows from the definition $f(a) = 10a$. The three equations together show that if $a_1 < a_2$, it must be true that $f(a_1) < f(a_2)$. Definition 4.4 applies, and f is an increasing function.

The careful reader may have noticed that the horizontal test for a one-to-one function is very much related to the behavior of a function. In fact, we have the following useful theorem. If the output of a function is allowed to flatten out, it can never be a one-to-one function.

Theorem 4.2. If a function is either strictly increasing or strictly decreasing, then it is a one-to-one function.

Why do we care about classifying the behavior of functions? From a practical standpoint, remember that these functions represent a relationship between predictors and response. If the response no longer "responds" to changes in the predictors, this would be valuable information to know.

In the sales example, we were trying to capture the relationship between advertising dollars spent (predictor), a, and the resulting sales (response), s. If spending more money on advertising has either no effect on sales (nonincreasing), or it causes a decrease in sales, we would not recommend spending more money on advertising.

Theorem 4.2 also allows us to classify a function as one-to-one if we know that it is increasing or decreasing. This naturally leads us to ask why we care about one-to-one functions! The answer is in the next section: one-to-one functions have *inverses*.

Exploration Exercises _____

4.1. Draw a sketch similar to Figure 4.7 or 4.11 representing each of the following relations
   (a) A relation that is not a function
   (b) A function that is not one-to-one
   (c) A function that is one-to-one
   (d) An increasing function
   (e) A decreasing a function
   (f) A function that is not monotonic

4.2. In your own words, define a *function*, and give a real-world analogy of functional behavior.

4.3. Write a paragraph explaining why the vertical line test works for determining whether the plot of a relation is a function. Include a sketch or computer printout.

4.4. Does the equation $y = \sqrt{1-x^2}$ describe the same relation as the equation $x^2 + y^2 = 1$? Why or why not?

4.5. Express the following descriptions in functional notation.

(a) Predictor: x; function: g; response: z

(b) Predictors: x and y; function: h; response: z

(c) Predictors: x_1 and x_2; function: f; response: z

(d) Predictors: p, qr, θ; function: g; response: z

(e) Predictors: z and x; function: Θ; response: z

(f) Predictors: n_1, n_2, n_5, n_3, n_6, and n_4; function: f; response: z

4.6. Identify which of the following relations are functions. In each case, let y be the dependent variable. For those relations that are functions, write them in functional notation, and specify the domain and the range. You may find it helpful to plot the functions.

(a) $x + y = 6$

(b) $x^2 + y = 6$

(c) $x + y^2 = 6$

(d) $\sin(x) + y = 1$

(e) $x + \sin(y) = 1$

(f) $\sqrt{x} + \sqrt{y} = 1$

(g) $xy = 1$

(h) $\sin(xy) = 1$

4.7. Demonstrate that each of the following functions is a one–to–one function, either algebraically or graphically. Then, determine the value of the response using the predictor value stated.

(a) $f(x) = x$; $x = 9$

(b) $f(z) = z^3$; $z = 2.5$

(c) $f(x) = x^5$; $x = -2$

(d) $f(w) = w^k$, k an odd integer; $w = 4$

(e) $f(w) = \sqrt{w}$; $w = 312$

(f) $f(x) = \ln(x)$; $x = 103$

(g) $f(z) = \exp(z)$; $z = 4.1$

4.8. Demonstrate that each of the following functions is not one-to-one, either algebraically or graphically. Then, restrict the domain for each so that the function is one-to-one over the restricted domain.

(a) $f(x) = |x|$

(b) $f(x) = x^2$

(c) $f(y) = y^3 + y^2 + 1$

(d) $f(x) = x^4$

(e) $f(z) = \sqrt[4]{|z - 1|}$

(f) $f(x) = \sin(x)$

(g) $f(w) = \cos(w)$

4.5 INVERSES

From a modeling perspective, we generally want to know what the response will be given that we know the value of the predictors we are using in our model. Given a set of values for our predictors, we get exactly one response value

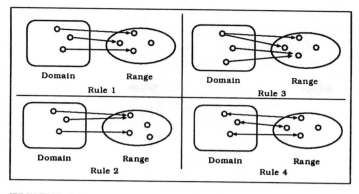

FIGURE 4.12
Four rules for relating inputs to outputs. Which are one-to-one?

in return. This is the nice aspect of a functional relationship existing between response and predictors.

Sometimes, it's useful to get information in a slightly different way: We observe the response, and we would like to identify the predictor that generated this response. This may not be possible if more than one predictor is assigned that response value by the function, as in Rule 1.

We've reproduced the rules in Figure 4.12 for convenience. Take a look at Rules 2 and 4 again. For Rule 2, we can determine which predictor produced each response for all but one of the responses in its range. For the response that has two predictors assigned to it, we have no way of distinguishing which of the two produced that particular response.

Contrast Rule 2 with Rule 4. In Rule 4, we can tell which predictor produced each response in the range. Rule 4 represents a one-to-one function.

The rule, or relationship, that recovers the unique predictor of a response is called the *inverse* of the function.

> **Definition 4.8.   Inverse Function.**   Let $y = f(x)$ be a function. Let g be a function such that $x = g(y)$ for all y in the range of f. Then g is the *inverse* of the function f, and we write $g = f^{-1}$.

NOTATION
It is very easy to confuse the notation for the inverse of a function, $f^{-1}(x)$, with ALERT!!
the reciprocal of the function, $f(x)^{-1}$. Please notice that

$$f^{-1}(x) \neq \frac{1}{f(x)}$$

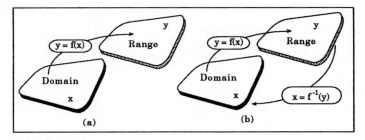

FIGURE 4.13
A function $y = f(x)$, and a function with its inverse relationship $x = f^1(y)$.

If we want to write the reciprocal of $f(x)$, we will write

$$\frac{1}{f(x)}$$

or, infrequently, $(f(x))^{-1}$. The location of the exponent sets the inverse and reciprocal notation apart.

This definition of an inverse function is illustrated in Figure 4.13.

Note *carefully* the domains and ranges of f and f^{-1}. The domain of f is the range of f^{-1}, and the range of f is the domain of f^{-1}. That is because f assigns a response to each predictor, and f^{-1} assigns a predictor to each response.

We have a useful theorem that is motivated by Rule 4, Figure 4.12.

Theorem 4.3. The function f has an inverse if and only if f is one-to-one.

4.5.1   Finding the inverse of a function

Although there are several techniques for finding the inverse of a function, we introduce two here. One is graphical, and the other is algebraic.

The graphical technique relies on the standard practice of plotting the response variable on the vertical axis. Let $y = f(x)$ be a one–to–one function. Method 1: We know that $f^{-1}(y)$ exists by Theorem 4.3. If we plot the graph of $y = f(x)$ with Graphic y on the vertical axis, we have a plot that looks like the left plot in Figure 4.14.

The right-hand plot is a mirror image of the graph of $f(x)$ about the line $y = x$. The vertical axis is now the x axis, because for the inverse function, the old domain is the new range. We see the graph of $f^{-1}(y)$ in the right-hand plot.

This method works because if (x, y) is a point on the graph of $f(x)$, then (y, x) must be a point on the graph of $f^{-1}(y)$, since $x = f^{-1}(y)$. Switching the x and y coordinates on the plot is the equivalent drawing the mirror image of $f(x)$ about the line $y = x$, as shown.

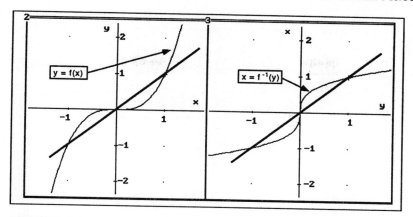

FIGURE 4.14
A function and its inverse reflected about the line $y = x$.

We need to illustrate a fundamental difference between the way that spreadsheets and CASs plot information. A CAS will create axes scales according to the normal Cartesian spacing, i.e. the tick mark spacing is consistent. This is good. The default setting for a spreadsheet, on the other hand, will attempt to flex the x-axis and $f(x)$-axis scales according to the data you are using. This is not so good if you are trying to graph the inverse of a function because it may distort the plot into an incorrect inverse function representation. The next example should clarify this point.

Example 4.15. Suppose that we had two-column table of x values and $f(x)$ values in a spreadsheet. We normally would choose to graph these values with the x values on the horizontal axis and the $f(x)$ values on the vertical axis. This is shown in Figure 4.15 for the function $f(x) = x^3$. **VERY IMPORTANT!**

However, we could plot these values with the $f(x)$ values on the horizontal axis and the x values on the vertical axis. Because this is the same as graphing the mirror image of the function plot $f(x)$ about the line $y = x$, we should obtain a plot of the inverse of $f(x)$. If we were using a CAS, this is exactly what we would see. However, to plot the inverse function $f^{-1}(x)$ correctly in a spreadsheet, that is, with the appropriate distances between tick marks, we need to adjust the scales on both the horizontal and vertical axes. Otherwise, the inverse function appears as a straight line, as it does in the right-hand plot of Figure 4.15. This is a good example of how a spreadsheet is not designed to represent symbolic expressions, which we mentioned in Chapter 2.

We have an algebraic method of finding inverses, too. If we write $y = f(x)$ and solve for x, we will obtain $x = f^{-1}(y)$, which is the inverse function. **METHOD 2: ALGEBRAIC**

Example 4.16. Suppose that we have the one-to-one function: $y = f(x) = x^3$, which is the function plotted in the left hand side of Figure 4.14. We can calculate

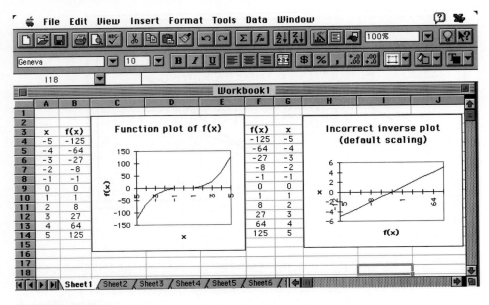

FIGURE 4.15
The incorrect scaling in the right-hand plot makes the inverse of $f(x) = x^3$ appear linear.

$f^{-1}(y)$:

$$y = x^3$$
$$\sqrt[3]{y} = \sqrt[3]{x^3}$$
$$\sqrt[3]{y} = x \tag{4.14}$$

From Equation 4.14, we have that $x = f^{-1}(y) = \sqrt[3]{y}$, which is plotted in the right hand side of Figure 4.14.

Both methods produce the same inverse function, which they should. Which method you use depends upon the situation you are faced with. It is sometimes difficult to algebraically solve for $x = f^{-1}(y)$, although *Derive* can be a great help.

We will use the properties of inverses in the chapter on trigonometry.

4.5.2 Restricting domains to obtain inverses

What if the function we are dealing with is not a one-to-one function? Can we still somehow find its inverse?

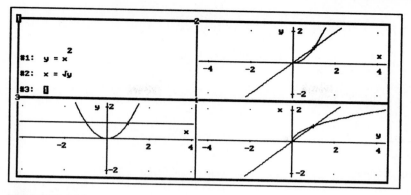

FIGURE 4.16
A restricted domain inverse.

The answer is no. Not across the entire domain of the function. There is a technique, however, that we can use to find an inverse of the function over a restricted domain.

Often, we can restrict the domain of a function sufficiently so that the function is one-to-one over the restricted domain. We will then be able to find an inverse. However, we must always bear in mind that the inverse is valid only for the restricted domain. Let's work an example.

Example 4.17.
Let $y = f(x) = x^2$. We plot this function in window 3 of Figure 4.16. Selecting $y = 1$, we apply a horizontal line test to the plot of the function. Since it crosses the plot in two locations, $f(x)$ is not a one-to-one function. By Theorem 4.3, $f(x)$ has no inverse across its entire domain.

In window 2 of Figure 4.16, we have restricted the domain of $f(x)$ to the nonnegative real numbers. We see that the function is now one-to-one over this new, restricted domain. As a result, the function now has an inverse. Reflecting the plot of $f(x)$ over this restricted domain, we plot its inverse in window 4.

Algebraically, we obtain the inverse as follows:

$$y = x^2$$
$$\sqrt{y} = \sqrt{x^2}$$
$$\sqrt{y} = x$$

We select the positive square root of x^2 because we know that the original x was nonnegative—we restricted the domain of x to guarantee it.

4.6   MULTIPREDICTOR FUNCTIONS

What happens if we identify more than one predictor for an observed response? In Chapter 3, we often had multiple predictors, and these predictors become the

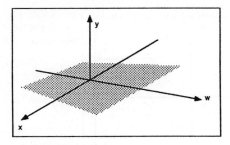

FIGURE 4.17
MultiPredictor domain.

independent variables for our model. Can we apply our function ideas when we have more than one argument?

The short answer is yes. We will need to alter our definitions to accommodate multiple predictors (or arguments), but it is a straightforward extension. The language is a bit stiff, but it is important to be precise here. If you examine the definition carefully, you will see all the ingredients that we need to satisfy the function requirements.

First, we need to define what a multiple predictor argument looks like.

ORDERED

n-TUPLE

Definition 4.9.   Ordered n-tuple. Let $(x_1, x_2, \ldots, x_n)$ be a set of n independent variables corresponding to n predictors, where x_1 is the value of the first predictor, x_2 is the value of the second predictor, and so on. $(x_1, x_2, \ldots, x_n)$ is called an *ordered n-tuple*.

Definition 4.10.   Function of Several Variables. Let f be a rule that assigns a unique real number to each ordered n-tuple. Then, f is called a *function of several variables*. We write $y = f(x_1, x_2, \ldots, x_n)$ to show that the response y is a function of these n predictors. The set of all allowable n-tuples comprises a set of all possible values for the predictors. We call this set the *domain* of the function f. The set of all possible y values is the *range* of the function.

We work four quick examples that will be used later in the chapter.

SUM

Example 4.18. Let $y = f(x, w) = x + w$. This is a function of two variables: a rule that assigns a unique real number by adding two predictors together.

This is a function because the sum of two real numbers is uniquely determined—there is no ambiguity. The domain of this function is the set of all ordered pairs (x, w), where x and w are real numbers. Figure 4.17 shows a graph of the domain of this function to be the entire (x, w)-plane, with axes x and w. The range of this function is the set of real numbers. The graph shows only the nonnegative values of y just for convenience.

Geometrically, $f(x, w) = x + w$ describes a plane, as we shall see later.

FERENCE

Example 4.19. Let $y = f(x, w) = x - w$. This also is a function of two variables, with the same domain and range as the preceding example. This function also describes a plane, although one that tilts differently. The gasoline station example used earlier had a function of this kind, using the predictors (TP, p).

Example 4.20. Let $y = f(x, w) = xw$. This is a *product function*, a function PRODUCT that takes two values of the predictors, and multiplies them together to yield a response. Since the product of two numbers is uniquely determined, this is also a function. Again, the domain is the set of all order pairs (x, w) from the real numbers, and the range is the set of all real numbers.

Example 4.21. Let $y = f(x, w) = x/w$. This is the quotient function. Its QUOTIENT domain is not quite the same as the preceding three examples, because division by zero is not allowed in the real numbers. The predictor x can be any real number, but w cannot be zero. The range is the set of all real numbers.

We end with one slightly more involved example.

Example 4.22. Let $y = f(x, w) = \sqrt{xw}$. What is the domain and range of this function?

   We know that we can not take the square root of a negative number, so $xw \geq 0$. The domain of f is the set of all ordered pairs (x, w) such that $xw \geq 0$. The range of f is the set of all nonnegative real numbers.

This last example introduces a technique of manipulating functions called the *composition of two functions*, which is discussed in the next section.

   As a last note, a single function containing more than one predictor rarely has an inverse. The predictors contain individual pieces of information that are being collapsed into a single number. Except in some very special cases, it is impossible to recover the original predictor information starting at a single response value.

Exploration Exercises

4.1. Why is Theorem 4.2 true?

4.2. Why does f have an inverse if and only if it is one-to-one?

4.3. Why does a graph that fails the horizontal line test fail to have an inverse? Use a sketch or computer printout to support your explanation.

4.4. For each of the following functions, determine if it is one-to-one. If it is, find its inverse. If not, restrict its domain so that the function is one-to-one, and find an inverse on this restricted domain.
   (a) $f(x) = x + 1$
   (b) $f(x) = 7x - 4$
   (c) $g(x) = x^2 - 4$
   (d) $g(x) = \sin(x)$
   (e) $h(x) = x^3 - 1$

(f) $f(w) = 1/w$ (Careful!)
(g) $f(z) = z^3 + z + 1$
(h) $g(x) = x^4$

4.5. For each of the following functions, determine if the proposed predictor value is allowable as input. If it is, evaluate the function to determine the corresponding value of the response. If it is not, explain why.

Function	Input
$g(x) = x^2 - 4x + 1$	(-3)
$f(x) = -3.2x + 5$	(12)
$f(x, y, z) = xy + 2x^3 - 6zx$	$(2, 1, 5)$
$g(x) = x + 9$	(-7)
$g(x_1, x_2, x_3, x_4) = x_1^2 - 6x_2 + x_3x_2 - 3x_4x_1$	$(4, -2, 3, 1.5)$
$g(x) = \sqrt{x^2 + 1}$	(-1)
$f(x) = \sqrt{x}$	(-4)
$g(t) = \sqrt{t^2}$	(-7.14)
$g(x) = (\sqrt{x})^2$	(-3)
$f(x) = x^3 + x$	(d)
$f(x) = x^2 - 4x + 1$	$(6, 3)$
$h(x) = \frac{15}{x-1}$	(1)
$h(x) = \frac{x-1}{15}$	(1)
$f(x) = \sqrt{x + 9}$	(-9)
$g(x) = \frac{1}{x}$	(0)
$f(x, y, z) = \frac{1}{x+y+z}$	$(0, 1, 3)$
$g(x) = 4$	(115)

4.7 OPERATIONS ON FUNCTIONS

In many real-world modeling situations, we find it to our advantage to adopt a "divide and conquer" strategy. After converting the mess to a problem, we attempt to break the problem into pieces, modeling each piece separately using functions. When we are done, we construct the complete model we need by combining the functions we built individually.

This raises the issue of how to work with functions. What can we do with functions? Can we add them? Subtract them? Multiply them? Divide them? With only one exception, the answer to each of these questions is yes.

However, before we examine algebraic operations with functions, let's examine the *composition of two functions* (mentioned at the end of the last section).

4.7.1   Composition of functions

The strategy of 'divide and conquer' motivates the idea of *composition of functions*, which is useful when analyzing a rather complicated function expression. A *composition* of functions is a function that uses another function as its argument. For example, $f(g(x))$ is the composition of two functions: f uses $g(x)$ as its argument.

COMPOSITION

Some calculus books use a special notation for the composition of two functions: $f \circ g(x)$, read "f of g of x." We prefer the nested version $f(g(x))$.

We take the approach of working from the inside out to identify the function's domain and range. This means that for a function such as $f(g(x))$, we first analyze $g(x)$, applying the function g to the predictor x, and then apply function f to $g(x)$.

This "divide and conquer" approach only works if $g(x)$ is in the domain of f, because f can only operate on an allowable input.

Why would we use this? Let's return to our first sales example.

Example 4.23. The sales model introduced earlier was given as $s = f(a)$, where s was sales, a was the amount spent on advertising, and $f(a) = 10a$.

Imagine we had another piece of this mess modeled as a function that describes the amount of money we spend on advertising as a function of the previous month's sales. We assign the previous month's sales the variable p, so that $a = g(p)$. Without getting specific, lets say that as p goes down, a goes up. In other words, we spend more on advertising when our sales are low.

Then the amount of sales we expect this month is given by

$$s = f(a) = f(g(p))$$

We substitute in $g(p)$ for a.

This is called the composition of two functions. It helps us divide and conquer, by building models that can work from the top down or bottom up.

Example 4.24.   Linear sales.   Again, recall that the sales example used the function model $s = f(a) = 10a$ to describe sales as a function of advertising dollars spent. Let $a = g(p) = 100 - p/20$ be the function that describes the relationship between advertising dollars spent in the current month a, and the dollar amount of the previous month's sales p.

For g to make sense, we require that p must be positive (no negative sales), and that $p \leq \$2000$ (no negative advertising budgets). This advertising budget spends less money when sales are high, and more when our previous month's sales are low.

We could debate the wisdom of the advertising policy represented by this function, but we'll just work with it for now. (Is this advertising function valid? Is it credible? Is it adaptable?)

What are our projected sales for this month, if we had p sales in the previous month?

Applying the composition of the sales and advertising functions, we have

$$s = f(g(p)) = f(100 - p/20) = 10(100 - p/20)$$

If last month's sales were $p = \$1000$, this month's sales would be $s = 10(100 - 1000/20) = \$500$. On the other hand, if last month's sales were $p = \$500$, we project sales for this month at the level $10(100 - 500/20) = \$750$.

Example 4.25.   Ants. Let's make a very simple model for the probability that ants build a nest in our back yard. Here our dependent variable (or response) will be p, the probability that the ants build in our backyard. Our first predictor will be the soil hardness, which we will denote by the variable h, so that $p = f(h)$. We also believe that the probability is affected by the moisture in the soil. We will represent the amount of moisture as m.

If we believe that the hardness of the soil is completely determined by m, we can write $h = g(m)$, and a composition of the two functions would give

$$p = f(g(m))$$

It is more likely, however, that moisture has other effects on the probability than just its effect on soil hardness. It is also not likely that soil hardness is completely explained by the soil moisture. A better model might be that the probability was a function of two variables hardness and moisture. Then we would write

$$p = f(h, m)$$

In this second model, we do not have a composition of functions. We have a function of two variables.

4.7.1.1   RECURSION.

We very quietly introduced an interesting effect in the composition function of Example 4.24. We did something very different with the output of a function: We fed it back into another function—the previous month's sales were the input for the current month's sales projections.

RECURSIVE   Models in which the output of a function becomes the next input to the
FUNCTIONS   function are called *recursive* functions. Some of the properties of recursive functions extend beyond the scope of this book, but we will indicate some of the characteristics briefly in this section for completeness, and then revisit recursive equations in Chapter 9.

Figure 4.18 shows an illustration of the recursive input–output structure. Here's a dilemma: If the output of a recursive function becomes the input for itself, a recursive model can't have input without output. So, to start this input–output cycle, we specify an *initial value* of the model's predictor(s), usually labeled with a subscript of zero.

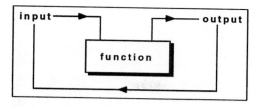

FIGURE 4.18
Recursive structure.

Example 4.26. Suppose that the sales total in the very first month is given by the initial value p. We want to predict sales in the future using our sales model. Sales as a function of the previous month's sales was given by the composition function

$$s = f(p) = 10(100 - p/20)$$

along with the constraint $0 \le p \le \$2000$.

We will have a lot of these s's and p's around shortly. We need a way to keep them all straight. Let's use an index: s_i represents the sales for the ith month, with s_0 denoting sales in the initial month.

Consequently, we have $s_0 = p$. We also know that the sales amount in any month is a function of the total sales of the previous month, so that $s_i = f(s_{i-1})$. This last equation is called the *recursive equation*. We can use these two conditions to find our sales for any month.

$$s_0 = p$$
$$s_1 = f(p)$$
$$s_2 = f(f(p))$$
$$s_3 = f(f(f(p)))$$
$$\vdots$$

It might appear tedious to do these calculations, although they are quite simple to solve in practice by using a spreadsheet. Figures 4.19 and 4.20 show the projected sales for $p = \$1000$ and $p = \$1200$. These spreadsheets support a fact we will leave for you to verify: No matter what value of p we choose, the projected sales will always level out at $666.66!

In both of the spreadsheet examples shown, we set the value of p in cell B2. Then, by varying this value, the spreadsheet automatically recalculates the recursion equations throughout all the cells, and updates the accompanying graph.

As mentioned earlier, the spreadsheets suggest that the sales level off at 666.666. Can we confirm this algebraically?

Example 4.27. If, as the spreadsheet figures suggest, sales eventually level off at some value, say l, then the sales from the previous month would be the same as the

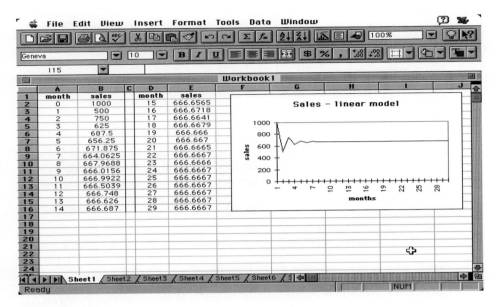

FIGURE 4.19
Spreadsheet showing the sales projections for our sales model, with initial sales equal to $1000.

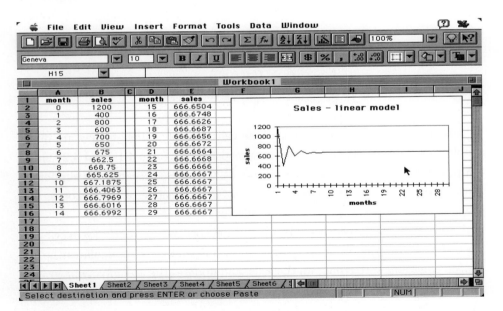

FIGURE 4.20
Spreadsheet showing the sales projections for our linear sales model, with initial sales equal to $1200.

projected sales for the current month, or $l = f(l)$. Substituting this relationship into the recursive equations yields $l = f(l)$, or $l = 10(100 - l/20)$. After collecting the l terms and simplifying, we obtain

$$l = \frac{\$2000}{3} \approx \$666.666$$

This agrees with the results of our spreadsheet analysis.

A value l that causes the recursive equations to level off as in the previous example is called an *equilibrium value*. Finding and studying equilibrium values for recursive functions is an exciting and lively branch of current mathematics. Surprising things can happen!

4.7.2 Algebraic operations with functions

If we think of functions as mathematical objects, then we can actually manipulate them in ways that are already familiar to us. Besides creating a composition of functions, we can add, subtract, multiply, and divide functions much in the same manner as we do with variables or any other mathematical object. The important thing to watch when manipulating functions is to keep our eyes on the domain and range of the functions before and after combining them.

This next theorem answers three of the four questions posed earlier concerning algebraic combinations of functions. It needs to be stated because of the examples of combining functions that we introduced in a previous section: $f_1(x, w) = x + w$, $f_2(x, w) = x - w$, and $f_3(x, w) = xw$. These are all functions of two real number variables.

> **Theorem 4.4.** The sum, difference, or product of two functions that have the same domain is another function that has that same domain.

This is a handy fact to keep in mind. It says that if two functions have the *same* domain prior to manipulating them in one of the ways stated, the resulting function will also have the same domain; it remains unaltered. Notice that this theorem requires all of the original functions to have the same domain.

To make the connection with the previous examples, which were simply functions of two real variables, we can let the variable x represent a function: $x = g_1(z)$ and let the variable w represent a different function $w = g_2(z)$. Now, if we assume that g_1 and g_2 have the same domain, then

- $f_1(x, w) = x + w = g_1(z) + g_2(z)$ is a function of just z, and its domain is the common domain of g_1 and g_2.

- $f_2(x, w) = x - w = g_1(z) - g_2(z)$ is a function of just z, and its domain is the common domain of g_1 and g_2.

- $f_3(x, w) = xw = g_1(z)g_2(z)$ is a function of just z, and its domain is the common domain of g_1 and g_2.

4.7.3   Division of functions

The algebraic operation that we have left to consider is division. What about the quotient of two functions? From Example 4.21, we know that the denominator cannot be zero, since division by zero is an undefined operation in the real number system. And, this is the only restriction that we have to keep in mind. Other than this restriction, we have no difficulties.

NO DIVISION BY ZERO

> **Theorem 4.5.** The quotient of two functions $f(x)/g(x)$ that have the same domain is another function with the original common domain less any x values such that make $g(x) = 0$.

This theorem is actually harder to read than to work with, as the examples that follow show.

> **Example 4.28.** Consider the functions $f(x) = 3x + 2$ and $g(x) = 4x - 8$. The domain of both f and g is the set of all real numbers. By Theorem 4.5, the quotient of the two functions, $f(x)/g(x)$, is another function, say $h(x) = f(x)/g(x)$ with domain of $h(x)$ equal to the set all the real numbers, except $x = 2$, which would cause $g(2) = 0$. To avoid division by zero, we must exclude $x = 2$ from our domain.

In modeling, it is a common practice to assemble mathematical models after first constructing their individual pieces. These "pieces" are smaller functions that get assembled using addition, subtraction, multiplication, division, or composition into one larger function that becomes the overall model. Theorems 4.4 and 4.5 above are important because we need to know if, in the process of putting the smaller pieces together, we have possibly changed the problem's original domain without realizing it.

Exploration Exercises

4.1. Decide whether each of the following statements is true or false. Explain your reasoning.

(a) The sum of two functions is a function.
(b) The product of two functions is a function.
(c) The sum of two 1–1 functions is a 1–1 function.
(d) The sum of two increasing functions is an increasing function.
(e) The product of two 1–1 functions is a 1–1 function.
(f) The product of two increasing functions is an increasing function.

4.2. Let $f(x) = x^2$, $g(x) = \sqrt{x+1}$, and $h(x) = (1-x^2)^{-1}$. For each of the following compositions, build up the composition of functions, plot the end result, and identify the composition's domain and range.

(a) $f(g(x))$
(b) $f(h(x))$
(c) $g(f(x))$
(d) $g(h(x))$
(e) $h(f(x))$
(f) $h(g(x))$
(g) $h(f(g(x)))$

4.3. True or false: $f(g(x)) = g(f(x))$. Explain your answer.

4.4. In our sales example, we modeled our advertising budget with the function $a = f(p) = 100 - p/20$. Comment on the credibility and validity of this model. Does it make sense in a real-world setting?

4.5. Analyze the sales model given by $s = f(a) = 26,000 - 10(a-50)^2$ as a recursive model, using an advertising function given by $a = f(p) = 100 - p/400$. Do the total sales tend to stabilize at one equilibrium value? Does the choice of the initial sales amount p affect the result?

4.8 DISCRETE FUNCTIONS

For some events that we observe, it doesn't make sense to think of the predictors as being able to take on all possible values. In this case, we restrict the domain of a function to be a collection of individual values, rather than a collection of intervals as in the case of piecewise continous functions.

For modeling situations such as

- Representing the total number of magazines sold on a monthly basis, as opposed to the dollar amount of sales

- Observing, recording and describing the number of births and deaths of a population of wolves in Alaska

- Monitoring the number of aircraft landing and taking off at Seattle-Tacoma Airport in Washington State

it is more appropriate to restrict the predictors to integer values.

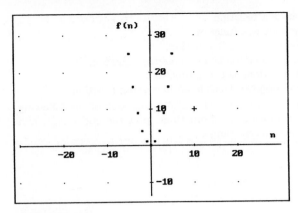

FIGURE 4.21
Discrete squaring function.

The natural ability of spreadsheets to represent individual data points makes them an excellent tool for analyzing discrete functions.

Example 4.29. Suppose that the population level of wolves p, which is the response variable, at the end of time period t was specified by the function

$$p = f(b, d)_t = 2b_t - d_t \qquad \text{for all } t = 1, 2, \ldots \tag{4.15}$$

where $b_t =$ the number of wolf births in month t, and $d_t =$ the number of wolf deaths in month t. This relationship indicates that there are approximately 2 births for every death during each time period t. The the domain of the function $p(b, d)$ is restricted to the collection of nonnegative integer pairs (b, d). Predictor values such as $b = 1.3$ and $d = 12.5$ do not make sense here.

This domain restriction is the essence of a discrete function. The predictors influence the response by changing in steps. The response variable, on the other hand, has no such restriction, and can take on fractional values. However, the response is not defined for values lying between predictor values.

Definition 4.11. Discrete function. A *discrete function* is a function whose domain consists of a finite or infinite set of individual values.

Example 4.30. A discrete squaring function:

$$s = f(n) = n^2 \qquad n = 1, 2, \ldots \tag{4.16}$$

The response values of this discrete function would then be $f(1) = 1^2 = 1$, $f(2) = 2^2 = 4$, etc., as shown in Figure 4.21. There is no output defined for predictor values such as $n = 1.5$, $n = 7.1$, and so on.

In this example, n is the predictor variable. We use the notation $n = 1, 2,$ ... to specify the domain of f, the values that the predictor n can take on. The dots "..." indicate that the values do not end; the domain is *infinite*.

Example 4.31. A discrete cube root function:

$$f(n) = \sqrt[3]{n} \qquad n = 1, 2, \ldots, \tag{4.17}$$

has all the positive integers specified as its domain. Its range is given by the infinite set $\{\sqrt[3]{1}, \sqrt[3]{2}, \ldots\}$

Example 4.32. The discrete linear function:

$$f(n) = n + 3/4 \qquad n = -3, 4, 5 \tag{4.18}$$

has only three values specified in its domain: $\{-3, 4, 5\}$. The response values are $\{-2.25, 4.75, 5.75\}$.

When a discrete function's domain is not infinite, but too large to conveniently list, we show an ending value, such as $n = 1, 2, \ldots, 9$, and use dots to indicate that there are additional values not shown. In this case, the domain set consists of the values $\{1, 2, 3, 4, 5, 6, 7, 8, 9\}$.

Discussion Ideas

⇒ Suppose that we claim "if a discrete function has an infinite domain, such as with $n = 2, 3, \ldots$, then the range of this function will also be infinite." Is this always a true statement? Can you give an example of a discrete function for which this would be true, and one for which this claim will be false?

⇒ Besides the three modeling situations mentioned, can you think of another situation in which predictors might be better represented with integer values?

4.8.1 Sequences

If we further limit the domain of a discrete function to consist of only the positive integers, also known as the *natural numbers*, the function is called a *sequence*.

Definition 4.12. Sequences. A *sequence* is a function whose domain is the set of positive integers (natural numbers) and whose range consists of real numbers.

Sequences are often associated with lists of numbers, without reference to their underlying function. It is more appropriate to view a sequence as the response of a discrete function, where each response value is a new term in the sequence, as in the next example.

Example 4.33. The discrete function

$$a_n = f(n) = 2n + 1 \qquad n = 1, 2, \ldots \tag{4.19}$$

is a sequence. We introduce the notation a_n here because it is often used to denote the nth response term of the sequence. We prefer the discrete function notation $f(n)$.

The first response term of this sequence would be calculated by substituting the predictor value $n = 1$ into the function

$$f(1) = 2(1) + 1 = 3 \tag{4.20}$$

Likewise, the 10th, 37th, and 1279th response terms of this sequence are

$$f(10) = \qquad 2(10) + 1 = \qquad 21$$
$$f(37) = \qquad 2(37) + 1 = \qquad 75$$
$$f(1279) = \qquad 2(1279) + 1 = \qquad 2559$$

Example 4.34. The discrete function defined by

$$f(1) = (-1)^n \sqrt{n} \qquad n = 1, 2, 3, 4, 5, 6, 7, 8, 9 \tag{4.21}$$

is a sequence whose domain consists only of the positive integers from 1 to 9. The 9 response terms of this sequence are as follows.

Input	Function substitution		Sequence response term
1	$f(1) = (-1)^1 \sqrt{1} =$	-1	$= -1.0$
2	$f(2) = (-1)^2 \sqrt{2} =$	$\sqrt{2}$	≈ 1.414
3	$f(3) = (-1)^3 \sqrt{3} =$	$-\sqrt{3}$	≈ -1.732
4	$f(4) = (-1)^4 \sqrt{4} =$	$\sqrt{4}$	$= 2.0$
5	$f(5) = (-1)^5 \sqrt{5} =$	$-\sqrt{5}$	≈ -2.236
6	$f(6) = (-1)^6 \sqrt{6} =$	$\sqrt{6}$	≈ 2.449
7	$f(7) = (-1)^7 \sqrt{7} =$	$-\sqrt{7}$	≈ -2.645
8	$f(8) = (-1)^8 \sqrt{8} =$	$\sqrt{8}$	≈ 2.828
9	$f(9) = (-1)^9 \sqrt{9} =$	$-\sqrt{9}$	$= -3.0$

4.8.2   Long-term behavior

In addition to describing a sequence as infinite or finite, which we can determine from its domain, we are also interested in two aspects of its behavior as n

increases. The first describes trends in the response values. Are the response values steadily increasing? Decreasing? Flattening out? The second describes where the response is heading. Is the response approaching, or *converging*, on a single equilibrium value, as in the case of our earlier sales example? Or, does it *diverge*?

The definitions describing the long term behavior of sequences parallel those introduced earlier for continous functions, with the exception of adding the idea of *monotone*, or unchanging, behavior. The correspondence between definitions is shown in the following table.

CONTINOUS:	strictly increasing	$f(x_1) < f(x_2), \; x_1 < x_2$
DISCRETE:	monotonically increasing	$f(n) < f(n+1)$
CONTINOUS:	nondecreasing	$f(x_1) \leq f(x_2), \; x_1 < x_2$
DISCRETE:	monotonically nondecreasing	$f(n) \leq f(n+1)$
CONTINOUS:	nonincreasing	$f(x_1) \geq f(x_2), \; x_1 < x_2$
DISCRETE:	monotonically nonincreasing	$f(n) \geq f(n+1)$
CONTINOUS:	strictly decreasing	$f(x_1) > f(x_2), \; x_1 < x_2$
DISCRETE:	monotonically decreasing	$f(n) > f(n+1)$

For small, finite sequences, diagnosing behavior can be accomplished by inspecting the ordered response terms.

Example 4.35. The output sequence $\{1, 2, 4, 6, 7, 10, 100, 115\}$ is monotonically increasing. Assuming that these values are in order of increasing n, no output value in the sequence is ever less than or equal to a value that has come before it.

Example 4.36. The output sequence $\{100, 99, 98, 97, 94, 23, 1, 0, -5\}$ is monotonically decreasing.

Example 4.37. The output sequence $\{10, 0, 0, -1, -15, -15, -20, -21\}$ is monotonically nonincreasing.

Example 4.38. The output sequence $\{35, 39, 39, 39, 48, 59, 60, 60, 72\}$ is monotonically nondecreasing.

For infinite sequences with only positive response terms, there is a useful algebraic test called the *ratio test* that we can use to identify a sequence's long-term behavior.

Definition 4.13. Ratio Test. If $f(n) > 0$ for all n, calculate the ratio

$$\rho = \frac{f(n+1)}{f(n)} \tag{4.22}$$

IF	THEN
$\rho > 1$ for all n	monotonically increasing
$\rho \geq 1$ for all n	monotonically nondecreasing
$\rho \leq 1$ for all n	monotonically nonincreasing
$\rho < 1$ for all n	monotonically decreasing

The next example has an obvious result since the value of each term

$$\frac{n}{n^2} = \frac{1}{n}$$

gets increasingly smaller as n increases. However, it is a clear example on how the analysis is performed, so we'll include it.

Example 4.39. The infinite sequence

$$f(n) = \frac{n}{n^2} \qquad n = 1, 2, \ldots \tag{4.23}$$

is monotonically decreasing since

$$\rho = \frac{f(n+1)}{f(n)} = \frac{\frac{n+1}{(n+1)^2}}{\frac{n}{n^2}} = \frac{n+1(n^2)}{(n+1)^2 n} = \frac{n}{n+1} < 1 \tag{4.24}$$

for all n.

Just as in the case of continous functions, discrete functions such as sequences have inverses only if they are one-to-one. Because there is a natural matching between n and $f(n)$, it is tempting to assume that all sequences will have an inverse. This is clearly not the case, as the next example shows.

Example 4.40. The sequence

$$f(n) = (-1)^n \qquad n = 1, 2, \ldots \tag{4.25}$$

is not one-to-one, and therefore has no inverse. Starting at any value of the response, say -1, it is impossible to determine the predictor value n that generated this response.

We can perform the same horizontal test on a discrete function as on a continous function. By assuming the discrete function is continous, $f(x) \approx f(n)$, and then applying the algebraic test or a horizontal line test, we can determine whether $f(n)$ has an inverse. The cryptology project included in this chapter relies on your ability to identify a discrete function that is one-to-one.

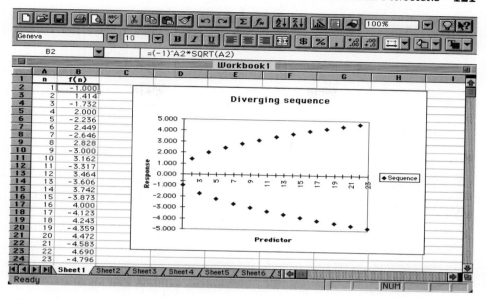

FIGURE 4.22
Graphical spreadsheet display of a diverging sequence.

4.8.2.1   GRAPHICAL ANALYSIS.

Whether a sequence converges to, or approaches, a single equilibrium value can sometimes be determined by examining a plot of the points $(n, f(n))$ as n increases. To determine whether a sequence is converging, we look for the response terms to approach a single value.

A discrete function has a domain and range composed of individual points. This makes a spreadsheet a good investigative tool for identifying converging behavior. However, we also show how to use *Derive* to accomplish the same graphical analysis, because *Derive* has the ability to Zoom in on questionable sections of its plot.

Example 4.41. Let's examine the behavior of the infinite sequence

$$f(1) = (-1)^n \sqrt{n} \qquad n = 1, 2, \ldots \tag{4.26}$$

Figure 4.22 shows an Excel spreadsheet with the first 23 predictor values in cells A2–A24, along with the corresponding 23 response term values in cells B2–B24. The command line at the top shows the function form. The graph shows a plot of the corresponding points $(n, f(n))$

This sequence jumps back and forth across the x-axis as n increases, alternating between positive and negative response values. The response terms also seem to be splitting apart as n increases, which is one way that a sequence can

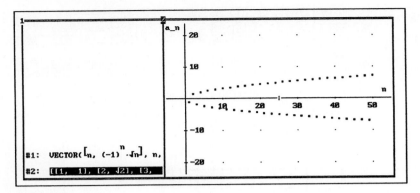

FIGURE 4.23
Alternating sequence plot.

fail to converge. This sequence is diverging. The sequence is also nonmonotonic, since each of the terms is neither only greater nor only less than its predecessor.

The same type of analysis can be accomplished using *Derive*.

To create, say, the first 50 predictor and response terms of the sequence, we can think of the response terms as an ordered list of components. The Calculus Vector command prompts you to enter the name of the sequence variable, the starting value of the sequence, the ending value of the sequence, and the step size that you want to use (usually equal to 1).

Alternatively, we can author the expression Vector($[n, (-1)^n \sqrt{n}]$, n, 50), which will create the ordered predictor-response pairs $(n, f(n))$ for $n = 1, \ldots,$ 50, using a step size of 1. Setting the Options State to Discrete will plot the sequence as points, and not as a connected curve. As shown in Figure 4.23, the results are similar.

In contrast to this last example, let's take a look at a sequence that converges.

Example 4.42. Examining the sequence

$$f(1) = (-1)^n 10\sqrt{1/n} \qquad n = 1, 2, \ldots \qquad (4.27)$$

we can see evidence of its converging behavior in the *Derive* plot in Figure 4.24. Although the response terms of this sequence also alternate back and forth across the x-axis, as n increases the two paths seem to be pinching in on the value $f(n) = 0$, although never quite getting there.

Increasing n to 100 shows this converging behavior even more (Figure 4.25). Notice also that, although the output terms of this sequence converge to zero, the sequence is still nonmonotonic.

Example 4.43. Examining the sequence

$$f(n) = 10/n^2 + 1 \qquad n = 2, 3, \ldots \qquad (4.28)$$

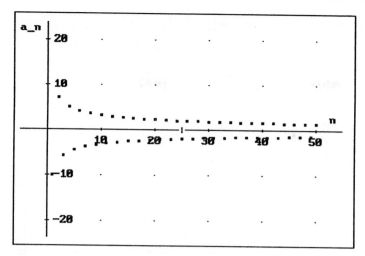

FIGURE 4.24
Converging alternating sequence.

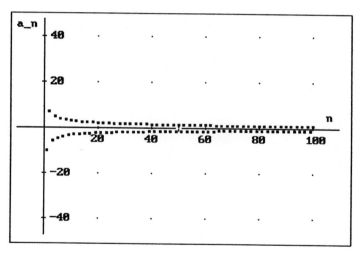

FIGURE 4.25
Nonmonotonic behavior.

we can see from the first 22 response terms in Figure 4.26 that, as n increases, the response terms of the sequence appear to be closing in on the value of $f(n) = 1$. This is a converging sequence.

Additionally, notice that, as n increases, each successive response term is less than its predecessor. The sequence is monotonically decreasing, which can be verified algebraically: $f(n) < f(n+1)$ for all n.

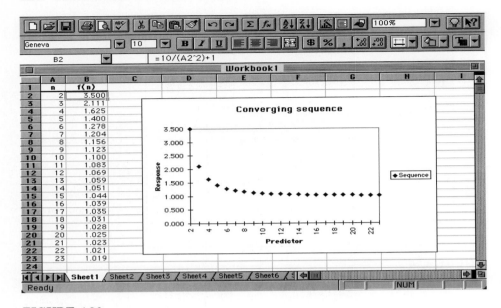

FIGURE 4.26
Converging monotonic sequence.

terms converge or diverge, and whether the sequence is monotonic in its behavior. Use the Ratio Test to confirm your graphical analysis, if it applies.

(a) $f(n) = 2n/(5n - 3)$, $n = 1, 2, \ldots$

(b) $f(n) = (1 - n^2)/(2 + 3n^2)$, $n = 1, 2, \ldots$

(c) $f(n) = (n - 1)/(n + 1)$, $n = 1, 2, \ldots$

(d) $f(n) = (-1)^n \left(\frac{n+1}{n} \right)$, $n = 1, 2, \ldots$

(e) $f(n) = (-1)^n \left((n + 0.1)/(n) \right)$, $n = 1, 2, \ldots$ (Hint: You may want to use the *Derive* Zoom option for this one.)

(f) $f(n) = \left((n^2 - 1)/(2 + n) \right)$, $n = 1, 2, \ldots$

4.2. Why is it valid to approximate a discrete function as continuous to test for one-to-one?

4.3. Consider the following infinite sequence

$$f(n) = r^n \qquad \text{for all } n = 1, 2, \ldots \qquad (4.29)$$

Graphically investigate the following questions.

(a) For what values of r does the sequence appear to converge?

(b) When it does appear to converge, does it always converge to the same value?

(c) For what values of r does the sequence appear to diverge?

(d) Is the sequence monotonic or nonmonotonic? Or does it depend upon the value of r? Explain your reasoning in a short essay, and include enough printouts or sketches of the sequence behavior to support your conclusions.

value of r? Explain your reasoning in a short essay, and include enough printouts or sketches of the sequence behavior to support your conclusions.

4.4. Consider the following infinite sequence

$$f(n) = \frac{1}{n^p} \qquad \text{for all } n = 1, 2, \ldots. \tag{4.30}$$

Graphically investigate the following questions.
(*a*) For what values of p does the sequence appear to converge?
(*b*) When it does appear to converges, does it always converge to the same value?
(*c*) For what values of p does the sequence appear to diverge?
(*d*) Is the sequence monotonic or nonmonotonic? Or does it depend upon the value of p? Explain your reasoning in a short essay, and include enough printouts or sketches of the sequence behavior to support your conclusions.

4.9 PIECEWISE FUNCTIONS

Piecewise functions make up an interesting class of functions. They frequently have restricted domains composed of a mixture of discrete points and continous intervals. As a result, a plot of this type of function can jump, have holes, or change shapes throughout its range.

Example 4.44. Let f be the piecewise function defined by

$$f(x) = \begin{cases} (x-1) & \text{if } x < 3 \\ (x/2+2) & \text{if } 3 \le x \le 5 \\ (x+1) & \text{if } x > 5 \end{cases} \tag{4.31}$$

Figure 4.27 shows a plot of this function. Although the domain and range of f both consist of the entire set of real numbers, we can see from the plot of $f(x)$ that the function is not continuous. It changes definition and instantaneously jumps at the predictor values $x = 3$ and $x = 5$.

To plot a piecewise function in *Derive*, we make the observation that we want to "turn on" a function definition only when the predictor's value is in the appropriate region. Otherwise, we want the function definition "turned off." We accomplish this using the chi(a,x,b) function as a multiplier for the function definitions. The chi(a,x,b) function takes on a value of 1 when $a < x < b$, and 0 otherwise.

To plot the previous example, we authored the expression

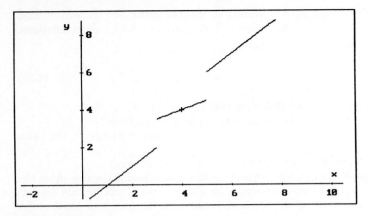

FIGURE 4.27
A piecewise discontinuous function.

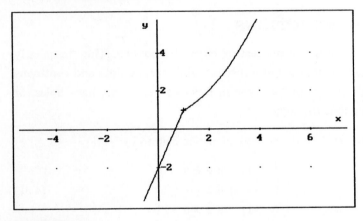

FIGURE 4.28
A piecewise continuous function.

```
(chi(-10,x,3)*(x-1))+(chi(3,x,5)*(x/2+2))+(chi(5,x,10)*(x+1))
```

which made each segment of the function definition active where appropriate, and inactive where it did not apply.

Example 4.45. Let g be the piecewise function defined by

$$g(x) = \begin{cases} (3x - 2) & \text{if } x < 1 \\ x^2 & \text{if } 1 \leq x \end{cases} \tag{4.32}$$

From Figure 4.28, we can see that the piecewise function g is continous, and it changes definition at the predictor value $x = 1$. As in the previous example, the domain and range of g consist of the set of all real numbers.

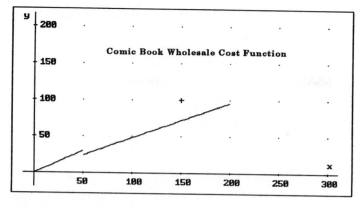

FIGURE 4.29
A piecewise wholesale cost function with a discontinous price break.

From a modeling perspective, piecewise functions are common. They are useful to capture the relationship between the response and predictor(s) whenever the situation specifies conditions on the response.

Example 4.46.   Price breaks. Many businesses can separate their operations into two activities—wholesaling and retailing—that dictate different pricing levels for goods and services. Consider the comic book business. The price that a magazine store pays a publisher for one new comic book is about $0.60. This is called the *wholesale price*. They, in turn, sell it to the public at the *retail price* of about $1.10. The mark-up in price that the public pays is determined by the store owner and designed to cover such costs as taxes that the store owner must pay, the costs of paying store employees their wages, the cost of keeping the store open, and a small amount of profit.

When the store orders a new batch of comic books from a single publisher, the publisher will usually price the comic books differently for volume purchases. The first 50 comic books might cost $0.60 apiece, whereas if they purchase between 51–200 comic books, the wholesale price is lowered to $0.48. The publisher actually makes out about the same or better in the latter case because they are moving more comic books out of inventory (saving storage costs, handling costs, labor costs, etc.) and getting a larger presence in the market.

Suppose that our modeling objective was to describe the cost of purchasing comic books from this publisher as seen from the perspective of the store owner. We'll select the response to be the cost c that the store owner realizes, in dollars. We'll let the predictor x equal the number of comic books purchased. The relationship between the response and the predictor is then given by

$$c = f(x) = \begin{cases} 0.6x & \text{if } x < 50 \\ 0.48x & \text{if } 50 \leq x \leq 200 \end{cases} \tag{4.33}$$

Figure 4.29 shows the effect of this piecewise function. Notice the *break* in price that the store receives at the predictor value of $x = 50$ comic books. This PRICE

BREAKS

idea of a price break corresponds to an instantaneous jump in the plot of price function $f(x)$.

As you will see in the project discussing price breaks, piecewise functions are very useful for modeling discontinuous cashflow structures. Although we focus on shipping charges in the project, you will encounter many applications of piecewise functions in your daily life (e.g. memberships in health clubs, CD club purchases, magazine subscriptions, automobile rentals) where organizations or companies want to reward actions that indicate a greater level of loyalty or participation in their business activities. In a later project dealing with pay scales, you will also see how effects such as promotion bonuses and pay raises cause instantaneous jumps at set times in an employee's career.

Exploration Exercises───────────────────────────────

4.1. Plot f and identify its range and domain.

$$f(x) = \begin{cases} (2x - 3) & \text{if } x < 2 \\ x^2 & \text{if } 2 \leq x \end{cases} \tag{4.34}$$

4.2. Plot g and identify its range and domain.

$$g(x) = \begin{cases} (1 - x^2) & \text{if } x < 0 \\ 3x + 1 & \text{if } 0 \leq x \end{cases} \tag{4.35}$$

4.3. Plot h and identify its range and domain.

$$h(x) = \begin{cases} (x + 2) & \text{if } x < -4 \\ \sqrt{16 - x^2} & \text{if } -4 \leq x \leq 4 \\ (2 - x) & \text{if } 4 \leq x \end{cases} \tag{4.36}$$

4.4. The idea of turning on and off different curve regions raises an interesting challenge: can you draw your initials on the *Derive* screen using the `chi(a,x,b)` function? Specify each initial that you have *Derive* as a piecewise function. The end result will be a function expression for your initials.

4.10   SUMMARY

This chapter presented some basic ideas about functions. We defined a function as a rule that assigns a unique response output to each predictor input. We learned how to identify functions graphically and algebraically, and how to use functional notation.

The set of allowable predictor values for a function is called the function's *domain,* and the set of response outputs is defined as the *range* of the function. We discussed restricted domains, which often become a necessity in modeling real world problems.

We examined discrete functions as sequences whose domains are restricted to be the positive integers. We also looked briefly at piecewise functions and how they arise in modeling situations.

We discussed some properties of functions (one-to-one, increasing, and decreasing, among others) and how these properties translated to discrete functions. An increasing function is always one-to-one, as is a decreasing function.

The horizontal line test is a graphical test used to determine whether a function is one-to-one.

One-to-one functions have inverses. An inverse function allows us to identify the predictor from its response. A function's inverse can be found graphically by reflecting its plot about the line $y = x$. Or, a function's inverse can be calculated algebraically.

Functions can be created from other functions. The composition of functions and algebraic operations with functions are two ways to do so. This chapter provides a foundation to build on in later chapters and to prepare you for future mathematical courses.

4.11   PROJECT: PRICE BREAKS

Catalog shopping is a very convenient way of purchasing merchandise without having to endure the challenges of traveling from one store to another. In addition to the price of the item ordered, taxes and shipping charges are also added to the customer costs. However, companies apply these charges differently, and their specific strategy is carefully constructed to meet the needs of their business.

This project is will examine two such strategies that will give you an appreciation for the usefulness of piecewise functions for modeling. The two companies are real, as are the charges listed. We've changed their names for this project.

CASE 1: CLOTHING RETAILER

Cool Digs, a clothing manufacturer that sells its merchandise by catalog, advertises the following shipping charges.

ORDER TOTAL	STANDARD (3–5 days)	EXPRESS (3 days)	EXPRESS PLUS (2 days)
Up to $30.00	$2.95	$8.95	$14.95
$30.01 to $60.00	$4.95	$10.95	$16.95
$60.01 to $90.00	$6.95	$12.95	$18.95
$90.01 to $120.00	$8.95	$14.95	$20.95
$120.01 to $150.00	$10.95	$16.95	$22.95
$150.01 to $200.00	$12.95	$18.95	$24.95
$200.01 and over	$14.95	$20.95	$26.95

Notice that this company bases its shipping charges on the dollar total of a customers's order. Let's take a closer look at these charges based on the modeling tools that we have learned. The focus question that we will use is "What is the best shipping strategy for a customer to use?"

Required Analysis

1. Identify an appropriate response and predictor, and specify each of the shipping options—Standard, Express, Express Plus—as a piecewise function of one variable.
2. Plot and describe the appearance of each of the shipping option functions. If there are points of discontinuity in the functions, identify them.
3. Is the clothing company giving the customer price breaks on shipping costs? If so, what are they and where do they occur? Are they significant?

Cool Digs is now considering changing the manner in which it charges the customer shipping costs to one based on either

1. the total number of items ordered, or
2. the total weight of the order.

Required Analysis

1. Do you recommend that the company changes to one of the new strategies, or stays with the current one? Explain why you recommend a particular strategy, and provide examples that support your reasoning.

2. Is there a single strategy that favors the customer? Why?

3. Is there a single strategy that favors the company? Why?

4. If Cool Digs sold furniture in addition to their clothing, would your recommendation change? Explain.

CASE 2: PLANT NURSERY

The Rustic Ridge plant nursery sells annual and perennial plants and flowers by catalog advertises the following shipping charges.

Order total	Charge	Order total	Charge
Up to $15.00	$5.95	$35.01 to $45.00	$8.95
$15.01 to $25.00	$6.95	$45.01 to $55.00	$9.95
$25.01 to $35.00	$7.95	$55.01 to $65.00	$10.95
Add $0.10 per each $1.00 of merchandise over $65.00			

As in Case 1, Rustic Ridge bases its shipping charges on the total dollar order of the customer. However, there exists an important difference between the two strategies. Notice how the shipping costs are *fixed* costs within predictor intervals for merchandise orders up to $65.00, and *variable* costs thereafter. Variable charges are charges that change either continuously or in small increments depending on the value of the predictor. Let's examine the effect of Rustic Ridge's strategy on the customer and see if there is some strategy that we could recommend for customers currently placing orders with Rustic Ridge.

Required Analysis_____

1. Identify an appropriate response and predictor, and specify the Rustic Ridge shipping strategy as a piecewise function of one variable.

2. Plot and describe the appearance of the resulting shipping function. If there are points of discontinuity in the functions, identify them.

3. Is Rustic Ridge giving the customer price breaks on shipping costs? If so, what are they and where do they occur? Are they significant?

4. What effect do variable charges have on the shipping cost function? Do these variable charges favor the company or the customer?

We now want you to see a subtle effect of *averaging* that is easy to overlook within the shipping cost structure used by Rustic Ridge. First, notice that it might appear that Rustic Ridge is basing its cost structure on the idea of $0.10 per $1.00 of merchandise ordered. But, is it really? What is the difference?

Required Analysis

1. Specify a continuous shipping function of one variable that represents a $0.10 per $1.00 of merchandise ordered for all merchandise orders.

2. Plot this resulting shipping cost function on the same graph as the piecewise shipping function currently being used by Rustic Ridge. At what points do the two strategies intersect?

3. Does a variable shipping cost strategy give the customer any price breaks? Explain.

4. Although one may argue that the *average* cost per $1.00 of merchandise ordered in the current strategy is $0.10, this hides the true effect of fixed-cost intervals. By employing the current shipping cost strategy, what merchandise ordering strategy is the customer being pressured into adopting? Why?

5. Which one of the two shipping cost strategies favors the company? Which favors the customer? Pay particular attention to the portions of the shipping cost functions where the two functions do not intersect.

6. A point that must be made: A cost savings passed on to the customer translates into revenue that is sacrificed by the company. If Rustic Ridge was to change to this new strategy, estimate the total amount of revenue that they would sacrifice in doing so. (*Hint:* What does the area between each function plot and the x-axis represent? A little geometry would help here.)

7. What merchandise ordering strategy would you recommend for customers of Rustic Ridge? (Assume that the current shipping cost strategy is being used.)

4.12 PROJECT: CRYPTOLOGY

In addition to using inverse functions to determine the predictor value(s) that might be causing a response we observe, they also have a very useful application all their own.

Codes and ciphers are ways to create privacy in messages sent over public transmission means. The *plaintext* is the message to be encoded. A *code* is a rule that assigns an address to each word in a set of words. A portion of a code might look something like

Codenumber	Plaintext
4021	bank
1304	credit
0010	name

In the encoded message sent in public, this means that the number 4021 replaces *bank*.

A *cipher* is a rule that assigns a numerical address to each letter in a message. A portion of a cipher for the English alphabet might look like

plaintext	a	b	c	d	e	f
cipher address	16	55	51	93	11	04

The study of codes and ciphers is called *cryptology*.

To be useful, the code and cipher rules must be one-to-one functions: We need to know what numerical address to assign to the pieces of our message, and we need to be able to decode the received messages.

To encrypt a message, we break it into words or letters, and apply our code and cipher functions. The output of the function is transmitted to our intended recipient. The recipient applies the inverse of the function we used to encrypt the message, and recovers the original message.

An eavesdropper only obtains the encrypted message, consisting of the numerical addresses. If the eavesdropper can successfully determine the inverse function being used, the code or cipher can be broken.

Secure encryption is a growing concern as more and more commerce moves onto the Internet. Many businesses would like for you to be able to order merchandise directly from their home page using a credit card. However, for money to be passed on the net, both the sender and the recipient want to make sure that no one can intercept their message, and more important, that no one can impersonate either party.

This project involves writing a short research paper investigating the use of functions in cryptology.

Required Analysis_____For

this project, assume that you are working for a communications company called EaseNet, Inc. EaseNet used to provide only telephone communications to its customers. Last year, they expanded their services to include on-line banking, private e-mail communications, and secure file transfers. Assume that you have been asked by your boss, Oke Sanduski, about the possibility of encrypting the company's financial records. Your requirement is to submit no more than a two page report that addresses your You need to accomplish three things.

1. Discuss what properties an encryption function and its inverse should possess.

2. Discuss how EaseNet, Inc. could send an e-mail message that proved the sender, and the sender alone, was the one who sent it.

3. Discuss the benefits to your company (and yourself) of having secure, private communications.

4.13 COMPLEMENTS

There are many excellent references available on the Internet that provide information on encryption ideas. Use your browser to find some references.

1. As this text is written, encryption on the Internet is a hot topic. Secure encryption algorithms, based on established mathematical properties, are freely available. These algorithms are used in private mail systems such as *PGP* (for Pretty Good Privacy). In the course of doing the project on Cryptology, you can find many, many useful sources of information on secure encryption on the Internet simply by searching on Yahoo! (http://www.yahoo.com).

2. You may want to perform a search using the following terms: encryption, V-chip, secure banking, secure banking, pretty good privacy.

3. A detailed, but not so technical account of cryptology is found in the book

   • *The Codebreakers: The Story of Secret Writing*, by David Kahn. MacMillan Company, New York, New York. First printing 1967.

CHAPTER 5

LINEAR MODELS

A great discovery solves a great problem but there is a grain of discovery in the solution of any problem. Your problem may be modest; but if it challenges your curiosity and brings into play your inventive faculties, and if you solve it by your own means, you may experience the tension and enjoy the triumph of discovery.

George Polya

Chapter Goals

⇒ Understand that all linear models have constant rates of change.

⇒ Understand why the initial model developed is often a linear model.

⇒ Fit linear models to data using technology.

⇒ Solve linear models.

⇒ Analyze fitted linear models to verify their appropriateness and to gain additional insights.

⇒ Understand how to report results, completing the 5 step modeling process.

Up to this point, we've examined many of the ideas of mathematical models, including our five-stage modeling process—*mess, model, solution, analysis, report.* We've also examined how to create functional relationships between predictors called *constraints.*

Now we are ready to focus on the response-predictor function and the various forms that it can take. This comprises the remainder of topics in this book, and is the last critical detail we need to start building, solving, and analyzing models. We'll start with linear models.

Linear models are fundamental models in applied mathematics. This is not to say that they are trivial. In fact, they are rich in ideas and insights, many of which extend to all the other models we examine in this text.

This chapter begins the part of the book that we find the most interesting—solving problems and thinking about the solutions. Although we could never hope to address every type of problem that you might encounter, we hope that the examples and problems that we do introduce will encourage you to attack similar problems of your own.

5.1   LINEAR FUNCTIONS: ONE PREDICTOR

Linear functions of one predictor are simple but very useful models. Let's first discuss the implications of using a linear model. Then we'll move on to discuss linear functions, and apply some of the ideas developed in Chapter 4.

This section lays a foundation for extending linear models to include functions of several predictors, and to building linear models from existing data.

The bottom line up front: Whenever the change in the response is *directly proportional* to the change in the predictors, a linear model is appropriate. In other words, for each unit of change in the predictor, the response always changes by the same constant multiple of this change in the predictor. An example will clarify the point.

Example 5.1. A helical spring is a measuring device with a small hook on the end of a spring that sport fishermen use to measure the weight of fish that they catch. The heavier the fish, the greater the extension of the helical spring, and the heavier the device indicates the fish weighs.

In a certain spring a fish of size x pounds causes an extension of y inches on the helical spring. The associated spring extension for six different sized fish

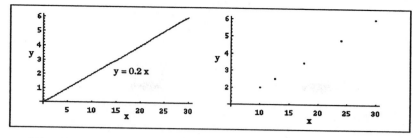

FIGURE 5.1
Graphical evidence of a directly proportional relationship.

is given by:

x	5.0	10.0	12.5	17.5	24.0	30.0
y	1.0	2.0	2.5	3.5	4.8	6.0

Each of the spring extension measurements results by multiplying the weight of the fish by 0.2. Therefore, if we were to model this helical spring device with x = weight of a fish as the only predictor, and y = the length of the spring extension, we would get the linear model $y = 0.2x$.

Notice two things: (1) for each value of the predictor x there is exactly one value of y, and (2) each value of the response y results by multiplication of the predictor x by exactly the same constant $c = 0.2$. This constant multiplier is called a *constant of proportionality*. These two qualities characterize direct proportionality.

By writing $y = 0.2x$ as $y/x = 0.2$ we can clearly see the idea that y is proportional to x in this linear model.

Figure 5.1 shows the graphical evidence of direct proportionality. If we were to plot each of the points (x, y) on a rectangular coordinate system as we did on the right-hand figure, and connect them with a continuous curve as we did on the left-hand figure, the points (x, y) will lie on a line *through the origin*. As we will examine in more detail later in the book, the plot on the left side of Figure 5.1 is called a *continuous* plot. The plot on the right side is called a *discrete* plot.

5.1.1 Lines and linearity

There are several different ways of writing an equation of a line. Each has its usefulness, depending upon the task that we are faced with.

- The *general* form of an equation for a line is given by $Ax + By + C = 0$. We will often use the slightly different form $Ax + By = C$ when we write linear constraints. You have already seen the constraint form as inequalities in linear programming models.

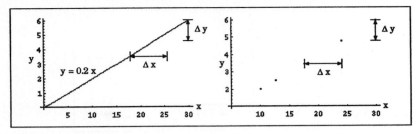

FIGURE 5.2
Notation representing the amount of change in both the independent and dependent variables.

- The *slope-intercept* form is given by $y = mx + b$, where m is the slope of the line and b is the y-intercept. Notice that we can write the expression for a line given by $Ax + By + C = 0$ in slope-intercept form as

$$y = \frac{-A}{B}x - \frac{C}{B}$$

- The *point-slope* form is given by

$$y - y_0 = m(x - x_0) \tag{5.1}$$

where (x_0, y_0) are the coordinates of one point known to be on the line, and m is the slope. When $x_0 = 0$, y_0 is the y-intercept. This form is a generalization of the slope-intercept form. We will make use of a modification of the point-slope form as

$$m = \frac{y - y_0}{x - x_0} \tag{5.2}$$

As we see in the exercises, each of these forms can be used to find all the others.

The key property we want to focus on is given by Equation 5.1, which we express as a theorem.

Theorem 5.1. Let $y = f(x)$ be a linear function, and let $y_0 = f(x_0)$ for some x_0 in the domain of f. Then the change in y, given by $\Delta y = y - y_0$, is always a constant multiple of the change in x, given by $\Delta x = x - x_0$.

The constant multiplier of Theorem 5.1 is the **slope** of the line. This property of a constant slope is unique to linear functions—every linear function it, and no others do.

Figure 5.2 shows the special notation that is used to capture the idea of change in a variable: the Greek capital letter Δ. So, the change in y as y moves

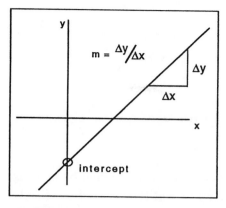

FIGURE 5.3
The relation between slope, intercept, Δx, and Δy.

away from some value y_0 is $\Delta y = y - y_0$. Likewise, the change in x is written as $\Delta x = x - x_0$. The slope is the ratio

$$m = \frac{\Delta y}{\Delta x} \qquad (5.3)$$

which follows from our definitions and Equation 5.2.

The fraction

$$\frac{\Delta y}{\Delta x}$$

is called a *difference quotient.* For a line, this difference quotient is constant, DIFFERENCE regardless of the initial point (x_0, y_0) we choose to use. QUOTIENT

Notice how this idea relates to the concept of proportionality previously introduced. A directly proportional relationship between two variables means DIRECT that $y/x = c$, where c is the constant of proportionality that never changes, PROPOR- regardless of where on the line that we look. Now, when we examine the slope, TIONALITY or *rate of change* of the resulting curve, we find that $\Delta y/\Delta x = m$, where m is AGAIN! a constant slope value, regardless of where on the line that we look. Both the values of x and y, and the changes Δx and Δy, are directly proportional.

A line is completely described by its slope and by the identification of one point on the line. Figure 5.3 illustrates these ideas.

There is a distinction we make between linear relations and linear functions. We will occasionally state that a set of linear predictors are related by a linear expression, such as $x_1 + x_2 = 1$, without focusing on the underlying function $x_2 = f(x_1) = 1 - x_1$ that the linear relation defines implicitly. Our motivation is that we will encounter nonlinear relations between predictors later, and we won't care that those relations are not functions.

For now however, let's continue to focus on describing the response-predictor relation as a function.

5.1.2 Linear functions

> **Definition 5.1. Linear Functions.** A linear function of one argument is a function of the form
> $$y = f(x) = mx + b$$

We can quickly verify that $f(x) = mx + b$ does describe a function by plotting any line that is not vertical. The vertical line test will then cross $f(x)$ exactly once.

We are excluding vertical lines within our modeling approach, because we can't express it in a form that reveals information about the response-predictor relationship $y = mx+b$. A vertical line is written as $x = k$, which tells us nothing about the response y, and which (obviously) fails the vertical line test!

When we model a response as a linear function of one predictor, we say that a plot of the response and predictor lies on a straight line. This was exactly the case using the example of a helical spring earlier. The response y (extension length of the helical spring) is a linear function of the single predictor x (weight of a fish). Consequently, we can write $y = f(x) = 0.2x$.

5.1.3 Analysis of linear functions

When we model the response as a linear function of the predictor, we automatically set the values of the slope and the intercept. Choosing a linear model asserts many things about the relation between the response and the predictor:

- Changing the value of the predictor has the same effect on the response, regardless of the value of the predictor we choose to change. This is the idea of Δy being directly proportional to Δx:
$$\frac{\Delta y}{\Delta x} = \frac{y - y_0}{x - x_0} = m$$

From this relationship, we see that

$$\Delta y = y - y_0 = m(x - x_0) = m\Delta x$$

for *every* set of values (x_0, y_0) that we could pick. By the way, if you solve for y in the equation $y - y_0 = m(x - x_0)$, you might recognize the result.

- The response has no maximum (or minimum) value, unless we restrict the domain or the line has $m = 0$.

  - If we restrict the domain, a maximum (or minimum) value occurs at an endpoint of the restricted domain. We can always get a positive (or negative) Δy by choosing an appropriate Δx.
  - If $m = 0$, the response y is a constant, and every predictor value x produces the "maximum" and "minimum" value of y. Notice that an endpoint of the domain still produces a maximum (or minimum) value— although this value is not unique.

These are strong assertions, although they may not appear so. They are often approximately true, even for nonlinear functions, if the function is smooth and the domain restricted.

We end this section with two theorems, which we ask you to verify in the exercises.

Theorem 5.2. A linear function of one predictor whose slope is nonzero is a one-to-one function.

This theorem follows immediately from the horizontal line test of the last chapter.

Theorem 5.3. A linear function of one predictor whose slope is positive is an increasing function; a linear function of one predictor whose slope is negative is decreasing.

5.1.3.1 INTERPRETING SLOPE.

Slope is the *rate of increase* of y, per unit of increase of x. Every one unit change in x results in a corresponding change in y of m units.

Example 5.2. The Automobile Association of America (AAA) publishes some great maps for traveling by automobile. One of the features that makes the maps useful is a small insert next to the legend section that shows the outline of the states that the map covers, along with a superimposed network diagram of the major highways connecting the cities. Labeled alongside each of the connecting lines is both the milage between the cities and the supposed time it should take to traverse the highway.

For example, from San Diego to Sacramento along Highway 5 and Highway 99 on the State of California map, the following information is provided:

From	To	Miles	Time (hrs:min)
San Diego	Long Beach	109	2:05
Long Beach	Los Angeles	24	0:30
Los Angeles	Bakersfield	114	2:14
Bakersfield	Fresno	104	2:00
Fresno	Merced	56	1:10
Merced	Manteca	54	0:59
Manteca	Sacramento	63	1:16

Two questions come to mind: (1) Do these values assume that we would be traveling at some specific rate of travel while on these highways? Perhaps the new interstate speed limit of 65 miles per hour? If so, then we should be able to identify this from the data. And, (2) are the quantities representing the location of the vehicle and the time of travel directly proportional to one another?

We can investigate the answers to these questions in several ways. We'll pick an approach that illustrates the point that we're trying to make in this section.

Using the city of San Diego as the starting point of our trip, we'll let $l =$ location of the vehicle from San Diego (in miles), and $t =$ the total time that has elapsed (starting at $t = 0$). This will change the tabular information we have slightly, since we now want elapsed distance and elapsed time. We'll also convert the units of hours and minutes to just minutes.

From	To	Elapsed miles	Elapsed time (min)
San Diego	Long Beach	109	125
Long Beach	Los Angeles	133	155
Los Angeles	Bakersfield	247	289
Bakersfield	Fresno	351	409
Fresno	Merced	407	479
Merced	Manteca	461	538
Manteca	Sacramento	524	614

If the rate of travel, or *rate of change of the vehicles position* is constant, then we know that no matter where we check the rate on the highways, we should see that

$$\frac{\text{Change in location}}{\text{Change in time}} = \frac{\Delta l}{\Delta t} = \text{ a constant}$$

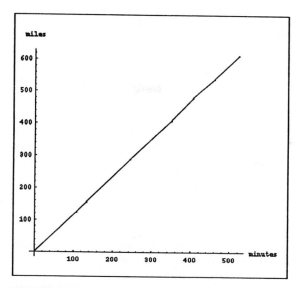

FIGURE 5.4
Piecewise linear plot of the rate of travel between San Diego and Sacramento.

From	To	$\Delta l / \Delta t$ (miles/min)	mph
San Diego	Long Beach	$109/125 = 0.87$	52.5
Long Beach	Los Angeles	$24/30 = 0.8$	48.0
Los Angeles	Bakersfield	$114/134 = 0.85$	51.0
Bakersfield	Fresno	$104/120 = 0.87$	52.2
Fresno	Merced	$56/70 = 0.8$	48.0
Merced	Manteca	$54/59 = .92$	55.2
Manteca	Sacramento	$63/76 = 0.83$	49.8

Figure 5.4 shows a plot of the the values of elapsed time versus elapsed distance for our data with sequential pairs of data points connected by a straight line segment.

From the evidence provided, the labeling information provided by AAA for traveling along this route does not assume that we will be traveling at a constant speed from San Diego to Sacramento. Certainly it does not assume that we would be traveling 65 miles per hour. But what are these values that we have computed? The answer is one of utmost importance for calculus.

First, each of these values represent a specific solution to the general expression

$$\frac{\text{distance traveled}}{\text{time elapsed}} = \frac{\Delta l}{\Delta t} = r = \text{ rate of travel}$$

This general expression is a model of how we are proposing that distance and time are related.

Secondly, each calculation is not just giving us a speed value between the cities. Each value represents the *average* rate of travel between the cities noted. And we can see from the expression

$$l/t = r \qquad \equiv \qquad l = rt$$

that each of these r-values is the slope of the line segment connecting pairs of data points.

Third, connecting the data points in this manner is the same as drawing a *secant* line between these points. And a secant line represents the average change $\Delta y/\Delta x$ between two points on a plot such as this. We still don't have a way of calculating how fast we would be traveling *at each instant* of the trip, called the *instantaneous* rate of travel. For this information, we need calculus.

Now, let's do some analysis. Why might the individual rate of travel values differ between cities? Would the map being out-of-date cause these values to differ? Most likely not. Even if the map we were using were outdated, and was printed while the old 55 mph limit was in effect, we would expect that this would simply shift each segment's rate of travel downward. It would not explain why each was different. Perhaps there is an error in the values reported?

What about the assumptions we are using? Here are a few questions that will illustrate how to challenge the modeling assumptions.

- The AAA map shows each of the cities noted as dots, with each of the highway segments connecting the cities as straight lines. However, cities are not dimensionless. They tend to cover a lot of square miles within their boundaries. If the highways go through the cities, perhaps the speed limits within the city boundaries is less than the open highways. Is the travel time between cities adjusted to compensate for this?

- Are there tolls or bridges along the roads, or something else such as interchanges that would cause the speed limit to decrease?

- Do the times that AAA is using include some kind of traffic factor that adjusts the estimated travel time around areas where heavy traffic is typically encountered?

We could (and should) investigate each of these assumptions, eliminating them one by one until the culprit introducing the differences is noted.

Our question on proportionality is intentionally posed, because the answer is not as obvious as we might first suspect. We know from earlier that a proportional model involving l and t would have

$$\frac{l}{t} = \text{a constant} \qquad \text{or} \qquad l = ct$$

Consequently, if we plot the data in the last table and connect the points with a continous curve, we should get a line going through the origin. Since we have pinned our starting point in San Diego and labeled this as $(l,t) = (0,0)$ in our table, we know that any curve that we use to connect the points will go though the origin. We just need the curve to be a line to conclude that a directly proportional relationship exists here.

Do we have a *single* line throught the origin? No. Do we have a single continuous curve going through the origin? Yes. And, in fact, it is linear; it is *piecewise linear*!

Between each pair of consecutive city pairs, the rate of change is constant since each curve connecting these pairs is linear. Within each travel segment, the two variables l and t are directly proportional. We just have not been able to specify a single r-value that would apply to the entire trip.

As an aside, make a mental note of what happens to the slope value at the connection points of these line segments. The slope values *instantaneously* change when we jump from one line segment to the next. These "corners" cause problems in calculus, when you will be working with instantaneous rates of change.

Barring any changes we make after checking out our assumptions, this piecewise linear model seems to be appropriate, given what we know intuitively about motion.

Lastly, by adopting this particular model, we mention that we are making some implied assumptions: the values of t are nonnegative, and if no time elapses then no distance is traveled.

Exploration Exercises

5.1. In the example just introduced, we saw that connecting two points on the data plot is the same as drawing a secant line between the two points. The slope of this secant line is the average rate of change $\Delta y/\Delta x$ between the two points. Since we don't have a way of determining the instantaneous rate of change without calculus, someone proposed that collecting the distance elapsed and time elapsed data at shorter intervals of time would enable us to approximate this quantity. What do you think? How small would you recommend the time intervals be? What happens to the plot of the secant lines under this scheme?

5.2. Someone else proposed that the data be used in a slightly different manner: knowing the time that has elapsed and the average rate of travel at a particular time allows us to calculate the distance elapsed at that particular time. For each interval, you know the value of slope and the two points that are connected by the secant line. Specify a piecewise linear function that describes the entire data set, and demonstrate how this model could be used in the way suggested.

5.3. We saw that the different rates of change correspond to the individual slopes of the line segments connecting the points. Because each of the slopes varied, no single straight line would go through all of the data points. However, if you were forced to pick or draw one line for the entire data set, how would you do it? Here are some suggestions to get you thinking.
   (a) Would you calculate the average value of all the slopes and then use this to draw your line?
   (b) Would you connect the first and last data points with a straight line and ignore the ones in the middle?
   (c) How do the linear models that result from these two approaches differ?
   (d) Which produces a model that better "fits" the data? Why?

5.4. When two quantities y and x are directly proportional, the resulting model is linear. Is this claim also true for the case when two quantities are *indirectly* or *inversely* proportional? Demonstrate your answer with a graphical plot.

Example 5.3. In the last chapter, we had a linear model for sales, s, as a function of the predictor $a =$ the preceding month's advertising expenditures. It was given by Equation 4.7:

$$s = f(a) = 10a$$

This model states that, for every \$1 spent on advertising, sales increases by \$10. It also implies that without money spent on advertising, sales will be zero. This is again an example of an assumption *embedded* in the model. If you use the model, you accept the assumption.

As in Example 5.2, here we are constraining both s and a to be nonnegative. The finite amount of wealth in the world would impose an upper bound on both s and a, although it may not matter to the problem.

5.1.3.2   INTERPRETING INTERCEPTS.

There are actually two intercepts associated with a linear response-predictor function using a single predictor. The first is the usual y-intercept. We also call this the *response intercept*. It is the value that the function will assume when the predictor equals zero: $y - \text{intercept} = f(0)$. The plot of the graph of $y = f(x)$ with a y-intercept of 0 goes through the origin, as in the case of the AAA example earlier.

There is also an x-intercept, similarly referred to as the *predictor intercept*. It is the value of the predictor that makes the response equal to zero: $0 = f(x)$. It is also known as a "root, or zero, of the function $f(x)$."

An x–intercept does not always exist.

Example 5.4. The linear function $y = f(x) = 3$ is a perfectly valid linear function, and it has no x-intercept. On the other extreme, the trivial linear function $y = f(x) = 0$ makes every point an x-intercept.

Linear functions with nonzero slope divide the cartesian coordinate system into two parts, which in turn causes the functions to have one x-intercept and one y-intercept, unless their domains have been restricted to exclude them.

Example 5.5. The DrinkWell company manufactures 16 ounce plastic cups that it sells to stadium beverage vendors. Suppose that the relationship between the response profit (p) as function of the predictor units sold (u) was given as

$$p = f(u) = 1.5u - 150 \tag{5.4}$$

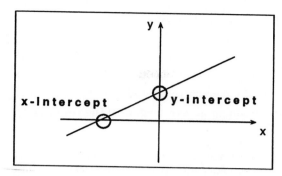

FIGURE 5.5
Intercepts for a linear function.

where each unit sold would generate $1.50 in profit, and the company faced a fixed set up cost of $150 to purchase the mold used to manufacture the plastic cups.

Since units sold is naturally restricted to values $u \geq 0$, the domain of $f(u)$ is likewise restricted. This results in a range for $f(u)$ of $p \geq -150$. Additionally, assuming that the plastic cups are sold in whole pieces, u must be an integer. We'll ignore this complicating restriction for now, and just impose that $u \geq 0$.

The predictor intercept would be $u = 100$, corresponding to the point $(u, p) = (100, 0)$. For any $u > 100$, profit is positive. For any $0 \leq u < 100$, profit is negative. We can interpret the value $u = 100$ as a *break-even point*. If the company sells enough plastic cups to bring their sales amount to this level, they have not made any profit, but they also are not experiencing a loss either.

BREAK-EVEN POINT

We note in passing that the response p is not limited on how large it can get. We use the terminology that the function $f(u)$ is not *bounded above*. Notice that $f(u)$ is bounded below: The minimum value of p is $p_{min} = -150$.

5.1.3.3 PREDICTION.

We often want to use the models we develop for prediction: What will be the response if a certain predictor value occurs? Prediction with a linear function is straightforward: Simply substitute the value of the predictor into the function for the corresponding response value.

Example 5.6. We can use the profit function $p = f(u) = 1.5u - 150$ to accomplish prediction. What can we expect profit to be if plastic cup sales reaches a level of 200 units?

Substituting the value of the predictor $u = 200$ into the profit function yields:

$$p = f(u) = f(200)$$
$$= 1.5(200) - 150$$
$$= 300 - 150$$
$$= \$150$$

The expected profit is \$150 when sales equals 200 units.

If a linear model is exactly correct—if it is completely valid—then we expect the predicted response to be the exact value given by the function. However, a model typically can have a small estimation error associated with the slope and intercept that will preclude us from obtaining an exact value of the response.

> **Example 5.7.** Let's return to our earlier example involving the trip from San Diego to Sacramento. Suppose upon checking our assumptions that AAA stated that they estimated each of the distances between cities, but were confident that their estimated values were within 2% of the true distance. Then, for each segment, the predicted value of r that we calculated would not be exact; it would have estimation error included in it. For example, a 2% error in the distance from San Diego to Long Beach would yield a value for the rate of travel as $51.27 \leq r \leq 53.36$. The value of r we would predict using this model is affected by the uncertainty in the distance data.

It is also possible that a response-predictor relationship is not exactly linear, or there could also be measurement error in the predictors. As a result, we say we *expect* the response to be the predicted value, but we may not be surprised if it varies slightly from the value predicted by the model.

The issues associated with *variation* between the true and predicted values are addressed later. How much variation is likely is a core issue in the study of applied statistics. How much is tolerable is a concern of every discipline that uses mathematical models.

5.1.3.4   INVERSES.

Finding the inverse of a linear function is a direct application of the ideas of the last chapter. A linear function with nonzero slope is one-to-one: It has an inverse.

> **Example 5.8.** Assuming that $m \neq 0$, we can directly solve for the inverse of the function $y = f(x) = mx + b$. By solving for x, we obtain directly
>
> $$x = \frac{y - b}{m} = f^{-1}(y) \tag{5.5}$$

Let's highlight the point that the inverse $f^{-1}(y)$ is valid only for those values of y that correspond to our (possibly restricted) original domain of $f(x)$.

> **Example 5.9.** The profit function $p = f(u) = 1.5u - 150$ has $m = 1.5$ and $b = -150$. Suppose that the question we want to answer is: How many cups do we have to sell to have a profit of \$2000? This type of question motivates finding

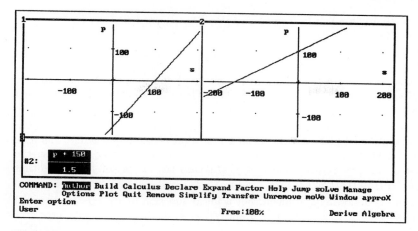

FIGURE 5.6
Graph of a profit function $p = 1.5s - 150$ on the left and its inverse $s = (p + 150)/1.5$ on the right.

the inverse of the profit function, which would then give us sales as a function of profit.

Using the approach of Equation 5.5 we can calculate its inverse:

$$u = \frac{p - (-150)}{1.5} = \frac{p + 150}{1.5} = f^{-1}(p)$$

Then, using this inverse function, we can answer the question posed:

$$f^{-1}(2000) = \frac{2150}{1.5} \approx 1434 \text{ plastic cups}$$

For what values of p is the inverse defined? Recall that the range of f consisted of all values of p such that $p \geq -150$, so that $s \geq 0$ because sales cannot be negative under our interpretation. This range of p values now becomes the domain of the inverse function $f^{-1}(p)$. In other words, the range of p becomes the input for the function $f^{-1}(p)$.

The inverse $f^{-1}(p)$ is defined for all values of p such that $p \geq -150$. Figure 5.6 shows a plot of the profit function $f(s)$ using s for units sold and its inverse $f^{-1}(p)$. Notice that by convention the horizontal axis is used to display the function domain (function input, or independent variable values, which are all the same idea). The vertical axis is used to display the function range (function output, or dependent variable values, which are also equivalent ideas).

Exploration Exercises

5.1. For the following linear functions with the indicated domains, find the slope, the response-intercept, the predictor-intercept, and the inverse. Be sure to specify the domain of the inverse functions.

(a) $y = f(x) = 3x + 1$, $x > 0$

(b) $y = f(x) = x - 7, \, x > 7$

(c) $y = f(x) = \sqrt{5}x + \pi, \, x > -5$

(d) $y = f(x) = 7 - x, \, x > 7$

(e) $y = f(x) = \frac{x+1}{2}, \, x > -1$

5.2. Compare the lines given by the equation $x + y = 1$ and the equation $2x + 2y = 2$. Can you see a relationship between the two? Can you write a general rule based on your observation?

5.3. Examining Figure 5.6, notice that if we were to draw the line $p = s$ in both plots shown, each plot appears to be a reflection of the other across this line. With this reflection idea in mind, answer the following: Since $f^{-1}(p)$ is the inverse of $f(s)$, does this mean that $f(s)$ is also the inverse of $f^{-1}(p)$, so that $f^{-1}(f^{-1}(p)) = f(s)$?

5.4. Consider the following statement: For a linear function of a single predictor, if we know that $x_1 < x_2$, $f(x_1) > 0$ and $f(x_2) < 0$, then $f(x)$ has a predictor intercept somewhere between x_1 and x_2.

  (a) What must we assume about the function $f(x)$ to make this a true statement? Give an example of a linear function that meets this requirement.

  (b) Without the assumption above, the statement can be false. Give an example of a linear function that demonstrates this.

5.5. Pick a familiar situation involved with one of your activities, and model some aspect of it using a linear function of one predictor. It will probably be easier to first think of a response that you can observe, and then think of a predictor that you can control that effects this response. Remember that a linear model would have a response that reacts in a directly proportional manner once you change the level of the predictor. Perhaps a predictor of the number of hours you study versus a response being the score you receive on a test? Or, here's another possibility: Find out how much it costs your household to make long distance telephone calls (response) versus the number of minutes the call lasts (predictor).

  (a) Identify the response, the predictor, the response-predictor function, and any predictor constraints you might need to make to restrict the domain of the response-predictor function.

  (b) Justify your choice of m and b in your response-predictor function.

  (c) State the domain and range of your linear function, and find its inverse.

  (d) Summarize your results in a short report, and comment on the reasonableness of your model for your given situation. How adaptable is your model?

  (e) Manipulating linear expressions:

  i.   Show that by knowing only the x- and y-intercepts, you can specify the equivalent linear function that goes through these points.

  ii. Starting with the linear function $y = f(x) = mx + b$, show that you can derive the equivalent general equation of the line.

  iii. Starting the linear function $y = f(x) = mx + b$, show that you can derive the equivalent point-slope form of the line.

  iv. Starting with the point-slope form of a line, $m = (y - y_0)/(x - x_0)$, show that you can derive the general form of the equation of the line.

  v.   Starting with the general equation of a line, derive the equivalent point-slope form. (Hint: Find one point on the line by setting $x = 0$ and solve for y.)

vi. Show that the point-slope form of the line can be written in the form $A(x - x_0) + B(y - y_0) = 0$, and find A and B in terms of m and (x_0, y_0).

(f) Let $y = f(x) = mx + b$. Show that the difference quotient is constant with value m regardless of the magnitude of Δx.

(g) Let $y = f(x) = mx + b$. Show that the difference quotient is constant with value m regardless of the value of x_0.

(h) Consider a model of dollars of sales s as a function of dollars spent on advertising a given by $s = f(a) = 10a$.

    i.   What is the domain of f? What are reasonable restrictions that we can place on that domain?

    ii. How credible is this sales-advertising model? Do you believe that every additional \$1 spent on advertising results in \$10 increased sales? In light of your answer, do you think that this simple linear model is appropriate? What other factors would you include in your revised model?

    iii. The model $s = f(a) = 10a$ implies that \$0 spent on advertising results in a prediction of \$0 in sales. Another model has been suggested that has the form $s = f(a) = 10a + c$, where c represents a fixed level of sales dollars. Using common sense as your guide, which model do you think is more appropriate? Why?

    iv. Which model do you think is more adaptable: $s = f(a) = 10a$ or $s = f(a) = 10a + c$?

(i) Show that Theorem 5.1 is true. (Hint: Remember the definition of slope.)

5.2 MULTIPREDICTOR LINEAR FUNCTIONS

When discussing predictors in Chapter 3, we often found that more than one predictor influenced the response. When the response is a linear function of several predictors, the corresponding model is surprisingly powerful. Multipredictor linear models are widely used in many disciplines. In fact, they are typically the first choice to try among several possible models when dealing with several predictors.

Just as a linear model with one predictor is based on the geometry of the line (one independent variable), a linear model with several predictors is based on the geometry of the plane—the analog of a line in higher dimensions. If we increase the dimension of a problem by increasing the number of predictors (independent variables), then it seems logical to expect that the geometric shape that represents the model will likewise increase in dimensions.

Let's begin our examination of multipredictor linear functions with a discussion of planes in three and higher dimensions.

A quick word on notation. We will represent the generic response variable

NOTATION   by y, to be consistent with earlier notation. The generic predictors will be x_1, x_2, etc. A fixed value of a predictor will be written with a double subscript, as in x_{1_0}, just as a fixed value of x was written as x_0. For particular modeling situations, we might use variables that remind us of the context, such as using s for sales and a for advertising.

If the response variable is not completely clear from the context of the problem, we will write explicitly $y = f(x_1, x_2, \ldots, x_n)$ to make sure we understand that y is a function of predictors $x_1, x_2, \ldots, x_n$.

Occasionally we write the response variable as z and the predictors as x and y when working in three dimensions, because it is the accepted axes notation.

5.2.1   Planes and linearity

There are several ways to write equations for planes, just as there were for lines. We will use three:

1. The *general* equation of a plane is given by

$$a_1 x_1 + a_2 x_2 + \cdots + a_n x_n + by + c = 0 \tag{5.6}$$

where $a_1, a_2, \ldots, a_n$, b, and c are constants. The response and predictors are not raised to a power (e.g., x_1^2), nor are they used in the argument of another function, such as in $(\ln(x_1))$.

Example 5.10. The multipredictor equations

$$3x_1 + 5x_2 - 7x_3 + 7y - 15 = 0$$
$$1.2x - 4z + 99w + 1 = 0$$
$$\pi y + \pi/2x_1 + 17z - 1.9 = 0$$
$$\pi^2 x_1 + \pi^3 x_3 - \pi^4 x_4 - y = 0$$

are all general equations of planes. The multipredictor equations

$$4.5x^2 - 3.0z + y - 15 = 0$$
$$x_1 + x_2^{-1} + y + 1 = 0$$
$$\ln(x_1) + 5\ln(x_3) - 11y - 10 = 0$$

are not general equations of planes.

2. The *function* equation of a plane is given by:

$$y = f(x_1, x_2, \ldots, x_n) = m_1 x_1 + m_2 x_2 + \cdots + m_n x_n + b \tag{5.7}$$

The constant b is the y-intercept—the value of y where the plane intersects the y axis. The m_i's are known as *marginal slopes* of the plane. They represent the MARGINAL slope of the plane looking solely along the direction of the ith coordinate axis. SLOPE

Example 5.11. The multipredictor functions

$$y = f(x_1, x_2, x_3) = 3x_1 + 5x_2 - 7x_3 + 7y - 15$$
$$z = f(x, w) = 1.2/4x + 99/4w + 1/4$$
$$y = f(x_1, z) = -1/2x_1 - 17/\pi z + 1.9$$
$$y = f(x_1, x_3, x_4) = \pi^2 x_1 + \pi^3 x_3 - \pi^4 x_4$$

are function equations of planes. The multipredictor functions

$$y = f(x, z) = -4.5x^2 + 3.0z + 15$$
$$y = f(x_1, x_2) = -x_1 - x_2^{-1} - 1$$
$$y = f(x_1, x_2) = 1/11 \ln(x_1) + 5/11 \ln(x_3) - 10/11$$

are not function equations of planes.

3. The *point-slopes* equation of a plane is given by

$$m_1(x_1 - x_{1_0}) + m_2(x_2 - x_{2_0}) + \ldots + m_n(x_n - x_{n_0}) - (y - y_0) = 0 \qquad (5.8)$$

As in the single predictor function, $(x_{1_0}, x_{2_0}, \ldots, x_{n_0}, y_0)$ represents a known point on the plane, $(x_1, x_2, \ldots, x_n)$ are predictor variables, y represents a single response, and the m_i's are again the marginal slopes.

Example 5.12. Using the known point $(x_{1_0}, x_{2_0}, x_{3_0}, y_0) = (-2, 3, -4, 9)$, with corresponding marginal slopes $m_1 = 17.3$, $m_2 = 4$, and $m_3 = 10$, the point–slopes equation of the plane passing through this point and having these slopes is given by

$$17.3(x_1 + 2) + 4(x_2 - 3) + 10(x_3 + 4) - (y - 9) = 0$$

We will see in the exercises that each of these forms is equivalent. Knowing one, we can find the others.

5.2.2 Analysis of Multipredictor Linear Functions

Let's begin by examining a linear function of two predictors given by

$$y = f(x_1, x_2) = x_1 + 2x_2 + 3 \qquad (5.9)$$

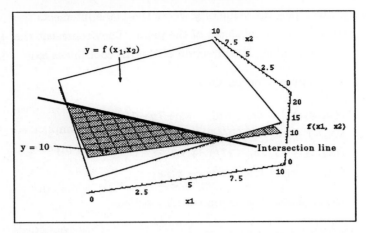

FIGURE 5.7
The graph of $y = f(x_1, x_2) = x_1 + x_2 + 3$ is a plane. By fixing the value $y = 10$ we create a second plane. The intersection of these planes is the line $x_2 = 7 - x_1$. There are an infinite number of points whose x_1 and x_2 values give a y value of 10.

What is the domain of this function? As written, x_1 and x_2 can assume any values, so the domain of $f(x_1, x_2)$ is the set of all real-valued ordered pairs (x_1, x_2).

Similarly, the range of $f(x_1, x_2)$ is the set of all real numbers, since y can assume any value.

Suppose that we were interested in calculating the inverse of this function. Is this function one-to-one? Let's consider a specific point in the range $y = 10$, and see if we can determine what predictor pair of (x_1, x_2) produced this response. How many points in the domain of $f(x_1, x_2)$ could have produced this value?

Setting $y = 10$, we get the expression $10 = x_1 + x_2 + 3$. This is an equation of a line in the (x_1, x_2) plane $x_2 = 7 - x_1$. How many points satisfy this equation? The answer is many more than one! Any two predictor values x_1 and x_2 that satisfy this equation will yield $f(x_1, x_2) = 10$. Geometrically, this result is stating that any point along the line that this equation represents will result in the function output $y = 10$. Figure 5.7 illustrates what is happening.

The function $y = f(x_1, x_2) = x_1 + x_2 + 3$ is not one-to-one. No linear function of more than one predictor, with an unrestricted domain, is one-to-one. The response value alone cannot represent enough information to recover the predictors that produced its value.

Since the function is not one-to-one, *it does not have an inverse!* This is immediately apparent from Figure 5.7.

This observation has many implications for working with functions containing several predictors:

- Faced with a general function of several predictors, with an unrestricted domain, we can almost never find which combination of the predictors resulted in a given response without more information. (There are certain complicated exceptions to this rule, but we don't typically encounter them in practice.)
- If we have a *linear* function of several predictors with an unrestricted domain, we can not find which combination of predictors resulted in a given output.
- If there are many potential combinations of predictors that allow the response-predictor function to achieve a certain response value, how do we choose among them?

In practice, we almost always restrict the domain when working with linear functions of several predictors. These restrictions often turn a problem with several predictors into a problem with only one predictor. We will discuss this at length when we study systems of linear equations.

5.2.3   Predictor constraints

In many situations, our predictors are not free to assume any set of values. It is often the case that resources must be completely used, or that the value of some predictors cannot be exceeded. For example, predictors are frequently required to be nonnegative for the results of a model to make sense.

Predictor constraints are used to restrict the domain of the response-predictor function. Linear relations (not functions) are used to express these constraints.

> **Example 5.13.** Some stores located at shopping malls like to employ young students on the weekends to do time-consuming tasks that help their business. One such store in Charlotte, North Carolina, uses students to distribute advertising brochures to shoppers to entice them to come into the store (in the hope that they buy something!). The store pays each student a flat fee of $30 per day, along with an additional $0.50 for each customer who purchases something from the store as a result of the student's efforts. A good focus question to ask is: How much money is it possible to make in a single day? Let's build a model to predict the student's earnings.
>
> We need to make a simplifying assumption first. In reality, the store has to withhold state and federal income tax, along with Social Security tax, from

the pay of the student. To simplify things just to get started, we'll ignore taxes and assume that what the student earns, the student gets paid. The impact of this assumption is that any amount T that our model predicts will be an overestimation of the amount that the student will actually earn.

Let T represent the total amount of money earned on a weekend day by the student. This is the response. Next, let x represent the number of customers that make store purchases as a result of the student's work. This is a predictor.

The relationship between the response and the predictor is pretty straightforward. Since every customer purchase x adds \$0.50 to the fixed \$30 payment, we can express this relationship by the linear, single-predictor model

$$T = 0.5x + 30$$

where 0.5 is the slope of our linear model. It represents the rate of change of T with respect to changes in x.

Let's do a quick reality check. If the student doesn't generate any store purchases, the model predicts that she will still receive \$30 for a day's work. And, for each purchase generated, x increases and the student will receive an additional \$0.50. Thus, our model appears to be a valid representation of the situation.

Let's use our model to answer the focus question. By substituting various values for the number of customers that make purchases in the store because of the student, we can predict how much money the student will earn:

Purchases (x)	Pay earned (T)	Purchases (x)	Pay earned (T)
0	\$30.00	2000	\$1030.00
10	\$35.00	5000	\$2530.00
20	\$40.00	10,000	\$5030.00
50	\$55.00	100,000	\$50,030.00
100	\$80.00	500,000	\$250,030.00
1000	\$530.00	1,000,000	\$500,030.00

What's wrong here? From the numbers in the table, this temporary job either looks like a weekend venture to get some spending cash, or one that competes with some of the better corporate executive salaries in the country! Given any typical Saturday or Sunday at a typical mall, it is doubtful that 1000 customers will purchase something from the store, let alone 1,000,000! For our model to be closer to reality, we need to restrict the domain of $T(x)$.

Figure 5.8 shows a plot of the function $T(x)$ versus x using a more reasonable domain restriction of $0 \le x \le 400$. The dark region that we added shows the *fixed* pay the student receives regardless of the value of x. The lighter shaded region represents the *variable* pay of the student whose total depends on the value of x. This domain restriction adds a predictor constraint to our model. The complete model is now given by both the total pay function $T(x)$ and the domain restriction:

$$T(x) = 0.5x + 30 \qquad 0 \le x \le 400$$

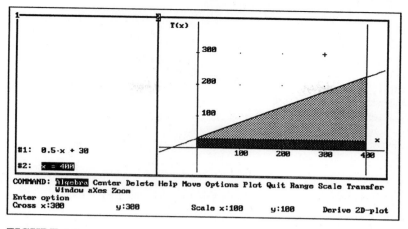

FIGURE 5.8

Graph of the student pay model with the domain restriction $0 \le x \le 400$. The dark region represents fixed pay, and the light region represents variable pay.

The positive slope of 0.5, which is constant throughout the domain of a linear function, will always increase $T(x)$ as x increases. Using our model with the reasonable domain restriction, we can answer the focus question now. The maximum value of $T(x)$ occurs at the right end of the domain, when $x = 400$:

$$T(400) = 0.5(400) + 30 = \$230.00$$

Example 5.14.   Television. Suppose that you are a teenager who has two favorite television shows that broadcast each weekend. One runs music videos and the other covers sports. Given the opportunity, you would sit and stare at them for hours even if you'd seen them before. However, your parents think that this behavior is insane, so they limit your viewing time to no more than 3 hours a day. In your mind, this means that you have *exactly* three hours of viewing time since you will always use as much time as your folks will allow.

There is an amount of pleasure p_1 and p_2 that we get out of watching each show. Let x_1 be a predictor that represents the amount of time (in minutes) you spend watching the music video show, and x_2 be a predictor that represents the amount of time (in minutes) you spend watching the sports show.

We can represent the total amount of pleasure you get out of watching your shows each day by using the response variable P. In this case, it is a linear function of x_1 and x_2:

$$P(x_1, x_2) = p_1 x_1 + p_2 x_2$$

So, for example, suppose that you get $p_1 = 2$ units of pleasure for each minute you watch music videos, and $p_2 = 3$ units of pleasure for each minute watching sports. If you were able to watch 90 minutes of music videos and 20 minutes of sports, you would get a total amount of pleasure

$$P(90, 20) = 2(90) + 3(20) = 240 \text{ units}$$

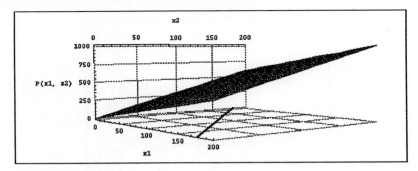

FIGURE 5.9
Graph of the television viewing model with the domain restriction $x_1 + x_2 = 180$.

as a response to these predictor levels.

You are limited to exactly 3 hours of viewing time per day, which we can state as the equality constraint

$$x_1 + x_2 = 180$$

This restriction allows you to to use any combination of show watching, as long as you don't exceed 180 minutes. Additionally, you cannot have negative amounts of viewing time, so both x_1 and x_2 are nonnegative.

Notice that we have to be careful to make sure the units of measurement match on both sides of the constraint. Otherwise, we might be tempted to mistakenly state the constraint as

$$x_1 + x_3 = 3$$

which would limit your viewing to 3 minutes per day. Although this may make your parents extremely happy, you might not like the results. The complete model we have formulated is

$$P(x_1, x_2) = 2x_1 + 3x_2$$
$$x_1 + x_2 = 180$$

The effect of this domain restriction can be seen in Figure 5.9. The only allowable values for x_1 and x_2 are those that lie on the line shown below the surface of the plane. Therefore, the only possible values of the response P are those that lie on the plane directly above the line $x_1 + x_2 = 180$.

Later on, we'll look at a way of building in your desire to *maximize* your total amount of daily viewing pleasure while recognizing that your time is constrained. This approach is called *linear programming*.

In a later chapter, we'll also discuss relations among predictors that contain inequalities as well as equalities. These restrictions on the domain of the predictors will continue to be an important part of our models.

5.3   RATES OF CHANGE

What does it mean to discuss rates of change for functions of several predictors? The complete answer to this question requires calculus, but that doesn't prevent us from gaining important insights by discussing just linear functions of several predictors. Let's examine the concept of slope in this context that introduces the idea of *directional slope*. These two ideas are even more important for functions with several predictors than they were for functions with one predictor.

When a model has only one predictor, it is pretty straightforward to determine if we should increase or decrease the value of the predictor to affect the desired response. We simply examine the value of the slope of the predictor.

Example 5.15. In the student pay model developed in the last section,

$$T(x) = 0.5x + 30 \qquad 0 \le x \le 400$$

the slope of the only predictor x in the model is 0.5. To increase T by 50, increase x by 100. To decrease T by 30, decrease x by 60.

With several predictors, determining which predictor should be changed to effect a particular response is a little more challenging. The proper answer may be to change one, two, or any combination of predictors.

In the total pleasure model for television viewing (developed in the last section), the slope coefficient for x_1 is 2, and the slope coefficient for x_2 is 3. If we wanted to increase the response P by exactly 50, how much should we increase the values of x_1 and x_2? The answer depends upon the amount of contribution each variable makes to the response. And this amount is determined by the coefficients of the variables in the linear model.

In the final chapter of this book, in which we preview calculus, we'll look at how easily and naturally these ideas form the basis for multivariable differential calculus.

5.3.1   Slope revisited

Imagine that we are standing on the side of a hill. Is it possible for us to walk sideways, and not go up or down in elevation? As Figure 5.10 shows, it is if we follow the *contours* of the hill. Are some directions going uphill steeper than   CONTOURS
others? Again, yes. We can walk straight up the hill, or we can angle off for a less steep ascent. That's the idea behind switchbacks on winding mountain roads. We

FIGURE 5.10
Contours indicate locations on a surface plot of a function with the same response values.

go up a steep hill gradually by not going up in the steepest direction. The road is longer, but easier to travel, especially in the winter! The slope of the road is less than the maximum slope, found by going uphill the steepest way possible.

Let's adapt these same intuitive ideas to planes.

Imagine that we are standing on a sheet of plywood that is lying on the ground on the side of a hill as illustrated in Figure 5.11. We'll say that y, the response, is the altitude above sea level, and we'll think of x_1 and x_2 as grid coordinates that give our location—perhaps latitude and longitude. Suppose further that the plane can be described by the function $y = f(x_1, x_2) = x_1 + 2x_2 + 3$. What do we mean by the slope of this plywood plane?

The slope we identify for the plywood plane is going to depend on the direction we are looking. If we are looking toward the top of the hill, the plane has a greater slope than if we are looking out of the picture in the direction of the x_2-axis. So, if we could only move 1 step, and we wanted the greatest increase in elevation, we would choose to move in the direction toward the top of the hill, which may not be a direction exactly aligned with one of the axes.

This is a key difference from the situation with one predictor. With one

FIGURE 5.11
Linear plane with 2 predictors that influence the slope of the plane.

predictor, our model has only one slope associated with the model, m_1:

$$y = f(x_1) = m_1 x_1 + b$$

To increase or decrease the response y, we had to consider an increase or decrease in the single predictor, x. Now, with a two predictor model,

$$y = f(x_1, x_2) = m_1 x_1 + m_2 x_2 + b$$

The slope of the plane that this represents is influenced by both predictor coefficients m_1 and m_2. So, now we have more choices. We can angle up the side of the plane in a shallow path, maybe even along a contour of the hill, or we can head up the plane in the steepest direction.

Several questions come to mind:

- How do we measure steepness?
- What is the direction of the steepest ascent or descent, and how steep is it?
- How do we find the steepness of a direction that isn't the steepest?

Let's tackle these one at a time, and in order.[†]

5.3.2   Marginal rates of change and the gradient

Let's continue to use the two predictor example we just introduced: $y = f(x_1, x_2) = x_1 + 2x_2 + 3$. We want to measure the steepness or slope of this plane.

Suppose that we fix the value of $x_2 = x_{2_0}$, and see what the change in y is for a change in only x_1. Let's also fix an initial point on the plane to be (x_{1_0}, x_{2_0}, y_0).

We have

$$\Delta y = y - y_0$$
$$= (x_1 + 2x_{2_0} + 3) - (x_{1_0} + 2x_{2_0} + 3)$$
$$= x_1 - x_{1_0}$$
$$= \Delta x_1$$

The difference quotient for a change in the x_1 direction is

$$\frac{\Delta y}{\Delta x_1} = 1 = m_1 \tag{5.10}$$

What happens if we fix x_1 and examine the change in y for a change in x_2? We get

$$\Delta y = y - y_o$$
$$= (x_{1_0} + 2x_2 + 3) - (x_{1_0} + 2x_{2_0} + 3)$$
$$= 2(x_2 - x_{2_0})$$
$$= 2\Delta x_2$$

The difference quotient for a change in the x_2 direction is

$$\frac{\Delta y}{\Delta x_2} = 2 = m_2 \tag{5.11}$$

[†]These questions are most easily answered using vectors and vector notation. We are going to avoid using vectors here, because they are not central to our main point. This will make our notation a little clumsier, but the main idea will hopefully be clearer. We will briefly touch on the vector concept in Chapter 7 when addressing linear inequalities.

Our motivation is to "freeze" the value of all but one predictor in order to examine the effects of its contribution to the response. The only predictor that can influence a change in the response is the one we did not fix; it is free to increase or decrease. It makes sense that this variable's slope coefficient is the only one that has a resulting impact upon the rate of change of the response. Thus, it's change, Δx, should be the only one appearing in the expression of the difference quotient.

Notice that we did not specify the exact value that we are using to fix each of the predictors. For what we are looking at here, it doesn't matter. We might as well use the value 0 for fixing predictors. This would be the same as if we simply ignored all the predictors in the function that we want to fix, when calculating the unfixed predictor's difference quotient. In fact, this is how it is commonly done.

Exploration Exercise

5.1. For each of the linear functions that follow, calculate the value of the difference quotients $\Delta y/\Delta x$ with respect to each of the predictors that appear in the function expression. Show by example that the difference quotient calculation is uneffected by the value chosen to fix the remaining predictors.

(a) $y = f(x, z) = 3x + 4z$

(b) $y = f(x_1, x_2) = 13x_1 + 22x_2$

(c) $y = f(x_1, x_2) = -11x_1 + 4x_2 + 9$

(d) $y = g(x_1, x_2, x_3) = 109 + x_1 - 33x_2 + 2x_3$

(e) $2y = g(x, w, z) = 1.4x - 2.3w - 11z + 10$

(f) $3y = f(x_1, x_2) = 23x_2 - (32 + x_1)$

(g) $y = g(x_1, x_2, x_3, x_4) = (x_1 + 11x_2) - (3x_2 - x_4) + x_3 + 11$

See the pattern? If we fix all the predictors except one, and then find the difference quotient for the response and that one predictor, we can calculate the rate of change of the plane with respect to the only predictor we are allowing to change.

Theorem 5.4. Let $y = f(x_1, x_2, \ldots, x_n)$ be a linear function of the form

$$y = f(x_1, x_2, \ldots, x_n) = m_1 x_1 + m_2 x_2 + \cdots + m_n x_n + b$$

Then for each x_i, the difference quotient for the response and x_i is given by

$$\frac{\Delta y}{\Delta x_i} = m_i$$

Theorem 5.4 tells us that, regardless of the initial point we select in the domain of the response-predictor multipredictor linear function, if we change the predictor x_i by one unit, y changes by m_i units.

For a one-predictor model, $y = f(x_1) = m_1 x_1 + b$, Theorem 5.4 states what we already know: The rate of change of the response y for a change in x_1 is given by the slope m_1. Theorem 5.4 extends this same idea to address linear functions with more than one predictor.

The quantity m_i is called the *marginal rate of change* for the ith predictor. This terminology is borrowed from economics. It means how much the response changes for one additional unit change in a particular predictor. This is the concept behind income tax rates known as *tax brackets*.

Example 5.16. Tax brackets. The statement that someone is in the 25% tax bracket is a statement of the marginal rate of change they will experience by earning \$1 in salary than they currently are receiving. If they currently earn \$30,000 a year, the next \$1 of earned income will be taxed \$0.25. This marginal rate of change in income tax reflects the rate of change of the response "income tax to be paid," for an additional one unit change in the predictor "earned income."

For nonlinear functions, the marginal rate of change of the response is not constant throughout the entire range of predictor values, as it is with linear functions. It depends on the predictor value that we select to examine! For linear functions, the marginal rate of change is constant, which is the point of Theorem 5.4.

Let's return to our example given by Equation 5.9.

Example 5.17. We know now that if we move in the positive x_1 direction by one unit, the response increases by $m_1 = 1$ unit. If we move in the positive x_2 direction by one unit, the response increases by $m_2 = 2$ units. Clearly, it is steeper in the x_2 direction, since our response changes twice as much.

Here is the \$64 question: Can there be a direction other than parallel to the x_1 or x_2 axis that has a greater steepness than $m_2 = 2$? The answer is yes!

Watch what happens if we change x_1 by $1/\sqrt{5}$ and x_2 by $2/\sqrt{5}$. This move is pictured in Figure 5.12.

Geometrically, how far have we moved? If we recall the distance formula from geometry and trigonometry, we have

$$d = \sqrt{(\Delta x_1)^2 + (\Delta x_2)^2} = \sqrt{(1/\sqrt{5})^2 + (2/\sqrt{5})^2} = \sqrt{1/5 + 4/5} = 1$$

To compare the marginal rates of change for various predictor values, we would like to be able to compare these changes on a common scale. This means we have to make some algebraic adjustment to the distance we intend to move.

In general, we can scale any move $(\Delta x_1, \Delta x_2)$ to have a length equal to one by dividing each component by the distance associated with the move:

$$\sqrt{(\frac{\Delta x_1}{d})^2 + (\frac{\Delta x_2}{d})^2} = 1 \tag{5.12}$$

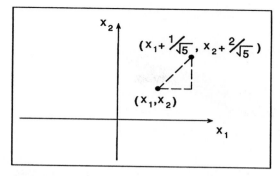

FIGURE 5.12
Changing (x_1, x_2) to $(x_1 + 1/\sqrt{5}, x_2 + 2/\sqrt{5})$, a move of length 1.

This means that a change of predictors given by

$$\left(\frac{\Delta x_1}{\sqrt{(\Delta x_1)^2 + (\Delta x_2)^2}}, \frac{\Delta x_2}{\sqrt{(\Delta x_1)^2 + (\Delta x_2)^2}} \right)$$

will always have length one.

How much has the response y changed? Although the notation is a bit awkward, by letting (x_{1_0}, x_{2_0}) represent the start point prior to the move, we have

$$\begin{aligned}
\Delta y &= y - y_0 \\
&= (x_1 + 2x_2 + 3) - (x_{1_0} + 2x_{2_0} + 3) \\
&= (x_1 - x_{1_0}) + 2(x_2 - x_{2_0}) \\
&= 1/\sqrt{5} + 2(2/\sqrt{5}) \\
&= \frac{5}{\sqrt{5}} = \sqrt{5} > 2 = m_2
\end{aligned}$$

We have found a way to simultaneously change our predictors that results in a greater change in the response than was possible by changing them individually! In other words, the greatest increase in y did not come not from making a change in x_1 alone, or x_2 alone. It came from changing both x_1 and x_2 at the same time. The underlying reason for why this happened is a very powerful idea stated in the next theorem.

Theorem 5.5. Let $y = f(x_1, x_2, \ldots, x_n)$ be a linear function of the form

$$y = f(x_1, x_2, \ldots, x_n) = m_1 x_1 + m_2 x_2 + \cdots + m_n x_n + b$$

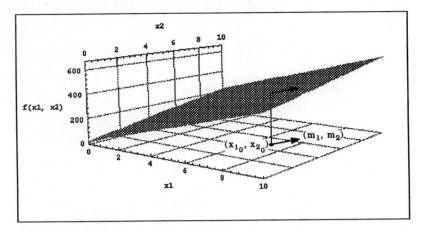

FIGURE 5.13
Direction of greatest increase is in the direction of the gradient (m_1, m_2).

The greatest change in the response y is achieved by making a change in the predictors $(x_1, x_2, \ldots, x_n)$ that is proportional to the marginal rates of change $(m_1, m_2, \ldots, m_n)$:

$$\Delta(x_1, x_2, \ldots, x_n) = k(m_1, m_2, \ldots, m_n)$$

where k is a constant not equal to zero.

GRADIENT

The ordered list of n elements, or n–tuple, representing the marginal rates of change $(m_1, m_2, \ldots, m_n)$, is called the *gradient* of the plane. The length of the gradient, given by $\sqrt{m_1^2 + m_2^2 + \cdots + m_n^2}$, represents the maximum slope of the plane, by Theorem 5.5. Any change in the predictors that is in proportion to the marginal slopes represented in the gradient is a change in the direction of greatest increase for the response. In other words, from any starting point on a plane, the fastest rate of change is attained by moving in the direction of the gradient.

Example 5.18. In the previous example, we changed the predictors in proportion to $(m_1, m_2) = (1, 2)$ by selecting the change $(\Delta x_1, \Delta x_2) = (1/\sqrt{5}, 2/\sqrt{5})$, which we scaled to have length 1 by dividing each proportional change by the distance $d = \sqrt{5}$. According to Theorem 5.5, this change of the predictors gives the greatest increase in y for all changes of predictors of length 1.

Figure 5.13 illustrates the idea of moving in the direction of the gradient of a plane given by the linear function $y = f(x_1, x_2) = 43x_1 + 22x_2 + 3$. From any starting point (x_{1_0}, x_{2_0}), moving in the direction $(m_1, m_2) = (43, 22)$ results in the greatest increase in the response y. In other words, if we change (x_1, x_2) in proportion to (m_1, m_2), that is by some positive multiple k of the gradient

$$(\Delta x_1, \Delta x_2) = k(m_1, m_2) = (km_1, km_2)$$

the increase in the response will be the greatest.

If a positive multiple of the gradient $(m_1, m_2, \ldots, m_n)$ results in the greatest increase in the response, then it makes sense that to achieve the greatest amount of decrease in the response, we make a change in the predictors that follows the *negative* gradient: $-(m_1, m_2, \ldots, m_n)$.

Example 5.19. For a change in the predictors of length one, the maximum change in the response y is

$$\Delta y_{max} = \sqrt{m_1^2 + m_2^2 + \cdots + m_n^2}$$

Let's reorient our thoughts for a moment. Remember that our motivation is to construct mathematical models of something that is happening in the real REALITY world. Sometimes the resulting model is a function, sometimes it is not. However, CHECK we are always trying to explicitly represent what we are observing in terms of a response, and the things that are influencing the response by predictors.

Being able to identify which direction to move to achieve the greatest change in the response is the same as asking "How should I change the value of the predictors so that I can observe the greatest response change?" This idea is extremely powerful for answering "what-if" questions when analyzing our models. If our modeling objective seeks the quickest change in response, we now know how to change each of the predictors: in proportion to their corresponding entries in the gradient.

You may have observed that the difference quotient $\Delta y / \Delta x$ for a change in the predictors depends on which predictors change, and how much they change relative to each other. Let's explore this idea further.

5.3.3 Directional slope

We know how to find the rate of change for the response of a linear function in the following situations

- We change just one predictor. Then $\frac{\Delta y}{\Delta x_i} = m_i$.

- We change the predictors in the direction of greatest increase, with a change of length one. Then

$$\Delta y = m_1 \Delta x_1 + m_2 \Delta x_2 + \cdots + m_n \Delta x_n = \sqrt{m_1^2 + m_2^2 + \cdots + m_n^2}$$

What about changes in predictor values that don't adhere to one of these two situations? How do we measure the rate of change of the response in some other direction? Let's restrict our attention for now to predictor changes that have a length of 1.

Theorem 5.6. Let $y = f(x_1, x_2, \ldots, x_n)$ be a linear function of the form

$$y = f(x_1, x_2, \ldots, x_n) = m_1 x_1 + m_2 x_2 + \cdots + m_n x_n + b$$

Any change in predictors can be scaled to have length 1 by dividing the changes by the square root of the sum of squared changes:

$$\Delta x = (\Delta x_1/d, \Delta x_2/d, \ldots, \Delta x_n/d)$$

where $d = \sqrt{\Delta x_1^2 + \Delta x_2^2 + \cdots + \Delta x_n^2}$.

For this case, the rate of change of y in the direction Δx is given by

$$\frac{\Delta y}{\Delta x} = m_1 \left(\frac{\Delta x_1}{d}\right) + m_2 \left(\frac{\Delta x_2}{d}\right) + \cdots + m_n \left(\frac{\Delta x_n}{d}\right) \tag{5.13}$$

NOTATION
ALERT!

We have changed our notation a bit because we are working with several predictors. The notation $\frac{\Delta y}{\Delta x}$ we are using to talk about the difference quotient of a function of several predictors is not really a fraction. It represents the rate of change of y in the direction of Δx, where $\Delta x = (\Delta x_1, \Delta x_2, \ldots, \Delta x_n)$. So, it can't be a fraction since we know that Δx is an n–tuple.

Example 5.20. Suppose that $y = f(x_1, x_2) = x_1 + 2x_2 + 3$. If we make a change of length 1 in the predictors x_1 and x_2 in equal positive amounts $\Delta x = (\Delta x_1, \Delta x_2) = (1/\sqrt{2}, 1/\sqrt{2})$, what is the rate of change of the response y?

Applying Theorem 5.6, we see that

$$\frac{\Delta y}{\Delta x} = 1(1/\sqrt{2}) + 2(1/\sqrt{2}) = 3/\sqrt{2} \approx 2.1213$$

So, the rate of change in the response by moving in this direction is approximately 2.1213. Since the gradient of this function is $(m_1, m_2) = (1, 2)$ and we're not making a change proportional to the gradient, we would expect the response change to be less than the maximum possible for a length one change, which would be realized by $\Delta x = (1/\sqrt{5}, 2\sqrt{5})$:

$$\frac{\Delta y}{\Delta x} = 1(1/\sqrt{5}) + 2(2/\sqrt{5}) = 5/\sqrt{5} \approx 2.2361$$

This completes our analysis of linear functions of more than one predictor. We next tackle constructing linear models from data sets, now that we know how to analyze them.

Exploration Exercises

5.1. Consider Equation 5.9, our example plane. What is Δy if our change in the predictors is $(\Delta x_1, \Delta x_2) = (-2, 1)$? What is Δy if $(\Delta x_1, \Delta x_2) = (2, -1)$? Is this just a coincidence, or can you identify a general rule?

5.2. Consider a linear function with two predictors, given by $y = f(x_1, x_2) = m_1 x_1 + m_2 x_2 + b$. What is Δy if $\Delta x = (-m_2, m_1)$?

5.3. Scale the following changes of predictors to have length 1:
  (a) $(\Delta x_1, \Delta x_2) = (1, 1)$
  (b) $(\Delta x_1, \Delta x_2) = (-1, 1)$
  (c) $(\Delta x_1, \Delta x_2) = (0, 1)$
  (d) $(\Delta x_1, \Delta x_2, \Delta x_3) = (7, 3, -4)$
  (e) $(\Delta x_1, \Delta x_2, \Delta x_3) = (-5, 1, 5)$
  (f) $(\Delta x_1, \Delta x_2, \Delta x_3) = (\sqrt{2}, 3, \pi)$
  (g) $(\Delta x_1, \Delta x_2, \Delta x_3, \Delta x_4, \Delta x_5) = (1, 0, 3, 7, 11)$

5.4. For the following functions, find the direction of greatest increase and the maximum rate of increase for changes in the predictors.
  (a) $f(x_1, x_2) = x_1 + x_2 + 1$
  (b) $f(x_1, x_2) = x_1 - x_2 - 3$
  (c) $g(x_1, x_2) = \sqrt{2}x_1 - \pi x_2 + 3$
  (d) $f(x_1, x_2) = 1.4x_1 - 66.3x_2 + 300$

5.5. For the following functions, find the direction of greatest increase and the maximum rate of increase for changes in the predictors.
  (a) $g(x_1, x_2, x_3) = 3x_1 + 2x_2 - x_3 + 4$
  (b) $f(x_1, x_2, x_3) = x_1 + x_2 - x_3$
  (c) $h(x_1, x_2, x_3) = 5 - x_1 - x_2 - x_3$

5.6. For each of the functions in Exercise 5.4, find the directional slope for the following changes of predictors.
  (a) $(\Delta x_1, \Delta x_2) = (2, -1)$
  (b) $(\Delta x_1, \Delta x_2) = (3, 1)$
  (c) $(\Delta x_1, \Delta x_2) = (-1, 2)$

5.7. For each of the functions in Exercise 5.5, find the directional slope for the following changes of predictors.
  (a) $\Delta x = (1, 1, 1)$
  (b) $\Delta x = (1, -5, 1)$
  (c) $\Delta x = (0, 3, 1)$
  (d) $\Delta x = (4, -1, 0)$

5.8. Calculate the gradient of the following functions.
  (a) $f(x_1, x_2, x_3) = 7x_1 - 3x_2 + 4.2x_3$
  (b) $g(x, w, z) = 11x - 3w - 4z$
  (c) $g(w_1, w_2, w_3) = 8.3w_1 + 3.9w_2 + 7.0w_3$

(d) $h(x_1, x_2, x_3, x_4) = 2.1x_1 + 3x_2 + 4.1x_3 + 8.0x_4$

5.9. The next couple of exercises are derivation exercises to give you some practice with algebraically manipulating equations.

    (a) Starting with the equation of a plane in the form of Equation 5.6, show that you can derive the equivalent forms of Equation 5.8 and 5.7.

    (b) Starting with the equation of the plane in the form of Equation 5.8, show that you can derive the equivalent forms of Equation 5.6 and 5.7.

    (c) Starting with the equation of the plane in the form of Equation 5.7, show that you can derive the equivalent forms of Equation 5.6 and 5.8.

MORE DIFFICULT   In our discussion in this chapter, we mentioned that there were complicated cases where functions of several predictors could be one-to-one. Can you construct or find a function of two predictors that is one-to-one? (Hint: it will not be linear.) If so, show that the function you identify is one-to-one. Show that your answer is not a linear function.

5.10. Verify Equation 5.12.

5.11. Case study: "Are we getting ripped off here?" A study of faculty pay scales at a college in the late 1970s used salary as the response variable, y. There were several possible predictors they considered to include in their model, but finally settled on three: gender, academic rank, and the number of years in current rank.

    The gender of the faculty member was represented by the predictor x_1, with $x_1 = 1$ for females and $x_1 = 0$ for males. Academic rank was represented by x_2, with $x_2 = 1$ for assistant professors, $x_2 = 2$ for associate professors, and $x_2 = 3$ for full professors. The predictor x_3 was used to represent the number of years in the current rank.

    Using gender alone as a predictor, and deriving a model from the pay scale data, we obtain the single predictor function $y = f(x_1) = -3340x_1 + 24,697$.

    Using gender, academic rank, and years in current position as predictors, we obtain the multipredictor linear function $y = g(x_1, x_2, x_3) = 603x_1 + 4747x_2 + 393x_3 + 11,011$.

    Let's compare the two models. Recalling that the predictors are combining to give us a prediction of the salary of a faculty member, what does the coefficient for x_1 mean in terms of faculty salary? (Hint: Interpret the coefficients of the two models in terms of marginal rates of change of salary.)

    Which model seems to be more credible? Based on the two proposed models, does there appear to be gender discrimination occuring at this college? Or does your answer to this question depend on which model we select? Explain your response. (Problem adapted from data in Weisberg, 1985. See the Complements section at the end of this chapter for full citation.)

5.4   FITTING LINEAR MODELS FROM DATA

In this section, we focus on creating linear models from a very important source: data sets. We'll look at a powerful and versatile modeling technique called *linear regression*.

Our goal is to introduce you to several fundamental concepts involved in models built using regression. In the process, we'll examine the applicability and limitations of these models. We'll focus on using both *Derive* and a spreadsheet to create these modes from any set of data.

The study of linear regression is usually a one-semester college course. Although we won't be able to completely cover regression in detail here, we'll discuss enough information to enable us to properly build and analyze linear functions based on this technique.

5.4.1   Predictors and response

In the process of constructing a mathematical model of some behavior, we're fortunate if we have some existing knowledge of the function form for representing the behavior. For example, we may already know from physics that the distance it takes for a vehicle to stop is a linear function of the speed of the vehicle when the driver applies the brakes. So, if we were investigating a traffic accident, we would have to gather enough data so that we could identify the particular coefficients of the linear model we needed to use, but we would already know the function form.

As we move from a mess to a model, identifying a response and predictors, we don't always have theory that suggests what the functional relation should be between the predictors and the response. However, we often might either have data or be able to easily collect measured data that may suggest an appropriate model to use.

For example, if we want to model the weight of adult males as a function of their height, we could measure the height and weight of a number of adult males and record this information. Then we could plot all of the different data points to see if some trend was evident that suggested a functional form for a model. The data that results is called a *data set*. This data set is then considered just one sample of the entire population of adult males.

There are many issues to contend with when selecting samples from a population, all of which are beyond the scope of this section. Statisticians have developed excellent mathematical procedures that they use to collect samples in such a way that important properties are preserved in the data. For this section, we provide several data sets for exploration that meet these requirements. References for further reading are provided in the Complements section at the end of this chapter.

TABLE 5.1
Height and weight data: adult males.

Height (inches)	Weight (pounds)
62	130
63	136
64	139
65	143
66	148
67	153
68	157
69	163
70	167
71	171
72	176
73	182
74	187
75	193
76	196

We can often find existing data sets that we can use to make our models, sparing us the problem of collecting the data. Rather than actually measuring different folks for our height and weight data example, let's use the reference data from the 1993 World Almanac.

Table 5.1 contains a data set of the average weight of American males, age 20–24, by height.[‡] Can the relationship between the height and weight data be adequately described using a linear function?

When working with data, an excellent first step is to plot the data to examine what it looks like. We can plot the height-weight data points using *Derive* to get an initial visual indication. We can also do this very conveniently with a spreadsheet.

MATRIX   In *Derive*, the most convenient way to enter data is to use a box-shaped array called a *matrix*. A matrix is specified by the number of rows (m) and

---

[‡]Source: *The World Almanac and Book of Facts*, Tharos, New York, 1993.

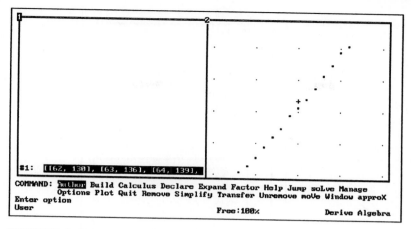

FIGURE 5.14
Height and weight data.

columns (n) it has, typically written as $m \times n$.

Since the columns contain the quantities of height and weight, we **Declare** a 15×2 **Matrix**, and enter the appropriate values from Table 5.1. We then highlight the resulting matrix, and **Plot** the points, and adjust the scale of the plot to get the best view of the data. The resulting display is shown in Figure 5.14.

The data appears to be dispersed in an approximately linear pattern. We next find the line that best describes, or best "fits" the data, which is easy to do using the **Fit** command in *Derive*. First we discuss the idea of the best fit.

5.4.2 Regression

There are several approaches that can be used to find the best line to represent data that appears to be linear. Consider the four plots of the same 11 data points that we show in Figure 5.15. The line in Figure 5.15(a) was drawn so that the furthest to the outside data points lie exactly on the line. The line in Figure 5.15(b) was picked to allow the inside data points influence the line the most. The line in Figure 5.15(c) was used because it passed through the greatest number of data points. Lastly, the line in Figure 5.15(d) was picked so that an equal number of data points lie above the line and below. Although any of these approximating lines could be used to describe the data, the line that we will use is based on another method—the method of *least squares*.

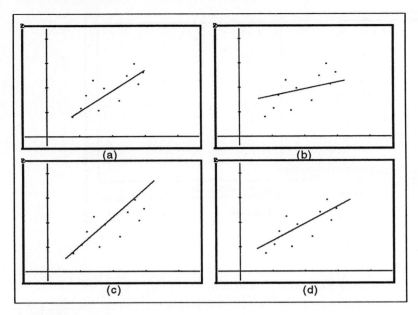

FIGURE 5.15
Possible choices for best fit lines.

5.4.3   Least squares

The method of least squares identifies a very particular linear function to describe the data. Notice in Figure 5.15 that, no matter which line we pick, there are some data points that will not lie exactly on the line. Suppose that we choose to use each point's vertical distance from the line to describe how far away each point is. If all the data points fell exactly on the line, corresponding linear function would perfectly describe the relationship between the two quantities. Since they don't, any line we use will have some error associated with it, i.e., the vertical distances between the points and the line.

Least squares gets it name from the fact that it selects a line that minimizes the sum of the *squares* of the vertical distances from the line to each point in the data set. The term *least* is used because we are minimizing. The term *squares* results from minimizing the sum of the *squares* of the vertical distances to each point from the approximating line. The line that "best fits" the data is called the REGRESSION *regression* line. We could pick this regression line by minimizing the sum of the LINE vertical distances themselves, but this approach causes a significant problem.

If each of the data points were to lie below the regression line, then the vertical distance $(\hat{y} - y)$ between the $\hat{y}$ value of the approximating point on the

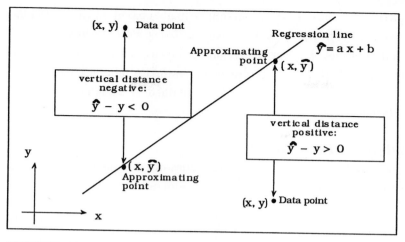

FIGURE 5.16
Positioning of data points.

regression line and the $\hat{y}$ value of the data point would be positive, and simply minimizing the sum of these distances would achieve the same effect as the least squares technique. However, if some of the data points were to lie above the regression line, or if the sum of the individual vertical distances to points lying above the regression line were greater than the sum to points lying below the regression line, we could get a negative value for the overall sum.

Figure 5.16 illustrates this effect. Minimizing a negative number forces it to be more negative. The end result would lead us to select a regression line as far below the data set as possible. Clearly this is not what we had in mind. Minimizing the sum of the square makes each distance quantity positive: $(\hat{y}-y)^2$, and results in the correct regression line being chosen.

There are other criteria that can also be used to fit the line, but we use the least squares criteria, which is the most frequently used.

5.4.4 Regression coefficients

Selecting a linear function using the least squares technique leaves us with the task of determining the values of a slope parameter, a, and an intercept parameter, b, in a linear model $y = ax + b$ that specifies the regression line. These parameters are called *regression coefficients*. We are going to examine two ways of doing this. First, we use the built-in functions of *Derive*, and second, we use a spreadsheet.

The regression coefficients we obtain are estimates based on the particular data we are working with. Different data give a different set of estimates.

To remind ourselves that our regression coefficients are estimates, we put little hats on them. We write $\hat{a}$ to represent our estimate for the true but unknown slope. We write $\hat{y}$ to indicate the values obtained by using our estimated regression coefficients $\hat{y} = \hat{a}x + \hat{b}$.

5.4.4.1   *DERIVE* COEFFICIENTS.

The *Derive* command for finding the proper values of regression coefficients is the `Fit` command. The form, or *syntax*, of the command has two arguments:

$$\texttt{Fit}\left([predictor\ variable,\ general\ form],\ A\right) \qquad (5.14)$$

The first argument: [*predictor variable, general form*], identifies both the predictor and form of the model we want to use, both enclosed in square brackets.

> **Example 5.21.** The first argument for the `Fit` command using the linear model $\hat{y} = \hat{a}x + \hat{b}$ would be $[x, ax + b]$.

> **Example 5.22.** Using the linear model $\hat{w} = \hat{a}h + \hat{b}$ to express the predicted weight $\hat{w}$ of adult males in terms of their average height h for the data of Table 5.1, the first argument would be $[h, ah + b]$. The parameters a and b are the unknown regression coefficients: slope and intercept.

The second argument in the `Fit` command, A, is the matrix of data we want to fit our model to. We enter this data matrix prior to using the `Fit` command. This matrix should be organized with the predictor values of the data points in the first column, and the response values in the last column. For our height-weight model, the values for h would be entered in the first column, and the values for w in the second. Once the data matrix is entered into *Derive*, this second argument is simply a reference to the line number of the data matrix, *e.g.*, #3, #10, etc. When we `Simplify` the complete `Fit` expression, *Derive* specifies the complete equation for the regression line that we seek.

Figure 5.17 illustrates these steps. The left *Derive* window shows the data matrix (#1), the `Fit` expression (#2), and the regression line (#3). The right *Derive* window shows the plot of the regression line through the data. The equation of the regression line, $\hat{w} = 4.8h - 165.01$, is the regression line that best fits the points in our data matrix, and has the smallest sum of squared vertical distances.

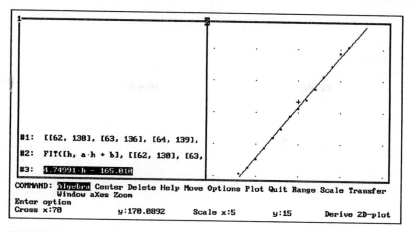

```
1 ┌─────────────────────────┬──────────────────────────┐
  │                         2                          │
  │                         │                          │
  │                         │                          │
  │                         │                          │
  │                         │                          │
  │                         │                          │
  ├─────────────────────────┼──────────────────────────┤
  │ #1:  [[62, 130], [63, 136], [64, 139],            │
  │ #2:  FIT([h, a·h + b], [[62, 130], [63,           │
  │ #3:  4.74991·h - 165.010                          │
  └─────────────────────────┴──────────────────────────┘
COMMAND: Algebra Center Delete Help Move Options Plot Quit Range Scale Transfer
         Window aXes Zoom
Enter option
Cross x:70          y:170.0892     Scale x:5        y:15      Derive 2D-plot
```

FIGURE 5.17
Fitting a line to height and weight data.

Let's think about this fitted linear function $\hat{w} = f(h) = 4.8h - 165.01$. What is its domain? What does the value $a = 4.8$ mean? What does the intercept tell us? How is the inverse useful?

The linear function $f(h)$ is defined for all values of h, but we should restrict the domain to values to stay close to the interval of the original predictor data—where our heights were between 62 inches and 76 inches.

The slope $a = 4.8$ means that the weight of the average man in this age range increases 4.8 pounds for every 1-inch increase in height.

The intercept alerts us to the dangers of working outside our data range. If we were to use this model to estimate the weight of a 2-year-old male of height 24 inches, we would obtain $w = -49.9$ pounds—a clear impossibility. The inverse reminds us that this model is a linear approximation of a data set, and is appropriate for describing the relationship between the response and predictor in the restricted domain of the original data.

We can use the inverse of this model to estimate the height of an adult male simply by knowing his weight. This could be useful in a criminal investigation, where the depth of a footprint provides an estimate of the suspect's weight.

As a further example, consider the next case of developing a linear model from sampled timber harvest data.[§]

[§]This data set is taken from the excellent book by Tom Tietenberg entitled *Environmental*

TABLE 5.2
Data for Douglas fir trees.

Age (years)	Volume (cubic ft.)
10	694
20	1,912
30	3,558
40	5,536
50	7,750
60	10,104
70	12,502
80	14,848
90	17,046
100	19,000
110	20,614
120	21,792
130	22,438
135	22,514

Example 5.23. The growth of Douglas fir trees in the Pacific Northwest is measured on a volume basis, typically by cubic feet for a particular site. The data in Table 5.2 represents different ages of a stand of Douglas fir trees, and the corresponding cumulative volume measured at that particular time. We would like to develop a model to describe the relationship between the age x of the stand and the volume v of trees, assuming that there is one. Here, our data set has 14 rows and 2 columns. We enter a 14 × 2 matrix into *Derive* with the predictor quantity "age" in the first column, and the response quantity "volume" in the second (Figure 5.18). Plotting the data matrix indicates a linear pattern in the data, so we decide to fit the data to the line $\hat{y} = \hat{a}x + \hat{b}$ using the *Derive* Fit command.

In the *Derive* screen shown in Figure 5.18, both of the regression coefficients are shown with their exact values expressed as fractions. Simplifying this resulting expression yields the regression line with decimal regression coefficients: $\hat{v} = 191.85x - 1441.39$, which we can subsequently plot to visually inspect the fit of our linear model (Figure 5.19).

and Natural Resource Economics, Scott, Foresman, and Company, Glenview, Illinois, 1988, Table 11.1, p.243.

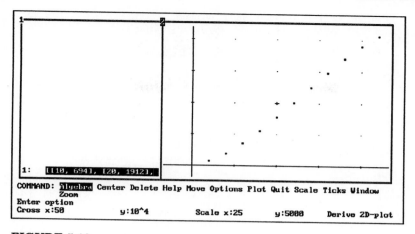

FIGURE 5.18
Derive window for Douglas fir data.

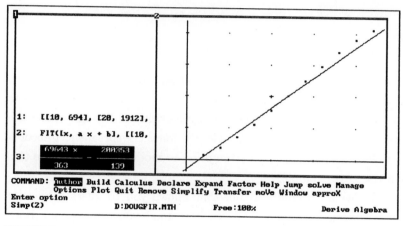

FIGURE 5.19
Regression line and data for the Douglas Fir harvesting example.

5.4.5   Spreadsheet least squares: approximation

Spreadsheets are very effective programs to use for determining the regression coefficients that we need to calculate best-fit lines. Most spreadsheets have an equivalent regression function preprogrammed into them, which makes determining a regression line a snap. In Excel, the technique is called "Adding a trendline," which we'll look at briefly in the next section. For more detail, we refer you to the User's Guide.

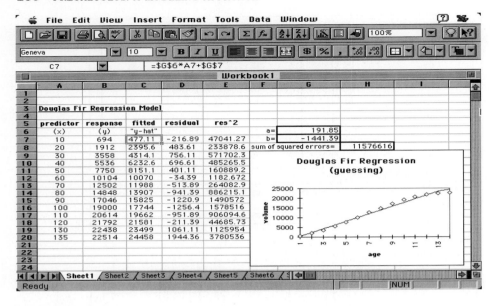

FIGURE 5.20
Excel spreadsheet layout for regression calculations.

Here, our goal is not to go from start to finish as rapidly as possible, but to use the task of identifying regression coefficients to illustrate how spreadsheets **EMPIRICAL** can be used experimentally to generate *empirical* evidence. We also make the **MODELS** point that this approach gives you access to easily *adapt* the spreadsheet according to the particular situation you are attempting to model. We'll illustrate this idea as part of the next example.

The overall idea is to create a tool that allows you to guess values for the regression coefficients a and b, and see how good your guesses are both numerically and graphically.

Figure 5.20 shows a layout for the Douglas Fir problem that we find particularly handy in general: placing the data set to the left-hand side of the page, a plot of the data set to the right, the values of the regression coefficients a and b and the sum of squared errors above a graph of our best fit line with the data. This way, our search for a and b can be guided by watching both a graphical plot of the regression line and the total value of the sum of squared errors that we are trying to make as small as possible. We simply manipulate a and b until it looks like we have a good fit graphically, then fine tune the values to make the numerical value of the sum as small as possible. This is a workbench approach to finding a and b.

We need four columns of information:

1. The predictor values x

2. The response values y

3. The predicted y-values lying on the regression line for each value of x, (typically labeled $\hat{y}$). Since we are working with $n = 14$ data points in the data set, these predicted y-values are obtained by substituting the x-values into the linear model we are using: $\hat{y}_i = ax_i + b$ for each data point $i = 1, 2, \ldots, 14$.

4. The squared vertical error associated with each data point $(\hat{y} - y)^2$.

The data for the columns with x and y are entered as is. The column with $\hat{y}$ should be absolute-linked to the boxed cells containing the values for a and b. This is typically accomplished in most spreadsheets by placing a $ sign before the cell letter and before the cell number. In Figure 5.20, you can see how this is done for the first $\hat{y}$ expression such shown in cell C7: =G6*A7+G7, where cells G6 and G7 contain our guesses for the values of a and b. By selecting cells C7–C20, and using the **Fill Down** command, the correct equation for each (x, y) data point is written in the correct cells. More important, each cell C7–C20 always looks to the cells G6 and G7 for the values of a and b that we supply as our guesses. So, for example, cell C18 will have the equation =$G$6*A18+$G$7. The dollar signs lock the reference for every equation to cells G6 and G7, rather than letting them change *relative* to the row that the equation is in.

Next, we use cell H8 for the sum of squared errors total value by placing in it the equation =SUM(E7:E20), where the cells E7–E20 hold the individual squared error terms $(\hat{y}_i - y_i)^2$ for each data point $i = 1, 2, \ldots, 14$. Lastly, we add a plot of two items—x versus y as discrete points, and x versus $\hat{y}$ as a line—so we can see how well the line seems to describe the data set. Getting Excel to plot two different types of plots is a little bit tricky, so we'll refer you to the manual for this. However, you can download this spreadsheet from our website. It's called **excel519** for Macintosh, and **excel519.xls** for Windows operating systems.

When we enter different guesses for a and b in the boxed cells, the cells that are linked to these cells are automatically recalculated. At the same time, the plot that we are using to graphically examine the quality of our guesses is also automatically updated. In Figure 5.20, we placed the previous coefficient values determined by *Derive* into the regression coefficient boxes so that you can

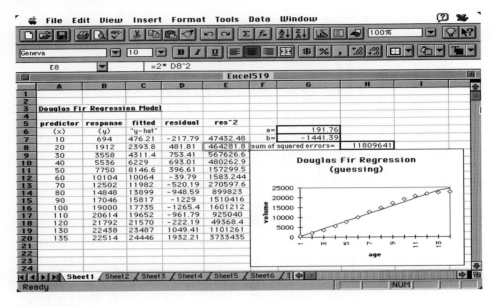

FIGURE 5.21
Changing the residual weight to reflect the increased importance of data point #2.

see how the data plot compares with the plot *Derive* generated.

The reason we mention this technique for finding solutions by trial and error is that you might not always have the exact software you need to find model parameter values such as the regression coefficients, or the software you do have is difficult to modify for your needs because of the way it is designed. It may be necessary to improvise, putting together a quick model that allows you to get at the information you need.

Example 5.24. Look closely at the sum of squared errors expression that linear regression seeks to make as small as possible:

$$\sum_{i=1}^{n} (\hat{y}_i - y_i)^2$$

and recall that the squared error terms $(\hat{y}_i - y_i)^2$, $i = 1, \ldots, n$ represents the vertical distance to the best fit line from each response value y in the data set. If we expand this expression to show the first three squared error terms:

$$(\hat{y}_1 - y_1)^2 + (\hat{y}_2 - y_2)^2 + (\hat{y}_3 - y_3)^2 + \cdots \tag{5.15}$$

you can see that each of these terms have the same coefficient, since Equation 5.15 is the same as

$$1(\hat{y}_1 - y_1)^2 + 1(\hat{y}_2 - y_2)^2 + 1(\hat{y}_3 - y_3)^2 + \cdots \tag{5.16}$$

If we think of each coefficient as a *weight* associated with each squared error term, then we can interpret these weights as indicating the importance of each data point's residual amount relative to the others in the set. For standard linear regression in which all data points have the same coefficients in the least squares expression, we can interpret this as meaning that all of the data points have the same degree of importance with regard to where the best fit line gets placed.

There are times when we won't want this assumption built into our model. For example, if we knew that data point #2 needed to be twice as important as any other data point in the set, then we would want our regression model to reflect this fact. Changing the least squares coefficient weights allows us to incorporate this information. The Excel spreadsheet we just built easily allows us to do this simply by changing the appropriate coefficient in the squared residual cell.

In Figure 5.21, making this modification changed the regression slope coefficient slightly, from $a = 191.85$ to $a = 191.76$. This new model now recognizes the importance of data point #2 with respect to the other data points in the set.

Spreadsheets are great for generating analysis results quickly, which is one reason they are so popular in the business world in which decisions frequently have to be made very quickly. Not everyone can afford the luxury of spending thousands of dollars on specialty software, especially small businesses (and students too!).

5.4.5.1   SPREADSHEET MACROS.

There are commands in most commercial spreadsheets that will find the regression coefficients without using the trial and error approach just described. We included the trial and error method above because it illustrates the point that the technique of least squares focuses on minimizing the sum of squared errors. Standard linear regression places equal weights on all data points, whereas changing the weights allows us to adjust the level of importance of certain data points relative to all the rest in the set.

Given two columns of data, the first containing predictor values and the second containing the corresponding response values, we can use built-in spreadsheet commands called *macros* to automatically generate regression models from data sets. For Excel, this option is called "Adding a Trendline."

Example 5.25. For the Douglas fir example, Figure 5.22 shows the results of using the trendline option to generate a linear model from data using regression. After plotting the original data set as points, selecting the points on the chart allows the trendline command to appear in the Insert menu option. We selected the linear trendline, and set the trendline option to display the resulting equation on the chart. The plot in the figure shows the data and the fitted line. Note the close agreement between the regression coefficients obtained by *Derive* and Excel.

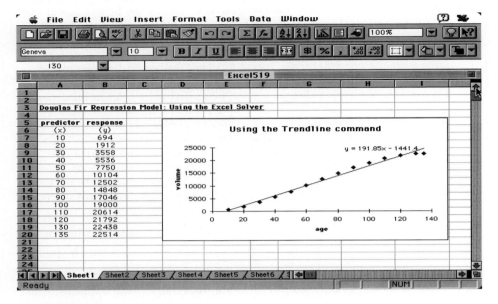

FIGURE 5.22
Fitting the Douglas fir example using the Trendline option in Excel. The resulting regression model is shown on the chart.

We would not expect a trial and error approach to do as well as either of these pre-defined operations.

We can also fit multipredictor linear functions using a spreadsheet. To do so, we list each predictor's values in a separate column. We then specify all the predictors as independent variables in the regression macro, and then follow the same procedures as we would for a single predictor model using a macro. We refer you to your spreadsheet documentation for the exact procedures.

We end with an example of how to fit a multipredictor linear function when using a *QuattroPro* spreadsheet.

Example 5.26. Table 5.3 lists some salary and qualification data on 52 teachers at a small Midwestern college. The data is from the 1970s. The variables are named as follows. The response, y, represents salary. There were several possible predictors: Gender of the faculty member (x_1), with $x_1 = 1$ indicating females and $x_1 = 0$ indicating males. We let x_2 represent academic rank, with $x_2 = 1$ for assistant professors, $x_2 = 2$ for associate professors, and $x_2 = 3$ for full professors. The number of years in the current rank was x_3. The highest degree held by the teacher was x_4, with 1 indicating a doctorate and 0 indicating a master's degree. The years since the highest degree was awarded was x_5. This data is available for down load from our Web site.

Case	x_1	x_2	x_3	x_4	x_5	y	Case	x_1	x_2	x_3	x_4	x_5	y
1	0	3	25	1	35	36, 350	27	0	2	11	1	14	24,800
2	0	3	13	1	22	35,350	28	1	3	5	1	16	25,500
3	0	3	10	1	23	28,200	29	0	2	3	0	7	26,182
4	1	3	7	1	27	26,775	30	0	2	3	0	17	23,725
5	0	3	19	0	30	33,696	31	1	1	10	0	15	21,600
6	0	3	16	1	21	28,516	32	0	2	11	0	31	23,300
7	1	3	0	0	32	24,900	33	0	1	9	0	14	23,713
8	0	3	16	1	18	31,909	34	1	2	4	0	33	20,690
9	0	3	13	0	30	31,850	35	1	2	6	0	29	22,450
10	0	3	13	0	31	32,850	36	0	2	1	1	9	20,850
11	0	3	12	1	22	27,025	37	1	1	8	1	14	18,304
12	0	2	15	1	19	24,750	38	0	1	4	1	4	17,095
13	0	3	9	1	17	28,200	39	0	1	4	1	5	16,700
14	0	2	9	0	27	23,712	40	0	1	4	1	4	17,600
15	0	3	9	1	24	25,748	41	0	1	3	1	4	18,075
16	0	3	7	1	15	29,342	42	0	1	3	0	11	18,000
17	0	3	13	1	20	31,114	43	0	2	0	1	7	20,999
18	0	2	11	0	14	24,742	44	1	1	3	1	3	17,250
19	0	2	10	0	15	22,906	45	0	1	2	1	3	16,500
20	0	3	6	0	21	24,450	46	0	1	2	1	1	16,094
21	0	1	16	0	23	19,175	47	1	1	2	1	6	16,150
22	0	2	8	0	31	20,525	48	1	1	2	1	2	15,350
23	0	3	7	1	13	27,959	49	0	1	1	1	1	16,244
24	1	3	8	1	24	38,045	50	1	1	1	1	1	16,686
25	0	2	9	1	12	24,832	51	1	1	1	1	1	15,000
26	0	3	5	1	18	25,400	52	1	1	0	1	2	20,300

TABLE 5.3
Data for the faculty salary example.

Using a spreadsheet, we obtain the following three models, which correspond to three different possible sets of predictors.

With just gender as a predictor, we obtain the model

$$\hat{y} = -3339.65x_1 + 24,696.79$$

The spreadsheet for this model is shown in Figure 5.23.

Including the three predictors gender, academic rank, and time in academic

	A	B	C	D	E	F	G	H	I
1									
2		Regression Output:							
3	Constant			11410.15					
4	Std Err of Y Est			2374.842					
5	R Squared			0.854718					
6	No. of Observations			52					
7	Degrees of Freedom			46					
8									
9	X Coefficient(s)		1241.792	5586.181	482.8598	-1331.64	-128.791		
10	Std Err of Coef.		885.56	663.967	91.71762	992.8543	75.58162		
11									
12		case	x1	x2	x3	x4	x5	y	
13		1	0	3	25	1	35	36350	
14		2	0	3	13	1	22	35350	
15		3	0	3	10	1	23	28200	
16		4	1	3	7	1	27	26775	
17		5	0	3	19	0	30	33696	

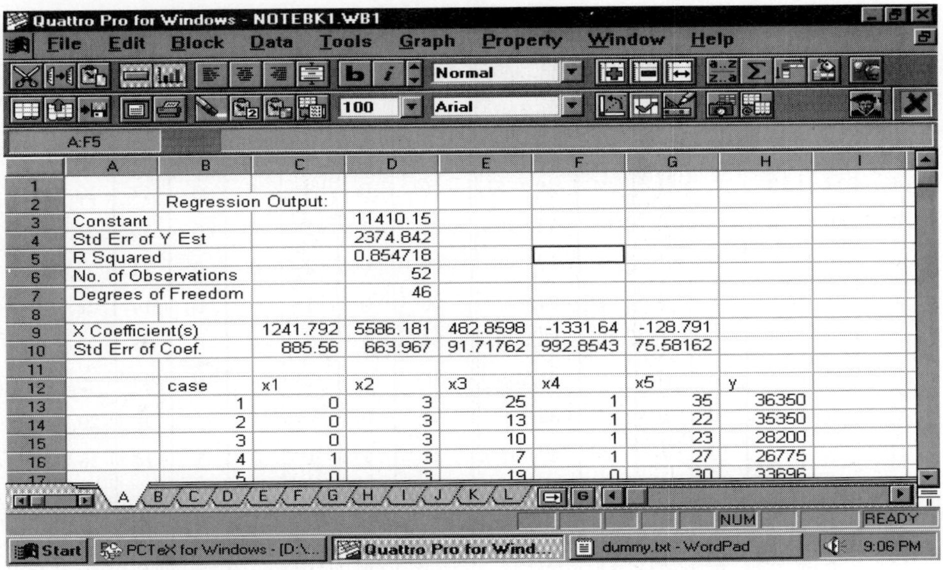

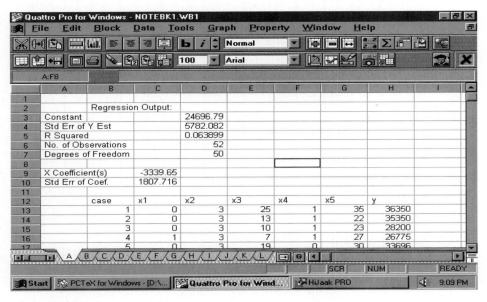

FIGURE 5.23
The QuattroPro spreadsheet fitting the single predictor, sex (x_1) to the response salary. The marginal slope of the predictor, -3339.65, is above it. The intercept is $24,696.79$.

	A	B	C	D	E	F	G	H	I
1									
2		Regression Output:							
3	Constant			24696.79					
4	Std Err of Y Est			5782.082					
5	R Squared			0.063899					
6	No. of Observations			52					
7	Degrees of Freedom			50					
8									
9	X Coefficient(s)		-3339.65						
10	Std Err of Coef.		1807.716						
11									
12		case	x1	x2	x3	x4	x5	y	
13		1	0	3	25	1	35	36350	
14		2	0	3	13	1	22	35350	
15		3	0	3	10	1	23	28200	
16		4	1	3	7	1	27	26775	
17		5	0	3	19	0	30	33696	

FIGURE 5.24
The QuattroPro spreadsheet fitting the three predictors x_1, x_2, and x_3, to the response salary. The marginal slopes are above the predictors: 603.77 for x_1, 4744.18 for x_2, and 393.86 for x_3. The intercept is $11,011.76$.

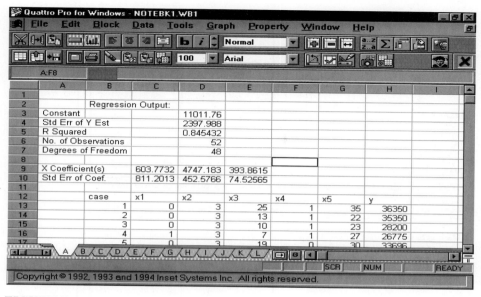

FIGURE 5.25

The QuattroPro spreadsheet fitting the five predictors x_1, x_2, x_3, x_4, and x_5, to the response salary. The marginal slopes are above the predictors: 1241.79 for x_1, 5586.18 for x_2, 482.86 for x_3, −1331.64 for x_4, and −128.79 for x_5. The intercept is 11,410.15.

rank, we obtain the model

$$\hat{y} = 603.77x_1 + 4744.18x_2 + 393.86x_3 + 11,011.76$$

as shown in Figure 5.24.

For the full model with all five predictors, we get

$$\hat{y} = 1241.79x_1 + 5586.18x_2 + 482.86x_3 - 1331.64x_4 - 128.79x_5 + 11,410.15$$

as shown in Figure 5.25.

5.4.6 Caveat user

There are some cautions worth mentioning concerning regression. First, regression will always find a best-fitting line for your data, even when the data is obviously nonlinear. The data points can even lie directly on a nonlinear curve, and regression will produce a linear approximation to the data. For example, let's take six points from a quadratic curve, plot them, and then find the least-squares line through these points.

Example 5.27. Consider the nonlinear equation for a parabola given by $w = h^2$. Six data points that lie directly on this quadratic curve are (1, 1), (-1, 1), (2, 4),

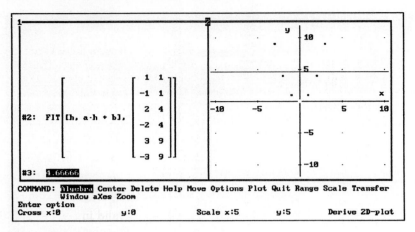

FIGURE 5.26
Regression line fitted to quadratic data.

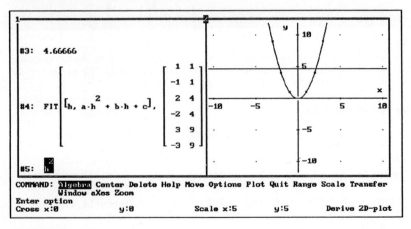

FIGURE 5.27
Quadratic regression curve fit to data.

(-2, 4), (3, 9), (-3, 9). The least-squares line resulting from the Fit command in *Derive*, together with the appropriate plot of the data is shown in Figure 5.26.

Notice that the line $\hat{w} = 4.66\bar{6}$ completely fails to capture the shape of the parabola, and is a very bad representation of the data. However, this is still the best-fit *line* for the data set. The plot of the data appears to indicate that the underlying relationship is nonlinear. So, using a line to describe the relationship between the two variables is inappropriate.

We see that it is always a good idea to plot the data before fitting a function!

The Fit command is much more versatile than it may first appear. We can also use the Fit command to fit nonlinear curves, as well as many other functions, to data sets.

Example 5.28. The syntax for the Fit command to find a least-squares quadratic regression curve is similar to that of finding a least-squares regression line. We would use $[h, ah^2 + bh + c]$ as the first argument, and follow exactly the same procedure as in Example 5.27. Applied to the data set of Example 5.27, this yields the great fitting regression curve $\hat{w} = h^2$, which we expected, since this is the nonlinear equation used to generate the six points of the data set (Figure 5.27).

Our second word of advice is to not use a regression curve to make predictions outside of the range of x values that generated it. Making predictions outside the range of x values is called *extrapolation*. Predicting within the range of x values is called *interpolation*. Although extrapolation is valid in some cases, the further you move from the range of your data to make predictions of y, the more dangerous it is. The next example illustrates this point.

Example 5.29. Consider again the data set containing height and weight data for adult males. We calculated a regression line that describes a relationship between height and weight based on the range of x data 63–76. Extrapolating outside these limits leads us to predict that an adult male 34.375 inches tall should weigh 0 pounds, and any adult male less than this height should have negative weight!

Exploration Exercise

5.1. Returning to the example of the data set generated by the quadratic equation $w = h^2$, let's further reinforce how the range of data collected affects our modeling effort.

(a) Using the equation $w = h^2$, generate two sets of data points. For the first data set, generate six points for $0 \leq h \leq 5/6$. For the second data set, generate eight data points for $2 \leq h \leq 10$.

(b) For each of the data sets, fit a least squares regression line to the data using the Fit command.

(c) In each separate case, plot the data points and the regression line and visually compare the fit of the line to data. How would you describe the quality of the fit? Why is this so? Would it be valid to extrapolate outside of the range of h given in the data set? Specify an example to support your claim.

(d) Next, fit a quadratic least squares regression curve to the same data, plot this curve. Would it be valid to extrapolate outside of the range of h using this regression curve? Why is this so? What assumption does this model have built into it that the least squares regression line does not? (Hint: think of how the data was generated.) Is it realistic to make this assumption for regression models developed from real sample data? Why?

5.4.7   Residuals

Although a visual inspection of the plot of the least-squares regression line with the data points suffices for determining how well our linear model $\hat{y} = ax + b$ seems to describe the data in the height–weight example, in general it may not. A more established means of assessing the fit of a regression line is to examine a plot of the individual vertical distances $(\hat{y}_n - y_n)$ for each of the n data points against their corresponding *fitted* values predicted by the regression line.

Recall that the sum of squared vertical distances is what the least squares method attempts to minimize. The quantity $(\hat{y}_n - y_n)$ represents the error associated with using a specific best fit regression line. This vertical distance associated with each data point is called its *residual*, and is typically denoted by $r_n = \hat{y}_n - y_n$.

We generally focus on two aspects of a residual plot: the relative size of the residuals $(\hat{y}_n - y_n)/\hat{y}_n$, and the dispersal of the points about the horizontal axis DIAGNOSING $y = 0$. If the values of the residuals are small relative to their fitted values $\hat{y}$, RESIDUALS then we have evidence of a good fit.

Conversely, many large values of residuals would cause us to question our choice of model since these deviations represent the difference between the actual response values observed and the ones resulting from our model. Additionally, we should not detect a noticeable systematic pattern of the data in this plot. A residual plot that looks like a random grouping of data points about the horizontal axis, with no apparent pattern, is an indication of a good choice of model.

We also might discover one or two data points that stand out from the rest OUTLIER in the residual plot. These potential *outliers* might have gone undetected in a plot of the data set.

Outliers can sometimes be attributed to errors in measurement, in which case new data should be gathered for this data point. In other cases, the outlying value is determined to be correct, and the outlier provides additional insight into the relationship being modeled. Determining whether a specific point is an outlier is beyond the scope of this section, and it a topic best left to studies in statistics.

Derive is not designed to specifically analyze residual plots for data sets. Plotting residuals r_n versus fitted values $\hat{y}_n$ requires that we calculate the individual residual value for each data point, then enter these values and their corresponding $\hat{y}$ values in a data matrix.

TABLE 5.4
Data and residuals for Douglas fir example.

x	y	$\hat{y}$	$\hat{y} - y$
10	694	477	217
20	1,912	2396	−484
30	3,558	4314	−756
40	5,536	6233	−697
50	7,750	8151	−401
60	10,104	10070	34
70	12,502	11988	514
80	14,848	13907	941
90	17,046	15825	1221
100	19,000	17744	1256
110	20,614	19663	951
120	21,792	21581	211
130	22,438	23500	−1062
135	22,514	24459	−1945

A far easier approach is to either directly use statistical software, or to use a spreadsheet to accomplish this analysis. For example, QuattroPro has an extensive regression toolkit that provides the equation of the best-fitting regression curve. It also produces useful statistical information for assessing how good the fit of this regression curve is.

With both statistical software and spreadsheets, it is very easy to enter the data set in two columns, specify a general residual expression in a third, automatically calculate the residuals, select the columns to plot, and examine various combinations of data plots.

The next example is given to illustrate how this type of analysis is accomplished using *Derive*.

Example 5.30. The first and second columns of Table 5.4 contain the original data points for the Douglas fir example. The third column contains the predicted response (the fitted value $\hat{y}$) on the regression line for each value of x. The fourth column contains the calculated residual for each data point.

Notice that some values are negative and some positive, and that the relative size of the residuals to the fitted values for each of the 14 points does not seem to indicate a problem with our model. However, the residual plot in Figure 5.28 reveals a pattern hidden in the table of numerical values. As a result of

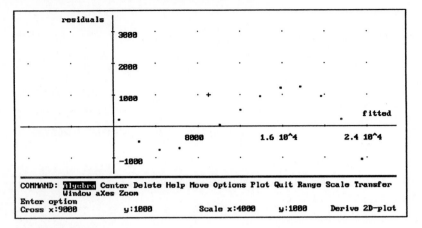

FIGURE 5.28
Residual plot for Douglas Fir model.

this pattern, we conclude that a least squares regression line was an inappropriate choice to model the relationship between the age of the Douglas fir stand and the cumulative volume of trees, even though the plot of the regression line versus the data in Figure 5.19 appeared to be acceptable at first.

Regression is a very powerful tool that is extremely useful in building models from data sets. It can be misused, however—and we should always check our models based on regression to make sure they make sense.

5.5 A SAMPLE REPORT

The last step of our problem solving process is to *report* our results: mess, model, solve, analyze, report. Many times these reports can get quite complicated. Since this may be the first time that you have written a technical report, let's keep the idea simple. After you get a feel for the general approach, you can use the format that we have included in Appendix A. Here, we illustrate a simple technical report for the faculty salary model in the exercises. Some general recommendations are in order.

A very effective technique used in most technical reports is to put the conclusions first: "Bottom line up front." This focuses the reader's attention on your main points and prevents them from getting lost in the details of the report.

You will also want to include a few key pictures, plots, or charts to represent results. These graphical examples are great because they can consolidate a number of pieces of information in one location where it is easy to understand.

A picture is worth a thousand words.

Brevity is also a virture. Try to keep reports as close to one page as possible for most of the exercises in this book. The projects will undoubtedly take more than a single page simply because you may want to include more information. In real-world modeling efforts, the corresponding technical reports can easily exceed several hundred pages. When this is the case, a one-page executive summary is presented in the very front of the document, serving the same purpose as a one-page report.

There is a rule of thumb that you should always follow, regardless of the length or topic of your technical report: Never leave it to your readers to draw their own conclusions from your work. Clearly state how *you* interpret the results of your analysis and the conclusions that are to be drawn from them.

Example 5.31.   Report.
MESS: Facing questions about our faculty salary structure, we modeled faculty pay as a linear function of the gender of the faculty member, academic rank (assistant, associate, or full professor), number of years in the current academic rank, highest academic degree, and years since the degree was granted.
MODEL: The full model that we developed incorporated all five of the predictor variables:

$$\hat{y} = 1241x_1 + 5586x_2 + 4883x_3 - 1332x_4 - 129x_5 + 11,410$$

Figure 5.30 shows both a plot of the fitted values $\hat{y}$ versus residuals r and the regression output.

Additionally, we developed two smaller models. The one-predictor model describes the relationship between the response and the gender of a faculty member. The three-predictor model describes the relationship between the response and the predictors: gender, rank, and years at the current academic rank.
SOLUTION: Not applicable. The regression model is designed to describe the relationship between the predictors and the response. It is not intended to be used to obtain a numerical solution.

ANALYSIS: The full model suggests that we pay women slightly more ($1241) than men of similar qualifications. This contradicts the results of the one-predictor model. The one-predictor model found that, on average, women faculty members earned $3339 less than men faculty members.

The three-predictor model confirmed the results of the full model: that women earned more than similarly qualified men ($603).

Since faculty pay, in our opinion, is more solidly based on all the predictors listed above, we believe the full model to be a more valid representation of the relationship between faculty pay and the predictors noted. It also appears to be more credible because of including these additional predictors.

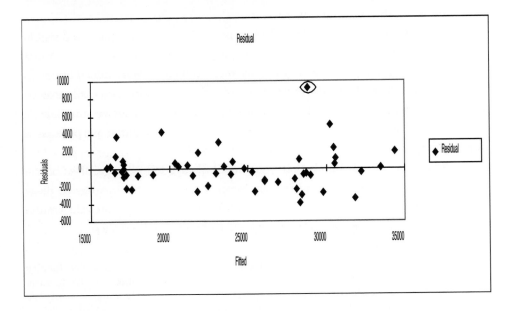

FIGURE 5.29
Plot of fitted values versus residuals for the full salary model. Note the one potential outlier.

	A	B	C	D	E	F	G	H	I
1		Regression Output:							
2	Constant			11410.15					
3	Std Err of Y Est			2374.842					
4	R Squared			0.854718					
5	No. of Observations			52					
6	Degrees of Freedom			46					
7									
8	X Coefficient(s)		1241.792	5586.181	482.8598	-1331.64	-128.791		
9	Std Err of Coef.		885.56	663.967	91.71762	992.8543	75.58162		
10									
11									
12		case	x1	x2	x3	x4	x5	y	yhat
13		1	0	1	3	0	11	18000	17028.21
14		2	0	1	9	0	14	23713	19539
15		3	0	1	16	0	23	19175	21759.9
16		4	1	1	10	0	15	21600	21134.86
17		5	0	1	2	1	3	16500	16244.03
18		6	0	1	2	1	1	16094	16501.61

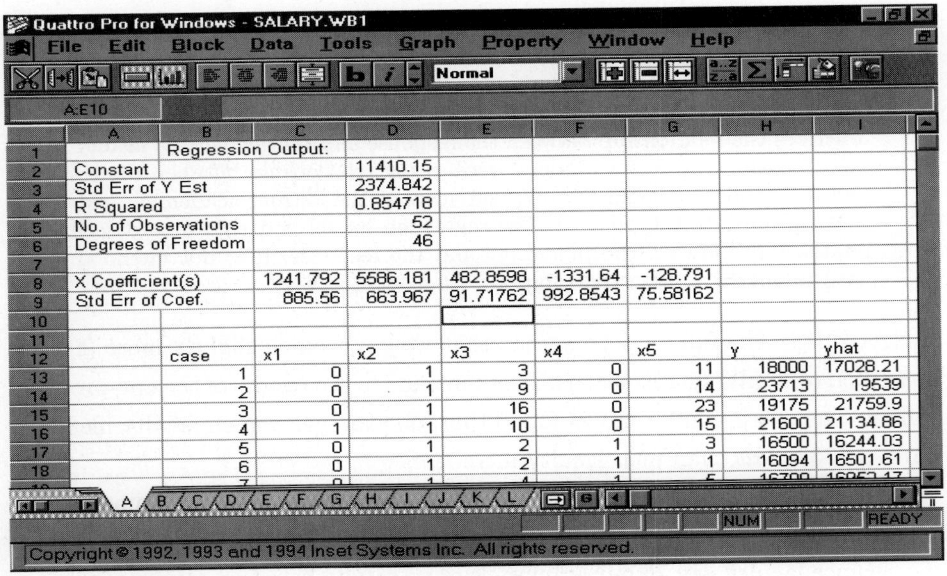

FIGURE 5.30
Regression output from the spreadsheet calculations for the full salary model. We're not using all the information available from the output; a statistical analysis would.

Faculty pay increases with faculty rank and number of years in rank. It decreases, surprisingly, with highest degree, and years since the highest degree was earned.

The diagnostic plot of fitted versus residuals for both the full and three-predictor models were unremarkable, except for one possible outlier. Case number 24 appears to earn $9037 more than the model would predict. This data point is raising the average woman's salary. Looking at the diagnostic plot, it appears that the average residual is about $2300, which means our model is correct within about $2300.

All of our models are based on the 52 faculty members at the college where the data was collected. It may or may not be valid for other years or other institutions. There may be other predictors that we have not included which would more completely explain the variation in faculty salaries.

We are available to answer any questions you may have.

Exploration Exercises

For each of the following data sets, first plot the data set. If a linear relationship is indicated between the independent variable and the dependent variable as a result of the plot, then determine the appropriate regression coefficients and regression line using the *Derive* Fit function. Either support or refute the use of your specific regression line by examining the plot of the regression curve on the data, and a residual plot for each data set.

5.1. Water resources of many regions of the world depend heavily upon melting winter snow accumulation to refill natural and man–made reservoirs. The National Aeronautics and Space Administration (NASA) creates computer models based upon *Landsat* (satellite) measurements of microwave emission in snow covered areas, and uses these models to predict potential water resources. These computer models are tested and refined based upon ground–based measurements of snow depth and temperature. Such measurements, when graphed, inevitably show a large amount of scatter, and it is the regression line for the data that is used as the standard for comparison. Table 5.5 contains data points for several ground based measurements. The snow depth is measured in centimeters, and temperature is listed in degrees Kelvin. ¶

5.2. Very high-energy particles (electrons and protons) are found in the radiation belts of some planets, and a plot of the number of particles found at different energies is called a *spectrum*. Often the spectrum has a shape that can be represented by a model of the form $N = KE^m$ where N is the number of particles

---

¶*Space Mathematics,* by Bernice Kastner, Department of Mathematics and Statistics, Simon Fraser University, Burnaby, British Columbia. A curriculum project of the National Council of Teachers of Mathematics (NCTM) jointly sponsored by NASA.

TABLE 5.5
Data for Landsat ground measurements.

$T_B(K)$	Depth(cm)	$T_B(K)$	Depth(cm)	$T_B(K)$	Depth(cm)	$T_B(K)$	Depth(cm)
195	25	243	1	250	2	243	6
209	17	247	3	255	1	248	4
211	21	245	1	207	19	209	15
218	19	251	3	210	25	217	22
227	20	211	20	214	21	230	13
232	13	223	14	218	16	233	8
233	18	232	17	228	22	239	16
235	21	237	5	231	18	242	5
237	12	240	4	233	11	247	2
239	6	243	3	236	8	252	2
240	8	249	4	238	8		
243	7	241	8	240	6		

TABLE 5.6
Data for spectrum equation.

Energy, E	Number, N
0.16	1.0×10^6
0.30	1.5×10^5
0.60	1.3×10^4
1.0	6.8×10^3
1.6	1.0×10^3
4.5	20
10.0	1
20.0	0.1

at a certain energy, E; K is a proportionality factor; and m is called the *spectral index*. Table 5.6 shows values of N measured a several energies during the flight of Pioneer 10 past Jupiter. Determine the best fit values of m and K for the model given. (Hint: Transform the model to a linear model using logarithms. Plotting $\log E$ versus $\log N$ will allow you to then find the appropriate regression coefficients for use in the model presented.)

5.3. The National Association of Underwater Instructors (NAUI) is an organization that provides all levels of certification for scuba diving. The safe-diving tables developed by NAUI provide numerical data that scuba divers can use to calculate

TABLE 5.7
Data for dive tables.

Start Depth (ft.)	NDL (min)
40	200
50	100
60	60
70	50
80	40
90	30
100	25
110	20
120	15
130	10
140	10

diving time limits for repetitive dives to avoid mandatory decompression stops. Table 5.7 shows the initial dive plan depth and corresponding decompression time limits (NDL) (in minutes) that specify the maximum time a diver can spend at that depth without having to perform decompression stops.

5.4. Experimental results of psychological studies of human decision-making are critical ingredients in the design of effective instrumentation panels for aircraft. The time it takes to respond when faced with varying numbers of choices becomes a limiting parameter as to the number of light emitting diode (LED) displays that can be built into a single pilot's panel. Table 5.8 shows a collection of experimental results for one such psychological study, where N is the number of choices presented to the test subject and R is the reaction time in seconds.

5.5. Postmortem blood drug concentrations are used to evaluate the role a drug has played in a death. Most morphine-caused deaths are associated with respiratory or cardiorespiratory failure, body functions controlled from the hind brain. Table 5.9 shows measured morphine concentrations in both blood and cisternal cerebrospinal fluid (CSF) in 20 cases of death resulting from morphine overdose.[||] Both measures of concentration are given in micrograms per milliliter (μg/mL). Is there a relationship between the measured quantities?

5.6. Because of both immediate and long-term problems, efforts are usually taken by health care professionals to identify newborns exposed to nicotine during pregnancy as soon as possible so that the appropriate intervention and follow-up can

---

[||]Logan, B. and R. Lüthi. "The Significance of Morphine Concentrations in the Cerebrospinal Fluid in Morphine Caused Deaths", *Journal of Forensic Sciences*, **39**, 3, p.702. (1994)

TABLE 5.8
Data for reaction times.

N	R
1	0.17
2	0.34
3	0.37
4	0.42
5	0.48
6	0.52
7	0.56
8	0.58
9	0.59
10	0.57

TABLE 5.9
Morphine levels in postmortem samples.

Case	Blood Morphine	CSF Morphine	Case	Blood Morphine	CSF Morphine
1	0.130	0.023	11	0.189	0.062
2	0.021	0.030	12	0.150	0.074
3	0.101	0.034	13	0.045	0.082
4	0.156	0.048	14	0.170	0.085
5	0.294	0.049	15	0.130	0.092
6	0.105	0.049	16	0.920	0.140
7	0.179	0.052	17	0.064	0.007
8	0.116	0.054	18	0.027	0.011
9	0.120	0.055	19	0.017	0.009
10	0.320	0.060	20	0.100	0.055

be done. Researchers in the health field have examined the effects of maternal smoking as a health hazard for the fetus by examining the concentration of nicotine in both mother and newborn infant soon after birth.[††] Table 5.10 shows the

---

[††]Kintz, P., Kieffer, I., Messer, J., and Mangin, P., "Nicotine analysis in neonates' hair for measuring gestational exposure to tobacco," *Journal of Forensic Sciences*, JFSCA, Vol. 38, No. 1, 119–123. (1993)

TABLE 5.10
Nicotine levels in hair.

NNC	MNC	NNC	MNC	NNC	MNC	NNC	MNC
11.8	61.0	5.4	40.7	1.2	14.0	0.2	1.1
1.1	2.5	0.8	4.0	0.81	2.4	0.3	2.4
1.1	7.0	4.8	36.1	4.3	25.5	3.7	9.8
7.5	36.1	0.8	2.0	0.7	5.2	6.08	46.0
8.6	25.5	7.75	50.2	2.3	9.1	1.8	15.2
1.3	2.48	6.48	12.5	3.4	17.0	0.6	2.0
3.6	60.0	1.4	2.5	1.2	19.5	1.4	18.0
10.7	63.0	0.14	2.8	3.4	27.5	3.6	18.3
0.9	5.8	6.4	13.5	7.35	42.0	6.4	36.4
7.35	42.0	6.4	36.4	0.2	3.3		

results examining hair samples of 37 mothers and their corresponding newborn infants gathered 1 to 5 days after delivery. The neonates' nicotine concentration (NNC) and the maternal nicotine concentration (MNC) are both expressed in units of nanograms per milligram (ng/mg). What relationship exists between the two measured quantities? What other information can you infer from the gathered data?

5.7. Mammals have gestation periods that differ by species. For example, the average gestation period for a human is nine months, whereas the average gestation period for a mouse is two weeks. We also know that the smaller the mammal, the faster its metabolism is, and the shorter its average life span. Is there a relationship between the average gestation period of mammals and their average life span? If there is such a relationship, what type of curve could be used to describe the relationship? If there is not, explain why.

5.8. We know from engineering mechanics that certain levers give us mechanical advantages in performing tasks. From watching basketball competitions in which most of the players are exceptionally tall, we can see that they can vertically jump a good distance. However, is it true that the taller a person is, the higher he or she can jump? Or, is the height a person jumps more related to the length of legs, height of knees, or length of feet?

5.9. We often assert that the more time someone spends studying for a test, the better the person performs on the test (usually measured by the grade that they receive). Is there a relationship between the two quantities? If so, conjecture what type of curve would best fit the data. If not, conjecture how the qualitative factor of "quality study time" might be affecting scores. How might we convert this qualitative factor into a quantitative factor? That is, how might we measure quality study time so that we could include it in a model?

5.10. As we have seen earlier in this section, the regression curve does not necessarily have to be a straight line of the form $\hat{y} = mx + b$. If your goal was to use an approximating curve to describe the relationship between the data in the plots

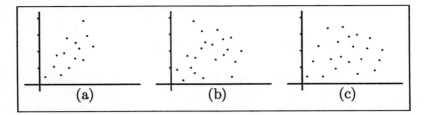

FIGURE 5.31
Data sets for approximating curves.

of Figure 5.31, what general form of a curve would you use? Assume that the plots are showing the raw data points (x, y) for different data sets.

5.6   SUMMARY

We have discussed a great deal of information concerning linear models in this chapter.

Whenever the change in response is proportional to the change in predictors, a linear model is appropriate.

All linear models have constant rates of change—the slope is the same regardless of the values of the predictors, and regardless where on the surface we examine the slope.

Linear models of one predictor with nonzero slope have inverses.

Linear models with more than one predictor do not have inverses.

For a linear function with more than one predictor, the slope depends on the direction of change of the predictors. The direction of maximum increase is given by the gradient. The length of the gradient is the rate of maximum increase.

Directional slopes other than along the main axes or in the direction of the gradient of the response-preditor function can be calculated using Equation 5.13.

Linear regression is a technique we can use to develop a linear model that best fits a data set. It should be used only when a plot of the data suggests that a linear relationship may exist between the response and preditors.

The domain of the regression function should be restricted to as close to original predictor intervals as possible.

The *Derive* Fit command and preprogrammed spreadsheet macros can be used to calculate the regression coefficients.

Adding or deleting predictors can greatly change the slopes of other predictors, and can completely change the results of a model.

A modeling problem is not completely solved until the results of the model have been clearly and concisely communicated.

5.7 PROJECT: MODEL ADAPTABILITY

The goal of this project is to test the adaptability of the the faculty salary model proposed in this chapter.

One of the questions left unanswered in the salary model is whether the results obtained are valid for other faculty at other schools, or limited to just the college where the data was gathered. This is a classic question of adaptability.

Required Analysis_____

1. First, gather similar data for the faculty at your school, and examine whether a linear model is suggested by a plot of the response and predictors used. If you can't find a data set for your school, we have a data set at our Web site that you can download and analyze.

2. Next, apply the one-predictor, three-predictor, and five-predictor models in the text to your data.

3. Calculate the sum of squared errors for each of the models applied to your data set. Do the predicted response values of the existing regression lines make sense for your data set? Would you expect them to?

4. Now, perform a one-predictor, three-predictor, and five-predictor regression on your data using the **Fit** command in *Derive*, or a spreadsheet macro. Explain why you selected the predictors you used for the one- and three-predictor models.

5. Examine a residual plot for each of the three models you developed. Are there any suspected outliers indicated in the residual plots?

6. Compare your results with the results from Section 5.5. Do your conclusions support those proposed in the text? Comment on the adaptability of the original three models presented in Section 5.4.

7. Write a short report summarizing your analysis.

5.8 PROJECT: BLOOD ALCOHOL ELIMINATION

The purpose of this project is to examine the functional relationship between the amount of alcohol in a person's bloodstream and the time it takes to eliminate it. The project data used here is actual data in which the names of the subjects have been intentionally not used. The data has not been "cooked" to yield a politically correct result.

Excellent objective scientific information concerning alcohol and other controlled substances can be found on the Internet at the Web sites that follow. We would encourage students and faculty to use these and other Internet resources as research for this project.

- The National Institute on Alcohol Abuse and Alcoholism (NIAAA), at

  http://www.niaaa.hih.gov/

- The National Clearinghouse for Alcohol and Drug Information (NCADI), at http://www.health.org/.
- The ETOH homepage for information searches from the NIAAA's Alcohol and Alcohol Problems Science Database at http://165.112.124.3

Blood alcohol uptake and elimination eventually becomes the concern of young adults in the United States sometime after their 21st birthday. Individual states have laws regulating the amount of alcohol that someone is allowed to have in their blood to legally operate a motor vehicle. For most states, this legal limit is defined as 0.08 grams per deciliter (g/dl) of blood.

A complete model that represents the uptake, or *absorption*, of alcohol along with elimination can be a complicated nonlinear process based on Michaelis-Menten first order enzyme kinetics that requires an understanding of how foods compete for absorption sites in order to model. This is beyond the scope of this project. Several references are cited at the end of this project description for further information and detail.

For alcohol uptake, this process can be simplified to say that alcohol is absorbed into the bloodstream instantaneously, beginning in the mouth and continuing throughout the digestive system. A peak blood alcohol level is typically attained approximately 20 minutes after the last drink is consumed.

Past the peak BAC point, absorption continues, but the process of elimination begins to dominate so that the total concentration of alcohol in the bloodstream begins to drop as the body converts the alcohol to the toxin acid aldehyde.

It is this elimination-dominated phase that captures our interest here, as well as peak BAC identification. We would like to know several pieces of practical information that set the stage for our project requirements.

Required Analysis

1. The Department of Transportation publishes a chart of approximate blood alcohol concentration levels given the weight of an individual and the amount of alcohol consumed. Using this information, develop a linear regression model that can be used to predict the approximate peak blood-alcohol concentration that will occur. What type of assumptions do you need to make this model valid?

2. Using the linear regression elimination model you developed, determine the time that someone would have to wait after consuming alcohol until safely within the legal limit of 0.08 g/dl.

3. The data in the following table, which was previously introduced in a Chapter 3 exercise, gives two examples of BAC profiles for two subjects, SP and JS, for two experimental situations in which they ingested 0.8 g/kg of alcohol on an empty stomach, and one week later immediately after breakfast. Graphically compare your linear regression model to the BAC profiles below. Do the profiles agree with what your model would have predicted, given the weight of the individuals and the amount of alcohol they consumed?

Time	Subject SP, 24 yrs, 73 kg		Subject JS, 23 yrs, 73 kg	
minutes	Empty mg/dl	Full mg/dl	Empty mg/dl	Full mg/dl
10	13	7	13	3
20	20	25	42	11
30	64	26	64	37
45	93	43	110	42
60	88	41	100	52
90	82	57	97	76
120	80	55	87	70
150	76	52	81	61
180	70	40	71	53
240	60	25	60	32
300	42	9	42	10
360	30	2	20	2

4. The two individuals below participated in a correlation study to track blood alcohol concentration levels using both blood (bl) and breath (br) samples. The test results indicate the BAC of the individual in grams per deciliter (g/dl). The times are reported in 24 hour notation. Check the performance of your linear regression model to compare its prediction with the actual data contained in these tables. What part of the domain of your model do these data represent? Can you approximate the peak BAC using your linear regression model and the data given? Comment on the adaptability and transferability of your model.

Person/weight/gender	Drinking Start-Finish	Time of sample	Test Result
J/182 lbs/M	1353–1412	1243	0.00
		1437	0.06 (br)
8 oz vodka		1443	0.08 (bl)
		1500	0.07 (br)
		1543	0.07 (br)
		1545	0.09 (bl)
		1613	0.06 (br)
		1643	0.05 (br)
		1645	0.08 (bl)

Person/weight/gender	Drinking Start-Finish	Time of sample	Test Result
S/140 lbs/F	1350–1415	1341	0.00
		1441	0.07 (br)
6 oz vodka		1445	0.08 (bl)
		1506	0.07 (br)
		1540	0.06 (br)
		1545	0.08 (bl)
		1620	0.06 (br)
		1641	0.05 (br)

5.9 COMPLEMENTS

1. There are many excellent references on regression. Two of our favorites that are quite comprehensive in their treatment of the topic are

   - *Applied Linear Regression*, 2nd edition, by Sanford Weisberg. John Wiley and Sons, Inc., New York, New York, 1985.
   - *Applied Linear Statistical Models*, 3rd edition, by John Neter, William Wasserman, and Michael H. Kutner. Irwin Publishing, Boston, Massachusetts, 1990.

2. The processes of alcohol absorption and elimination carry with them many legal as well as biochemical ramifications. The following list represents a very good start point to explore the topic further.

   - *Biochemistry*, 2nd edition, by Donald Voet and Judith G. Voet. John Wiley and Sons, Inc., New York, New York, 1995. Enzyme kinetics are covered on pp. 351–355.
   - *A Bibliography of Forensic Aspects of Alcohols*, by James G. Wigmore. Published by the Forensic Sciences Foundation, Inc., Colorado Springs, Colorado, 1992. This reference contains the largest reputable consolidated listing of published sources of information on blood alcohol that exists as of this writing. It is obtainable by contacting either the Forensic Sciences Foundation or the American Academy of Forensic Sciences. Both can be found by performing a Web search on their titles. The listings in the bibliography are divided into four parts for ease of organization:

(*a*) Alcohol and Driving, Boating, Flying; and Accidents

(*b*) Breath Alcohol, Solvents, Methanol, Isopropanol, Acetaldehyde and Cogeners

(*c*) Blood Alcohol, Other Fluids/Tissues, Postmortem, High BACs and Fatal BACs

(*d*) Pharmacokinetics of Alcohol, Miscellaneous

CHAPTER 6

MODELING WITH SYSTEMS OF EQUATIONS

All progress is precarious, and the solution of one problem brings us face to face with another problem.

Martin Luther King, Jr.

Chapter Goals

⇒ Understand how systems of equations arise in the modeling process.

⇒ Understand the underlying geometry of a system of equations.

⇒ Understand how to solve systems of equations.

⇒ Understand the usefulness of matrix descriptions of systems of equations.

⇒ Represent and solve simple systems of equations using matrices.

Last chapter, we discussed linear functions that connected a response with one or more predictors. In this chapter, we examine systems of linear equations.

These systems arise when the response must simultaneously satisfy several linear functions of the predictors. The systems also arise as relationships among the predictors, which may be linearly related.

6.1   BACKGROUND

There is a long history of solving systems of linear equations, dating before the first century A.Din China and from the third century A.D in Greece. As with much of mathematics, progress was slow until the development of a clear, concise notation. The Chinese work in this area may have been as early as 1100 B.C. Early Greek work is due to Diophantus around 275 A.D Advances in notation occurring toward the the end of the 16th century spurred the study of linear systems by simplifying the bookkeeping associated with solving such systems.

The methods and notation we use in this chapter date from the 19th century. They were developed in England by J. J. Sylvester and Arthur Cayley. We digress for a moment to share some stories about them.

Sylvester never actually graduated from Saint Johns College, Cambridge, refusing to sign a religious oath that conflicted with his Jewish faith. He taught briefly at the University of Virginia, but fled back to England after wrongly believing that he had killed, with his sword, a student who rudely read a newspaper in his class. Sylvester was forced to become a lawyer. While practicing law, Sylvester tutored many students in mathematics, including Florence Nightingale.

It is interesting that Cayley, after his graduation from Trinity College, Cambridge, also became a lawyer to support his mathematical hobbies, publishing about 250 mathematical papers in the 14 years he was a lawyer.

Sylvester and Cayley were life-long friends. Their friendship was forged during the period that they both practiced law at the courts of Lincoln's Inn, in London. Both eventually became professors of mathematics, Cayley at Cambridge and Sylvester at Woolrich, then John Hopkins, then Oxford. Both are credited with first-rate work in mathematics.

The main solution method we introduce for systems of linear equations is named after Johann Carl Friedrich Gauss and Marie Ennemond Camille Jordan. They were not collaborators, as they were born 61 years apart. Each contributed significantly to the theory of solving linear systems of equations.

Gauss is recognized as one of the greatest mathematical geniuses. His talent was recognized from the age of 7. He made several fundamental discoveries such as the method of least squares. His students included such notable mathematicians as Cantor, Dedekind, and Riemann—who would make their own fundamental contributions to mathematics.

Gauss studied financial markets, and became very rich from his successful investments.

Jordan studied at the École Polytechnique, a French military academy, where he taught for many years after his graduation. Jordan's students included Sophus Lie and Felix Klein, who greatly extended his work.

As you can see, we join the ranks of a notable and prestigious crowd as we study linear systems of equations!

Today, much of modern industrial management and economics depends on solving large systems of equations. Conservation laws in the sciences that require energy and mass to be neither created or destroyed result in balance equations, where the amount of each quantity must be accounted for. These, too, lead to systems of linear equations. The subject is important, and its use widespread.

Let's begin in a familiar setting.

6.2 INTERCEPTS AND INTERSECTION

In the last chapter, we introduced the idea of an intercept in conjunction with the slope-intercept form of a linear function: $y = f(x) = mx + b$.

After determining that we could identify the y-intercept by setting $x = 0$, the process became somewhat trivial. However, there is another valuable perspective on an intercept that's different from its role as a response-intercept: It's one component of the intersection point of two curves.

INTERSECTION

POINT

> **Example 6.1.** We calculate the response-intercept of $y = f(x) = 3x + 19$ by setting $x = 0$ and solving for y, yielding $y = 19$. Finding the intersection of the two lines $y = 3x + 19$ and $x = 0$ yields the point: $(0, 19)$.

> **Example 6.2.** Calculating the response-intercept of $y = f(x) = 0.8x^2 + 14x - 2$ yields $y = -2$. Finding the intersection of the two curves $y = 0.8x^2 + 14x - 2$ and $x = 0$ yields the point: $(0, -2)$.

See the pattern? Think of what the calculations are doing in this way: By setting $x = 0$ in the intercept calculation, we're specifying a vertical line that corresponds to the usual y-axis. Then, we're determining the y-value of the intersection point between the linear function and this vertical line. So, if we were interested in finding the intersection point of the two curves $y = 3x^2 + 4x - 2$ and $x = 1$, we would set $x = 1$ and solve for the y-component.

In a similar fashion, suppose that we are interested in finding the predictor-intercept of a linear function. The predictor-intercept corresponds to the line $y = 0$, or, equivalently stated, the usual x-axis. Solving for the predictor-intercept of a function is the same as solving for the intersection point of two expressions, one of which is the expression $y = 0$.

This is a similar approach to how we use the inverse of a function graphically. To identify the predictor that produced a specific response value, we draw the line $y = k$, and where it intersects the graph of our function, we find the corresponding x value, such that $x = f^{-1}(k)$.

This is also the idea behind finding the roots of an equation, which a symbolic software application such as *Derive* accomplishes with relative ease. But, before going on, we'd like you to think about and discuss the next ideas.

Discussion Ideas_____

Consider the task of finding the intersection of two lines where neither is horizontal or vertical?

$\Rightarrow$ How is this different than the task of finding the intersection of a line with one of the standard Cartesian axes? Is the task more complicated? In what way?

$\Rightarrow$ Now, think about how we perform the calculation for finding x- and y-intercepts in terms of isolating one variable and substituting the expression it is equal to into the other equation. Could you still perform the same steps for this case? If so, then you will be using the same step-wise solution procedure, i.e., the same *algorithm*. Is that the case here?

_____

Using *Derive*, we have several ways of finding intersection points other than those involving the standard axes.

Example 6.3. Suppose that we wish to solve for the intersection point of the two lines

$$y = \frac{1}{4} - \frac{3}{4}x$$

$$y = \frac{1}{2}x - \frac{7}{2}$$

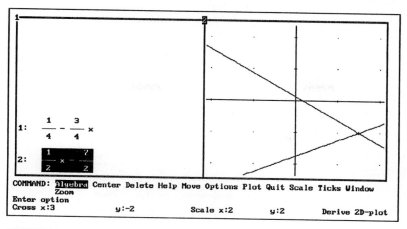

FIGURE 6.1
Intersection of linear curves.

Plotting both of these lines on the same graph enables us to graphically estimate the intersection point using the *Derive* crosshairs, which we move using the arrow keys. There is only one intersection point.

It appears that the intersection point is $(x, y) = (3, -2)$, as shown in Figure 6.1. We can quickly check if we are correct by substituting these values into both of the equations, since an intersection point must lie on each curve, and must satisfy both equations.

Graphical analysis for intersection points is useful as an approximation to the exact value of the intersection point, but it is only an approximation. For linear curves, this approximation can be quite accurate, as seen in the previous example. It can also be accurate for determining the intersection point(s) of nonlinear functions.

GRAPHICAL APPROXIMATION

Example 6.4. Suppose that we are interested in finding the point(s) of intersection of the nonlinear curve $y = 3x^3$ and the linear curve $y = 2x + 1$. Figure 6.2 shows these two expressions along with their corresponding plots in the second window.

It appears obvious that the two curves intersect. We can graphically estimate the intersection point by moving the *Derive* crosshairs over the point where the two curves cross. Doing so yields the point $(1, 3)$.

To get an exact solution, notice that both expressions are conveniently equal to y as written. Assuming that both expressions share the same value of y at a point of intersection, we can set one expression equal to the other, $3x^3 = 2x + 1$, and solve for the corresponding value(s) of x.

All CAS applications will be able to solve for the intersection point of these curves. A convenient way to accomplish this in *Derive* is to use the Build menu option. We specify the Build first expression as #1, the Build operator as the equals sign =, and the Build second expression as #2. Keeping the default

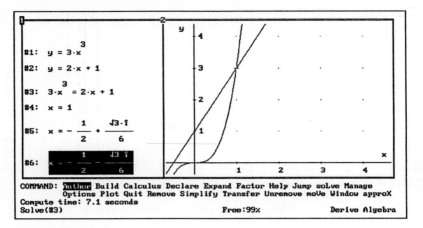

FIGURE 6.2
Intersection of a linear and a nonlinear curve.

Options, Precision in the Exact mode, we solve for the appropriate x value(s) using the menu option soLve. This results in one real valued solution

$$x = 1$$

and two imaginary, or complex solutions

$$x = \frac{\sqrt{3}i}{6} - \frac{1}{2}$$

$$x = \frac{-\sqrt{3}i}{6} - \frac{1}{2}$$

The graphical plot in Figure 6.2 shows the single real-number intersection point for these two curves. This value of x is the one we are interested in, since we assume that the problem has some sort of meaning in the (x, y)-plane of real numbers.

As an option, we could have highlighted this value of x and obtained an approximate value of $x = 1$ using the approX menu option. Similarly, by setting Options, Precision to Approximate, as opposed to the default setting of Exact, the menu option soLve would likewise yield $x = 1$.

Graphical methods are not always trouble-free. Consider the next example, which shows the difficulties that can arise even with a system of two linear equations.

Example 6.5. Using the crosshair of the *Derive* cursor, estimate the intersection point of the two curves:

$$y = \frac{1}{8}x - 2.1$$

$$y = \frac{0.96}{8}x - 2.09$$

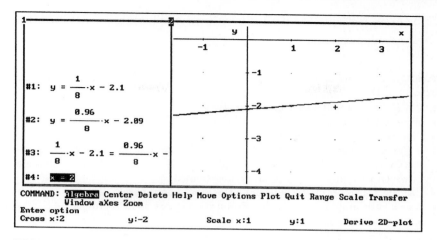

FIGURE 6.3
Two near-dependent lines. Where do they intersect?

They intersect at $x = -2$, but because they are so nearly parallel, we can't find the intersection point easily on the graph. See Figure 6.3.

These two equations are displaying a condition known as *near dependency* NEAR that we discuss in detail later in this chapter; one line is nearly the same as the DEPENDENCY other. The challenge presented in determining an intersection point doesn't go away when we use computers. And, when we are faced with a lot more than two equations, the problem can get *really* ugly.

At first glance, it seems much simpler to plot the expressions of interest and graphically examine them for intersection points. In fact, this is the case when we are working with low dimensional models involving linear expressions.

When expressions have nonlinear terms, the graphical plot can sometimes be inconclusive or misleading. Despite this possibility, it is still a good rule of thumb to first plot the information we are working with, whether the information is a data set or curves.

Our caution is that you keep in mind that the plots in *Derive*, or on a graphing calculator, are an approximation based on the default settings of the program. Finding exact intersections and solutions should be left to exact meth- NOTE! ods. For Example 6.4, *Derive*'s algebraic techniques yield a clear answer: The given curves intersect only once in the space of real numbers, and twice in the space of complex numbers; nowhere else. So, although our exploration began with a graphical examination of the information we possess, we rely upon it as a guide for the necessary algebraic exploration that follows.

Graphical methods are also useful checks of our final answers. If the answer we obtain by exact methods doesn't agree with our graphical approximation, we should always double check our work!

Exploration Exercise_____

6.1. For each of the following sets of expressions:
- Write the expression as a linear function.
- Write the expression as a general linear equation.
- Plot both expressions on the same graph.
- If the given curves intersect, graphically approximate the point(s) of intersection using the *Derive* crosshairs. Identify the x and y values of the scale at which this information could be determined.
- Use the soLve option to determine the exact coordinates.
- Check your graphical approximation using approX as in Example 6.4.

(a) $y = x^3 - 10^{-9}x$ and $y = 0$
(b) $\pi x - 3y = 12$ and $15y + 2x = -3$
(c) $-13x_1 - 7.2x_2 = 0$ and $-14x_1 - 7.2x_2 = -5$
(d) $\frac{6}{17}z - \frac{22}{119}w = 11.03$ and $\frac{11}{24}w + \frac{82}{83}z = 0$

6.3   SYSTEMS OF LINEAR EQUATIONS

Systems of linear equations form the core of a course called *linear algebra*. Linear algebra, in turn, provides a foundation for a broad range of other topics such as finance, economics, physics, chemistry, mathematics, earthquake engineering, biomedical engineering, electrical engineering, psychology, medicine, and forensic science, among others. The fundamentals of solving linear systems in this section should give you a sound understanding of the topic without overshadowing the remainder of the book.

The problem of determining the intersection points of two or more curves, if such points exist, was shown to be a problem of finding the point(s) that the curves share in common. In other words, we were attempting to determine what points, if any, *simultaneously* satisfy both equations at the same time. Such points are said to satisfy the *system of equations* specified by the given set.

The system of equations used in Example 6.4 is obviously not a linear system of equations because of the third-order term appearing in the first equation. In this section, we will concentrate on exploring systems of linear equations exclusively.

Systems of linear equations can arise naturally in modeling. We can associate a response with each observable aspect of an event that we are trying to model. If we choose to represent two different responses in a single model, we end up with two distinct dependent variables, each associated with various predictors.

Example 6.6. Suppose that we identify two responses y and z, each of which is influenced by the predictor x in a different way. It is then possible represent this as a system of equations such as

$$y = 3x - 1$$
$$z = -2x + 2$$

Systems of linear equations can also result when predictors must satisfy several linear functions simultaneously. Consider the following examples:

Example 6.7. Suppose that a small business is trying to determine the amount of dye it needs to purchase in order to make 22 gallons of a custom solution that it mixes and sells to a T-shirt manufacturer around the corner. The dye is commercially available in bulk, in whatever amount is needed. Additionally, the number purchased must meet the business's budget limitation.

Suppose that we select one predictor to be $x_1 =$ the number of gallons of dye 1, and a second predictor to be $x_2 =$ the number of gallons of dye 2. Dye 1 costs \$32 per gallon, and dye 2 costs \$34 per gallon. The business must spend exactly \$712.

The function modeling the number of gallons purchased is

$$f_1(x_1, x_2) = x_1 + x_2$$

a linear function. The function describing the cost of purchasing the dye is also linear:

$$f_2(x_1, x_2) = 32x_1 + 34x_2$$

The two limitations in the problem can be modeled as the constraints

$$f_1(x_1, x_2) = 22$$
$$f_2(x_1, x_2) = 712$$

We would need to find all the values (x_1, x_2) that satisfy both constraints simultaneously.

We could also be faced with a requirement to fit models from data where regression is not appropriate. We may be able to find the coefficients of our model by solving a system of linear equations, where we know the values of the variables corresponding to certain outputs. One such case is given in the next example.

Example 6.8. Suppose that we are in an arcade playing a new video game called "Hunter Fighter." The basic plot is that we navigate around alien defenses to try to destroy their fortifications before they stockpile enough forces to take over the Earth.

We have two basic weapons: smart bombs and laser death-ray blasts. This is such a popular game that the instructions that used to be printed next to the joystick on the front of the console are worn off. As a result, we don't know whether it is better to use our smart bombs or laser death-ray blasts.

We decide to conduct an experiment. For the first attack run at the alien fortifications, we buzz in low, drop 3 smart bombs on target, fire 1 laser death ray blast on target before getting shot down, and accumulate 50 points. On the next run, we attack with the sun behind us, drop 1 smart bomb on target, fire 2 laser death ray blasts on target before again getting shot down. This run accumulates 40 points.

The game awards points according to how many hits we get with each weapon. We suspect the response, number of points, is a linear function of the predictors x_1, the number of hits with the smart bomb, and x_2 the number of hits with the laser. The number of points per smart bomb hit is m_1, and m_2 is the number of points per laser hit.

The model is $f(x_1, x_2) = m_1 x_1 + m_2 x_2$. Since we are awarded no points when we have no hits, we omit the intercept term: $b = 0$. Now, how do we find m_1 and m_2?

From our data of the problem, we can write

$$f(3,1) = m_1(3) + m_2(1) = 50 \tag{6.1}$$

$$f(1,2) = m_1(1) + m_2(2) = 40 \tag{6.2}$$

This is a system of linear equations in the unknowns (m_1, m_2).

The simultaneous solution to this system is $m_1 = 12, m_2 = 14$. You can check that this answer is correct by substituting these values into Equations 6.1 and 6.2.

In other words, we get 12 points for a hit with a smart bomb, and 14 points for a hit with a laser. The function for $t =$ total number of points scored is

$$t = f(x_1, x_2) = 12x_1 + 14x_2$$

6.3.1 Prerequisites for systems of equations

For a system of linear equations to exist, we assume that common variables represent the same quantities in each of the equations. The variable y which appears in the two equations

$$y = 3x - 1$$

$$y = -2x + 2$$

is assumed to represent the same quantity, as does the variable x that also appears in both equations. The equations must have variables in common to

SYSTEM

LINKAGE

constitute a system. Without this linkage, the equations are said to be *separable*.

Example 6.9. The equations given by

$$x_1 + x_2 + x_3 + x_4 = 13$$
$$2x_1 + x_3 - 11x_4 = -52$$
$$7x_2 - x_3 = 19$$

constitute a system. All three equations are linked by the variable x_3. To solve this system for a simultaneous solution, we could first use the last equation to determine x_3 in terms of x_2, then substitute for x_3 everywhere it appears. This results in the equations

$$x_1 + 8x_2 + x_4 = 32$$
$$2x_1 + 7x_2 - 11x_4 = -33$$

which also possess the required system linkage.

Example 6.10. The set of equations

$$x_1 - 11x_3 + x_7 = 3$$
$$x_2 - 13x_4 + x_5 = 11$$
$$x_6 - x_8 = 44$$

lacks any linkage whatsoever. There are no common predictors in either equation. This set does not constitute a system of equations, and is separable. Information concerning the relationship between predictors in one equation provides no useful information about the relationship in the other equation.

There is a very important correspondence between intersection points and solutions to systems of linear equations. We state this correspondence in the form of a theorem.

Theorem 6.1. For the linear system of equations involving n variables and m equations

$$a_1x_1 + b_1x_2 + \cdots + n_1x_n = c_1$$
$$a_2x_1 + b_2x_2 + \cdots + n_2x_n = c_2$$
$$\vdots$$
$$a_mx_1 + b_mx_2 + \cdots + n_mx_n = c_m$$

in which at least one of the coefficients $a_1, \ldots, a_m, b_1, \ldots, b_m, \ldots, n_1, \ldots, n_m$ is different from zero, there exist only three possible outcomes for the simultaneous determination of a solution (intersection point):

1. No such solution (intersection point) exists and the system is called *inconsistent*.
2. A unique solution (intersection point) exists, and the system is called *consistent*.
3. Multiple solutions (intersection points) exist and the system has an infinite number of solutions, and the system is called *undetermined*.

Discussion Ideas

Here is a 3D conceptual aid that you can do right now. Take two pieces of paper approximately the same size and shape and hold them in front of you. Each piece of paper represents a plane, which, by definition, is a linear equation involving two independent variables and one dependent variable. Tilt and bring together the two sheets of paper to do the following.

⇒ Is it possible to align the two planes so that a unique solution to this system of two equations would result? Demonstrate with the paper sheets.

⇒ Is it possible to align the two planes so that there is no solution to this system of two equations? What condition must hold? Demonstrate with the paper sheets.

⇒ Is it possible to align the two planes so that multiple solutions to this system of two equations would result? Demonstrate with the paper sheets.

⇒ Can you think of a reason from algebra that would support the conclusions you were able to determine above? (*Hint*: It has something to do with the number of variables.)

We're writing the linear equations in this form, with the predictors and coefficients on the left and the constant on the right, because it will help clarify the notation we use to introduce matrices. Systems of linear equations have their own notation that differs from the standard functional notation. (Sylvester, Cayley, Driscoll, and Olwell apologize for the change of notation.)

SYSTEM STRUCTURE

The geometry of a system of linear equations provides important insight into what is known as the *structure* of the system. Each equation defines a plane or hyperplane (which is a plane in higher dimensions than we can visualize). The surfaces can either intersect or be parallel.

This structure directly affects whether solutions to the system can be found, and depends on both the number of variables (n) and the number of equations

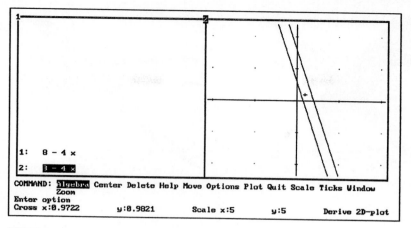

FIGURE 6.4
Inconsistent two-dimensional system of two equations.

(m). We explore the various possibilities in the next section, but mention the "no solution" case of Theorem 6.1 next to illustrate one aspect of this geometric structure.

6.3.2 The "no solution" case

When no solution exists for a system of equations, the equations defining the system have no points that are shared by all the equations. Another way of interpreting this situation is to say that some degree of parallelism exists in the geometry of planes of the system. Parallel surfaces do not intersect. Therefore, they cannot possess simultaneous solutions.

Example 6.11. Consider the inconsistent system of equations given by

$$4x_1 + x_2 = 8$$
$$8x_1 + 2x_2 = 6$$

Figure 6.4 shows a *Derive* two-dimensional plot of these two equations, which appears to indicate that the lines represented by these two equations are parallel. Checking this observation algebraically, we see that the second equation has the same slope as the first equation ($m = -4$). The two equations are parallel, differing only by a shift of 2 units in the x_2-intercept.

In three dimensions, an inconsistent system has the same parallelism present somewhere in its structure that prevents a common intersection point from occurring. Sometimes this parallelism is obvious, and other times it is not. Figure 6.5 shows two examples of this parallelism occurring.

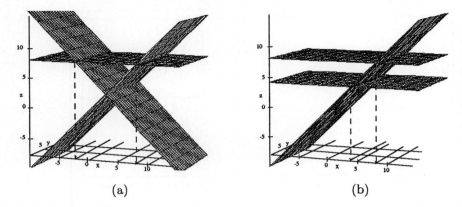

(a)   (b)

FIGURE 6.5
Two inconsistent systems of linear equations.

In generating Figure 6.5(a) and Figure 6.5(b), we chose z to be a response dependent upon both predictor x and y, so that a three-dimensional (3D) plot could be generated. The predictor y can assume any value without affecting the values of x and z. This is why equations with only two variables represent surfaces.

Example 6.12. Figure 6.5(a) represents the graphical structure of the system

$$z - x = 0$$
$$z + x = 6$$
$$z = 8$$

whose equations do not initially appear to be parallel. However, notice that the third equation is fixing the value of $z = 8$. Substituting this value into the remaining equations yields $x = -2$ and $x = 8$, which are two parallel vertical planes in the three-dimensional plot. By setting $z = -10$ for convenience, we can project the parallel intersections and redraw this solution-preventing parallelism in an (x, y)-plane.

Example 6.13. Figure 6.5(b) represents the graphical structure of the system

$$z - x = 0$$
$$z = 4$$
$$z = 8$$

STRUCTURAL

PARALLELISM

Here, the solution-preventing parallelism is obvious in the equations $z = 4$ and $z = 8$. These last two equations represent the two parallel surfaces shown in (b). Again, setting $z = -10$ conveniently projects the parallel intersections onto the (x, y)-plane.

When a system is inconsistent, the parallelism will be evident somewhere in the algebra while trying to solve the system. It may be revealed at the onset, during intermediate steps, or not until the very last step. It will always be present—we just have to find it.

Exploration Exercises

6.1. Identify the parallelism in the following inconsistent systems of linear equations. (Hint: Plot the two-dimensional systems.)

(a) $2x - 3y = 2$
$\frac{3}{2}y - x = -2$

(b) $x_1 + 4x_2 + 3x_3 = 1$
$3x_1 + \quad + x_3 = 1$
$4x_1 + x_2 + 2x_3 = 1$

(c) $\qquad r + 3s = 5$
$2.1r + 6.2s = 11.1$

(d) $3z + 2q = 9$
$-z - \frac{2}{3}q = 3$

6.2. Does Theorem 6.1 remain valid if the system of equations contains equations involving complex terms? For example, does the theorem hold for the two dimensional case: ADVANCED

$$a_1 x_1 + i b_1 x_2 = c_1$$

$$a_2 x_1 + i b_2 x_2 = c_2$$

6.4 SOLVING SYSTEMS OF LINEAR EQUATIONS

Algebraically solving a system of linear equations reduces to the task of manipulating a system of equations to isolate the independent variables.

Example 6.14. Solving the system of equations given by

$$x_1 + x_2 + x_3 = 1$$

$$x_1 + x_3 = 1$$

$$x_1 + 2x_2 + 3x_3 = 5$$

reduces to the task of manipulating these equations to end up with a system of equations that isolates each of the independent variables. This results in an equivalent system in the form

$$x_1 = \text{value}$$
$$x_2 = \text{value}$$
$$x_3 = \text{value}$$

In this case, isolating these variables yields the unique solution

$$x_1 = 1 \tag{6.3}$$
$$x_2 = 0 \tag{6.4}$$
$$x_3 = 2 \tag{6.5}$$

Isolating each of the variables in this way automatically identifies the solution to the system, if a solution exists. The values on the right make up the simultaneous solution to the original system of equations.

In the case of the previous example, if we start with three unknowns, and we want to end with one equation per unknown, we had best start with at least 3 equations. Not every set of m equations can be solved to produce a unique solution such as in the previous example.

In general, a system of linear equations must meet two requirements to produce such a unique solution:

1. The number of equations must equal the number of unknown variables.

2. The equations on the left-hand side must be *linearly independent.*

LINEARLY IN-
DEPENDENT
EQUATIONS

Definition 6.1. Independent Equations. An equation is called *linearly independent* if the left side expression of the equation is *not* a linear combination of the left side expressions of any other equations contained in the system. When all the equations of a system are independent, the system is called *independent.*

A linear combination of expressions is an expression formed by multiplying each expression by a constant and adding the result together.

Example 6.15. Consider the system of equations given by

$$5x + y = 3$$
$$x + y = 5$$
$$x - y = 13$$

The left side expression $5x + y$ is a linear combination of the two expressions $(x + y)$ and $(x - y)$. It is obtained by forming the linear combination:

$$3(x + y) + 2(x - y) = 3x + 3y + 2x - 2y = 5x + y \tag{6.6}$$

As a result, the first equation $5x + y = 3$, is not linearly independent of the remaining two equations. It is called a linearly *dependent* equation.

Notice that the concept of independence versus dependence again surfaces. Where else have you seen this idea?

The number of linearly independent equations in a system is called the *rank* of the system. We'll use *Derive* to determine the rank of a system, solve the system, and to determine which equations are linearly independent. RANK

Example 6.16. The system of equations given by

$$3x_1 + 4x_2 + 2x_3 = 2$$
$$5x_1 + x_2 + 5x_3 = 7$$
$$x_1 - x_2 + 2x_3 = 8$$

and the system of equations given by

$$5x + y - z = 3$$
$$x + y + 2z = 5$$
$$x - y + z = 13$$

each contain three linearly independent equations. As we will soon have a means of checking, none of the left side expressions within each system is a linear combination of the remaining equations in that system.

Here is the main point: The only way a unique solution to a system can occur is if each variable of the system has exactly one linearly independent equation associated with it. These independent equations can be manipulated until each variable is isolated on the left-hand side with its corresponding value on the right.

6.4.1 Solution methods

Solving a system of linear equations consisting of n variables means to determine all of the points of intersection, or all of the ordered n-tuples $(x_1, x_2, x_3, \ldots, x_n)$, that simultaneously satisfy all n of the equations.

There may be no such points, only one such point, or an infinite number of solution points. If there are an infinite number, they can lie on a line or a plane or a hyperplane. For discussion purposes, let's consider a system of two equations and two unknowns.

There are three common methods of solving a system of linear equations. In the *method of equating*, we algebraically isolate the same variable in both equations, set the equations equal to one another, and determine the value of the remaining variable that satisfies both equations. This value is then substituted into either original equation to get the value of the other variable. The method of equating is most commonly employed in computer algorithms used to solve systems of nonlinear equations to find their roots.

The second method is called the *method of substitution*. In this method, we isolate a single variable using one equation, and the result is substituted into another equation. This second equation is now a single equation containing a single unknown that we solve for. Again, we substitute this value back into the other equation and solve for the remaining variable. The method of substitution is most commonly used to simplify expressions, so you have undoubtedly seen a version of this before.

Here is a different perspective on the above techniques. Eliminating a particular variable using substitution is the same as performing a *projection* of the **PROJECTION** problem, just like projecting a shadow on a floor using a flashlight. Because a variable of the problem is eliminated, the problem that remains is in a lower dimensional space involving fewer variables. We have, in effect, made one coordinate axis disappear from the problem.

Eliminating one variable in a three-variable problem (which would require three axes to plot) makes the problem a two-variable problem (that requires only two axes to plot). This projects the problem onto a two-dimensional space. The value of the variable that we eliminated can easily be obtained after the reduced problem is solved, by using the relationship that defined the substitution.

Example 6.17. For the system of equations

$$-5x_1 - x_2 + 3x_3 = 3$$
$$3x_2 + 5x_3 = 8$$
$$2x_3 = -4$$

is a three-dimensional problem, requiring coordinate axes for x_1, x_2, and x_3. We can eliminate the variable x_3 from the problem by solving the third equation for $x_3 = -2$, and substituting this value into the other two equations. The resulting system

$$-5x_1 - x_2 = 9$$
$$3x_2 = 18$$

no longer requires an x_3 axis; the original problem has been projected into the two-dimensional plane involving only x_1 and x_2.

We could project the problem into a one-dimensional space by solving the second equation for $x_2 = 6$, and substituting this value throughout the system. The resulting equation

$$-5x_1 = 15 \tag{6.7}$$

is simply a line that requires a single coordinate axis for x_1. The solution to the original system is $x_1 = -3$, $x_2 = 6$, and $x_3 = -2$, exactly the values used to fix the values of the variables to project the problem into lower dimensional spaces.

We mention this idea here because it is used quite often in very large systems. Based on some rules, a certain number of variables are fixed at some values that make sense, and the remaining variables are solved for. Then, we use this solution to start with, fix different variables, and repeat this approach until some criteria is met that allows the process to stop.

The third method of solving a system of equations, called the *addition method*, has a variation that is far more famous—Gauss-Jordan elimination—which we will examine soon. To use this method, we first multiply each equation ADDITION of the system by a suitable constant. By choosing these constants wisely, the METHOD coefficients of one or more of the variables in the new equations will have coefficients with opposite sign from those in another equation. We then add these equations, and the variable having opposing coefficients cancels out. We repeat this process until we have only one variable left, and solve for it. The values of the eliminated variables are obtained by substitution in the same way as in the previous two methods.

Example 6.18. Suppose that we wish to solve the system of equations given by

$$3x_1 + 4x_2 = 1$$
$$x_1 - 2x_2 = 7$$

using the addition method. We can multiply the entire second equation by -3 so that we have

$$3x_1 + 4x_2 = 1$$
$$-3x_1 + 6x_2 = -21$$

Multiplying both sides of an equation by the same constant does not change the solution.

Next, adding the two equations together yields

$$10x_2 = -20$$

We then get $x_2 = -2$, which we substitute into either of the original equations to get $x_1 = 3$. Checking this solution (always a good idea when performing algebraic manipulations!) in the original equations verifies that $(x_1, x_2) = (3, -2)$ is a solution to the given system of equations.

Remember the idea that multiplying the entire second equation by a constant did not alter the solution to the system; we will need it again soon.

For a small number of equations, the three methods are equally efficient. It is a matter of experience and preference as to which method you choose to employ for a particular problem.

For larger systems of equations, such as the type that we see in modeling complicated events, computer software programs such as *Derive* rely exclusively on Gauss-Jordan elimination, or some variation of Gauss-Jordan elimination developed to speed up calculations. For this reason, we will concentrate on the Gauss-Jordan elimination method for solving systems of linear equations.

The Gauss-Jordan technique tries to isolate the variables of the system in the same manner introduced earlier. This is useful to keep in mind while executing the steps of the technique. We will examine several examples using the `row_reduce` command of *Derive* (which uses Gauss-Jordan elimination) to expose this pattern. First, however, we need to introduce the idea of a *matrix*, and link this idea to solving a system of linear equations.

6.4.2   Matrices

Matrices give us a compact way to write the coefficients of a system of linear equations. This notation will greatly simplify our work of finding solutions. Matrices also introduce a whole new branch of mathematics, called linear algebra, which is fascinating and useful in its own right.

For our purposes, we define a matrix in the following way.

> **Definition 6.2.   Matrix.** A *matrix* is a rectangular array of numbers. An $m \times n$ (read as 'm–by–n') matrix A has m rows and n columns. These are called the dimensions of the matrix A. If $m = n$, then the matrix is called *square*.

MATRIX
STRUCTURE   Matrices come in different sizes, depending upon the structure of the problem we are addressing. For example, here are several different matrices with their

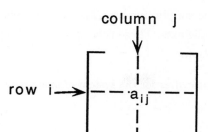

FIGURE 6.6
Referencing an entry in a two-dimensional matrix.

corresponding sizes (rows × columns) listed below each.

$$A = \begin{bmatrix} a_{11} & a_{12} \\ a_{21} & a_{22} \end{bmatrix}, \qquad B = \begin{bmatrix} b_{11} & b_{12} & b_{13} \\ b_{21} & b_{22} & b_{23} \end{bmatrix}, \qquad C = \begin{bmatrix} c_{11} & c_{12} \\ c_{21} & c_{22} \\ c_{31} & c_{32} \end{bmatrix}$$

$$2 \times 2 \qquad\qquad 2 \times 3 \qquad\qquad 3 \times 2$$

$$\begin{bmatrix} a_{11} & a_{12} & a_{13} \end{bmatrix} \qquad \begin{bmatrix} a_{11} \\ a_{21} \\ a_{31} \end{bmatrix} \qquad \begin{bmatrix} a_{11} \end{bmatrix}$$

$$1 \times 3 \qquad\qquad 3 \times 1 \qquad\qquad 1 \times 1$$

Matrices that have only a single row or a single column are typically called *vectors*. A 1×3 matrix is called a *row vector* because it is consists of one row. Likewise, a 3×1 matrix is called a *column vector*.

Each individual entry, or *component* of a matrix has a subscript label that identifies its (row, column) location in the matrix, as shown in Figure 6.6. The component labeled: a_{21}, for example, indicates that the value a is located in row 2, column 1 of matrix A.

This standard means of labeling components provides an easy reference as to the location of any component in the matrix. So, the matrix A has entries a_{ij}, NOTATION where i is some row and j identifies a column; a matrix D will have entries d_{ij}; a matrix T will have entries t_{ij}, and so on.

6.4.3 Creating matrices

The individual components of matrices come directly from the variable coefficients of a system of equations and their right-hand side values. To create a

COEFFICIENT particular *coefficient matrix* for a system, we simply line up all of the variables
MATRIX vertically and select their corresponding coefficients. These then get placed into
the coefficient matrix in the same configuration.

Example 6.19. Extracting the *coefficient matrix* for the system of linear equations given by

$$3x_1 - 2x_3 + x_2 = 9$$
$$x_3 - 12x_1 = 17$$
$$2x_2 + x_1 + x_3 = 14$$

is accomplished by

$$
\begin{array}{l}
3x_1 - 2x_3 + x_2 = 9 \\
x_3 - 12x_1 = 17 \\
2x_2 + x_1 + x_3 = 14
\end{array}
\rightarrow
\begin{array}{l}
3x_1 + x_2 - 2x_3 = 9 \\
-12x_1 \quad\quad + x_3 = 17 \\
x_1 + 2x_2 + x_3 = 14
\end{array}
\rightarrow
\begin{bmatrix}
3 & 1 & -2 \\
-12 & 0 & 1 \\
1 & 2 & 1
\end{bmatrix}
$$

The right-hand side values of each equation go directly into a column vector that gets appended, or added onto the coefficient matrix. A vertical line is used in place of the system's equal signs to keep the two collections of numbers separate.
AUGMENTED The following example shows how a complete *augmented matrix* representing a
MATRIX system of equations is obtained.

Example 6.20. The augmented matrix for the system of linear equations given by

$$3x_1 - 2x_3 + x_2 = 9$$
$$x_3 - 12x_1 = 17$$
$$2x_2 + x_1 + x_3 = 14$$

is found to be

$$
\begin{array}{l}
3x_1 - 2x_3 + x_2 = 9 \\
x_3 - 12x_1 = 17 \\
2x_2 + x_1 + x_3 = 14
\end{array}
\rightarrow
\begin{array}{l}
3x_1 + x_2 - 2x_3 = 9 \\
-12x_1 \quad\quad + x_3 = 17 \\
x_1 + 2x_2 + x_3 = 14
\end{array}
$$

$$
\rightarrow
\left[
\begin{array}{ccc|c}
3 & 1 & -2 & 9 \\
-12 & 0 & 1 & 17 \\
1 & 2 & 1 & 14
\end{array}
\right]
$$

Each column to the left of the vertical line in the augmented matrix represents the coefficients of a different variable, the single column to the right of the vertical line represents the right-hand side of each equation, and each row of the matrix represents a different equation of the system.

Example 6.21. The augmented matrix for the system of equations given by

$$15.7x + 22.3y + w - 1.5z = 109.3$$
$$45w - 11.2x - 35.2y = 27.5$$
$$2x + 32y + 10.1w = 11$$

has an augmented matrix given by

$$\left[\begin{array}{cccc|c} 15.7 & 22.3 & 1 & -1.5 & 109.3 \\ -11.2 & -35.2 & 45 & 0 & 27.5 \\ 2 & 32 & 10.1 & 0 & 11 \end{array}\right]$$

An augmented matrix is a convenient form for solving a system of linear equations by Gauss-Jordan elimination. Using a 3×3 system as an example, the GAUSS-overall approach is as follows. Through a series of algebraic steps starting with JORDAN the augmented matrix of a system

$$\left[\begin{array}{ccc|c} a_{11} & a_{12} & a_{13} & b_1 \\ a_{21} & a_{22} & a_{23} & b_2 \\ a_{31} & a_{32} & a_{33} & b_3 \end{array}\right]$$

we hope to end up with a final augmented matrix, called a *reduced matrix*, that has a staircase shape similar to

$$\left[\begin{array}{ccc|c} 1 & 0 & 0 & c_1 \\ 0 & 1 & 0 & c_2 \\ 0 & 0 & 1 & c_3 \end{array}\right]$$

which is *equivalent* to the augmented matrix of the original system of equations. This final augmented matrix is said to be in *reduced form*, defined precisely as follows.

Definition 6.3. Reduced Form. An augmented matrix is said to be in *reduced form*, and is called the *reduced matrix* for a system of equations if the REDUCED following conditions hold: FORM

1. The leftmost nonzero component of any row is 1, and it has only 0's above and below it in the same column.

2. If any row is comprised entirely of 0's, it is located below any row having at least one nonzero entry.

3. The augmented matrix possesses a staircase shape in which the leftmost 1 of any row is located strictly to the right of the leftmost 1 in any row above it in the augmented matrix.

Because the reduced matrix is algebraically equivalent to the original augmented matrix, any solution to the system represented by the reduced matrix, assuming at least one exists, is also a solution to the original system of equations. The solution can be read directly from this reduced matrix.

Recalling that each column on the left-hand side of an augmented matrix represents the coefficients of a different variable, translating the reduced matrix of Example 6.21 back to equation notation yields $1x_1 = c_1$, $1x_2 = c_2$, $1x_3 = c_3$; or $x_1 = c_1$, $x_2 = c_2$, $x_3 = c_3$.

We will use the augmented matrix format to solve systems of equations in *Derive*. So, how do we manipulate the system, and what type of operations are allowed that establish the equivalence we need?

Instead of simply listing the operations, let's explore a little graphically, keeping in mind the correspondence between seeking the solution(s) to a system of equations and identifying the intersection point(s) of the curves or surfaces these equations represent.

Exploration Exercises

6.1. Each of the following initial augmented matrices listed in the left column was extracted from a system of equations possessing a unique solution. Write out each augmented matrix in equation notation, selecting variable names as you see fit. Each of the final augmented matrices listed in the right-hand column was obtained by properly applying Gauss-Jordan elimination to an augmented matrix listed. Using the equation notation for the systems, match each system with its appropriate solution. Next, use the 2D plot option in *Derive* to plot the equations and verify that the initial augmented matrix representation is equivalent to the final matrix representation for each system. The problem with π as a coefficient is used to give you practice with using *Derive* special characters.

Augmented Matrix		Reduced Matrix

(a) $\begin{bmatrix} 4 & -1 & \vline & 2 \\ 1 & -2 & \vline & -3 \end{bmatrix}$

(1) $\begin{bmatrix} 1 & 0 & \vline & \frac{175(65637\pi^2-212474)}{69(196350\pi^2-241459)} \\ 0 & 1 & \vline & \frac{7437935\pi}{23(196350\pi^2-241459)} \end{bmatrix}$

(b) $\begin{bmatrix} \pi & 1.3 & \vline & 10 \\ -\pi & 2.5 & \vline & -30.5 \end{bmatrix}$

(2) $\begin{bmatrix} 1 & 0 & \vline & -\frac{18725}{757} \\ 0 & 1 & \vline & \frac{516310}{24981} \end{bmatrix}$

(c) $\begin{bmatrix} 467.34 & 392.7\pi & \vline & 1043 \\ 138\pi & 142.6 & \vline & 117\pi \end{bmatrix}$

(3) $\begin{bmatrix} 1 & 0 & \vline & 2 \\ 0 & 1 & \vline & 4 \end{bmatrix}$

(d) $\begin{bmatrix} 4 & 1 & \vline & 12 \\ 1 & 2 & \vline & 10 \end{bmatrix}$

(4) $\begin{bmatrix} 1 & 0 & \vline & 1 \\ 0 & 1 & \vline & 2 \end{bmatrix}$

(e) $\begin{bmatrix} \frac{3}{7} & \frac{11}{15} & \vline & \frac{41}{9} \\ 3.74 & \frac{33}{4} & \vline & 78 \end{bmatrix}$

(5) $\begin{bmatrix} 1 & 0 & \vline & \frac{1293}{76\pi} \\ 0 & 1 & \vline & -\frac{205}{38} \end{bmatrix}$

6.2. Use the linear systems from the previous exercise to graphically explore the following questions.

(a) If we were to switch the order in which the equations (rows) of a linear system appear in an initial augmented matrix, how would this affect the solution?

(b) You are sitting in a group doing homework, when someone proposes the idea "If I were to pick out one of the rows of an augmented matrix and multiply each component of the row (including the component to the right of the vertical divider) by a nonzero number, then the entry in the reduced matrix for that row will scale by the same amount." Do you agree or disagree? Support your opinion with a graphical plot.

(c) How does multiplying an entire initial augmented matrix by a nonzero number affect the solution of the system? Justify your response algebraically and graphically.

(d) Suppose that we select one complete row of an initial augmented matrix, multiply it by a nonzero scalar, and add the resulting row to another row of the augmented matrix. How is the original solution affected?

(e) Suppose that we simply add up all of the equations of a particular system of equations. Will the solution to the original system of equations also satisfy this *surrogate* equation? Justify your response.

6.4.4 Gauss-Jordan elimination

Gauss-Jordan elimination is a systematic method to write an augmented matrix in row-reduced form. Let's see how *Derive* solves systems of equations using the `row_reduce` command, which applies Gauss-Jordan elimination.

Example 6.22. Consider the system of equations given by

$$3x_1 + 2x_2 - x_3 = 11$$
$$6x_1 - x_2 + 2x_3 = 8$$
$$4x_1 + 3x_2 + 5x_3 = 7$$

The augmented matrix for this system is

$$\left[\begin{array}{ccc|c} 3 & 2 & -1 & 11 \\ 6 & -1 & 2 & 8 \\ 4 & 3 & 5 & 7 \end{array} \right]$$

We enter the augmented matrix into *Derive* in two pieces: the left-hand side and the right-hand side. Entering the left-hand side, we Declare a Matrix of 3 rows and 3 columns. *Derive* then prompts us for each component according to its (i, j) location in the augmented matrix.

ROW_REDUCE   When complete, *Derive* displays the appropriate matrix. We then Declare a Matrix of 3 rows and 1 column, and again enter the appropriate values, which *Derive* displays upon completion.

Next, we Author the *Derive* function `row_reduce(#1, #2)`, where #1 and #2 correspond to the *Derive* expression number for the left-hand and right-hand sides of the augmented matrix. *Derive* then displays the complete function.

Figure 6.7 shows the *Derive* screen for these steps. Selecting the Simplify option from the *Derive* menu results in the reduced matrix

$$\left[\begin{array}{ccc|c} 1 & 0 & 0 & \frac{68}{33} \\ 0 & 1 & 0 & \frac{58}{33} \\ 0 & 0 & 1 & -\frac{43}{33} \end{array} \right]$$

This system has a unique solution given by $x_1 = \frac{68}{33}$, $x_2 = \frac{58}{33}$, and $x_3 = -\frac{43}{33}$ which can be read directly from the reduced matrix.

The left-hand side of the reduced matrix of Example 6.22 is known as an *identity* matrix. An identity matrix is a square matrix that has all 1's as compo-
IDENTITY   nents starting in the upper left corner and ending in the lower right corner. This
MATRIX   diagonal line of components is called the *main diagonal*. All other components are zero. It is called an identity matrix because this is the matrix equivalent

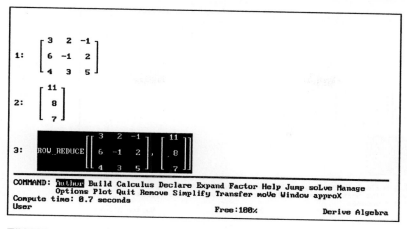

FIGURE 6.7
Steps for using row_reduce in *Derive*.

to the number 1 in algebra: Multiplying another matrix by the identity matrix leaves its components unchanged.

Example 6.23. We can alter the system of equations used in the previous example to cause the case of no solution to result. Recall that we have to introduce some degree of parallelism to prevent any point from being a common intersection point for all the equations. So, if we make the left-hand side of the second equation a multiple of the left-hand side of the first equation, so that the system becomes

$$3x_1 + 2x_2 - x_3 = 11$$
$$6x_1 + 4x_2 - 2x_3 = 8$$
$$4x_1 + 3x_2 + 5x_3 = 7$$

We have created two parallel planes whose intercepts differ. Again, simplifying the row_reduce expression, we get the *Derive* screen shown in Figure 6.8.

This example illustrates the classic Gauss-Jordan elimination indicator of a linear system not having a solution: A row of the final reduced matrix yields an algebraic contradiction. In this example, the third row of the final reduced matrix has $0x_3 = 1$, or $0 = 1$, which is never true. This tells us there is no solution to the system, as there is no x_3 that satisfies $0x_3 = 1$.

The final case we need to examine is a linear system that yields multiple solutions. Reading the solution of such a system directly from the reduced matrix is slightly more complicated, but still straightforward.

We can again alter the system of Example 6.22 to cause multiple solutions to occur. The key is to create a situation in which the system does not have enough equations to uniquely specify a solution for each variable. This relates

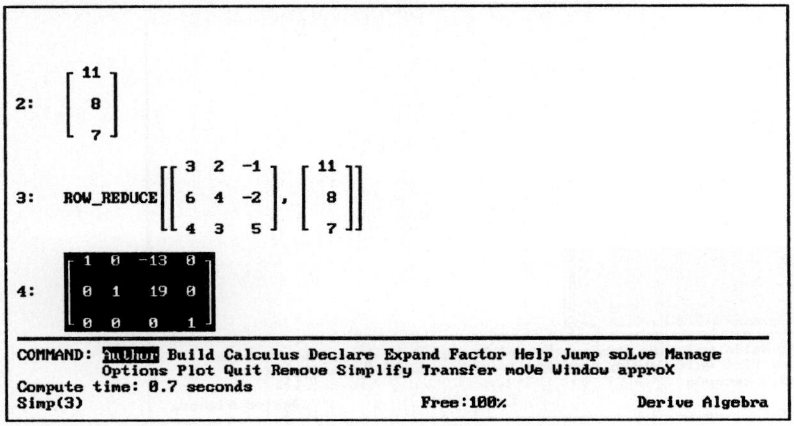

$$2: \quad \begin{bmatrix} 11 \\ 8 \\ 7 \end{bmatrix}$$

$$3: \quad \text{ROW\_REDUCE}\left(\begin{bmatrix} 3 & 2 & -1 \\ 6 & 4 & -2 \\ 4 & 3 & 5 \end{bmatrix}, \begin{bmatrix} 11 \\ 8 \\ 7 \end{bmatrix}\right)$$

$$4: \quad \begin{bmatrix} 1 & 0 & -13 & 0 \\ 0 & 1 & 19 & 0 \\ 0 & 0 & 0 & 1 \end{bmatrix}$$

COMMAND: **Author** Build Calculus Declare Expand Factor Help Jump soLve Manage
Options Plot Quit Remove Simplify Transfer moVe Window approX
Compute time: 0.7 seconds
Simp(3)   Free:100%   Derive Algebra

FIGURE 6.8
Derive results using row_reduce.

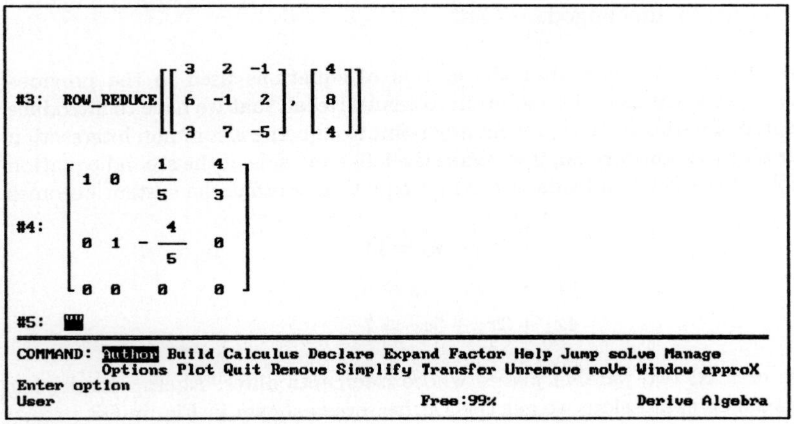

$$\#3: \quad \text{ROW\_REDUCE}\left(\begin{bmatrix} 3 & 2 & -1 \\ 6 & -1 & 2 \\ 3 & 7 & -5 \end{bmatrix}, \begin{bmatrix} 4 \\ 8 \\ 4 \end{bmatrix}\right)$$

$$\#4: \quad \begin{bmatrix} 1 & 0 & \dfrac{1}{5} & \dfrac{4}{3} \\ 0 & 1 & -\dfrac{4}{5} & 0 \\ 0 & 0 & 0 & 0 \end{bmatrix}$$

#5: ▓

COMMAND: **Author** Build Calculus Declare Expand Factor Help Jump soLve Manage
Options Plot Quit Remove Simplify Transfer Unremove moVe Window approX
Enter option
User   Free:99%   Derive Algebra

FIGURE 6.9
Results indicating multiple or infinite solutions.

to the algebra rule that states that you need two independent equations to solve for the unique values of two unknowns; three independent equations for three unknowns, etc.

Let's rewrite the last example. Instead of two parallel planes with different intercepts, we will write two parallel planes with the *same* intercept. In other words, we have the same equation twice, resulting in two different equations and three unknowns.

Example 6.24. Consider the linear system of equations given by

$$3x_1 + 2x_2 - x_3 = 4$$
$$6x_1 - x_2 + 2x_3 = 8$$
$$3x_1 + 7x_2 - 5x_3 = 4$$

The corresponding augmented matrix for this system is

$$\left[\begin{array}{ccc|c} 3 & 2 & -1 & 4 \\ 6 & -1 & 2 & 8 \\ 3 & 7 & -5 & 4 \end{array} \right]$$

After entering the augmented matrix in *Derive*, we again simplify the `row_reduce` expression, resulting in the *Derive* screen shown in Figure 6.9.

To read the solution directly from the reduced matrix, keep in mind that any solution we specify must somehow show that there is more than one solution to the system. Each column of the reduced matrix corresponds to the coefficients of the same variable as the augmented matrix. So, we can translate the reduced matrix into equation notation to see how the solution is revealed:

$$x_1 + 0x_2 + 0.2x_3 = 1.3\bar{3}$$
$$0x_1 + x_2 - 0.8x_3 = 0$$
$$0x_1 + 0x_2 + 0x_3 = 0$$

In this form, the fact that multiple solutions exist is evident by isolating the variables that have coefficient values of 1:

$$x_1 = 1.3\bar{3} - 0.2x_3$$
$$x_2 = 0.8x_3$$

Notice that each time we select a different value of x_3 in Example 6.24, we get different values for the two other variables that satisfy the system of equations; and our choice for x_3 is unlimited. Because the value of x_3 is free to be specified as we choose, it is called a *free variable*. Hence, we have multiple or infinite solutions to this system of linear equations. FREE VARI-
ABLE

We will see in the next section that these solutions all lie on a line. Each value of x_3 determines one point on this line. This line is the intersection of the two unique planes represented by the two equations in the original problem.

6.4.5 The geometry of free variables

To further illustrate the geometric role of a free variable, we consider another three variable problem, so that the solution can be displayed in a three-dimensional plot.

Example 6.25. Consider the linear system of equations given by

$$x + y + 2z = 10$$
$$-x + y + z = -3$$

The corresponding augmented matrix for this system is

$$\left[\begin{array}{ccc|c} 1 & 1 & 2 & 10 \\ -1 & 1 & 1 & -3 \end{array}\right]$$

Using `row_reduce`, we arrive at the reduced matrix

$$\left[\begin{array}{cc|c} 1 & 0 & \frac{1}{2} & \frac{13}{2} \\ 0 & 1 & \frac{3}{2} & \frac{7}{2} \end{array}\right]$$

The solution to this system of equations, in equation notation, is

$$x = \tfrac{13}{2} - \tfrac{1}{2}z$$
$$y = \tfrac{7}{2} - \tfrac{3}{2}z$$

As in Example 6.24, this system has multiple solutions, evidenced by the free variable z.

The solutions to this system of equations lie along a line created by the intersection of the two planes $x + y + 2z = 10$ and $-x + y + z = -3$. Figure 6.10 shows these two planes, along with a superimposed intersection line.

The two solution expressions in Example 6.25, $x = 13/2 - z/2$ and $y = 7/2 - 3z/2$, describe the x and y coordinates of points on this line as the value of the free variable z changes. As we alter the value of z, we generate coordinate points of the form $(x, y, z) = (13/2 - z/2, 7/2 - 3z/2, z)$. For example, when $z = 2$, we get the point $(5.5, 0.5, 2)$ on the intersection line, which is also a solution to the given system of equations.

A line created in this manner is called a *parametric* curve, because the PARAMETRIC x and y coordinates rely on the value of the *parameter* z to determine their CURVE values. By plotting the line in a three-dimensional space, we get to see the value of z. Later on, we'll introduce the idea of parameterizing curves where the plot of these curves hides the value of the parameter that is generating the other variable values.

Regardless of the number of variables involved in a system of equations, or whether the intersection is a line, plane, or hyperplane, the role played by fixing the value of a free variable is the same: It identifies one possible solution out of

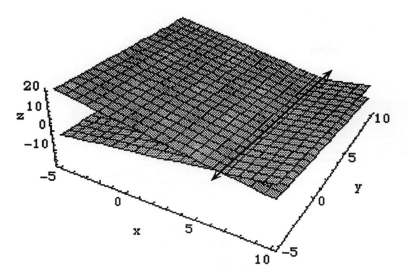

FIGURE 6.10
Multiple solutions along intersection of planes.

an infinite number of choices. Free variables allow an infinite number of choices
to be made for a simultaneous solution to a system.

The case of multiple solutions is actually the most interesting of the three.
If the previous example's system were modeling a particular problem in business, having multiple solutions would give the decision-maker a lot of freedom
in deciding which solution to use. This can be quite an advantage, since there
may be other considerations affecting the problem that were not included in the
formulation.

6.4.6 "What if" explorations

"What if?" questions that arise in business typically involve changes to the
right-hand side values of a system of equations, because these quantities limit
the values that the variables can take on. They typically represent some physical
requirement that must be met exactly (in the case of equations).

Suppose that, in Example 6.22, the right-hand side values 11, 8, and 7
represent only one of, say, three possible right-hand sides for the system. The
other two are given by a set of high values {14, 9, 9}, and a set of low values

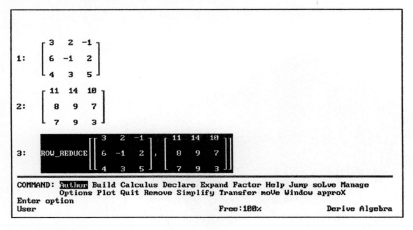

FIGURE 6.11
Row_reduce setup for multiple right-hand sides.

$\{10, 7, 3\}$. If we allow the system to use the high values or low values, how will it affect the solution we find? The **row_reduce** command in *Derive* is useful to explore such possibilities, as the next example illustrates.

Example 6.26. The three possible systems of linear equations that we need to solve are given by

$$3x_1 + 2x_2 - x_3 = 11 \qquad 3x_1 + 2x_2 - x_3 = 14 \qquad 3x_1 + 2x_2 - x_3 = 10$$
$$6x_1 - x_2 + 2x_3 = 8 \qquad\quad 6x_1 - x_2 + 2x_3 = 9 \qquad\quad 6x_1 - x_2 + 2x_3 = 7$$
$$4x_1 + 3x_2 + 5x_3 = 7 \qquad\quad 4x_1 + 3x_2 + 5x_3 = 9 \qquad\quad 4x_1 + 3x_2 + 5x_3 = 3$$

Because all three systems have exactly the same coefficient values on the left-hand side of the equations, they will all have exactly the same left-hand sides when put into an augmented matrix. And, after Gauss-Jordan elimination is applied, they will all have the exact same left-hand sides in their reduced matrices.

This fact enables us to use the **row_reduce** command efficiently. We need only enter the left-hand side values once. Interestingly, we need only do the same for the right-hand side values also.

Recall that the right-hand side values of a system are represented by a column vector of values. We can enter these three column vectors as columns in a single right-hand side matrix. Figure 6.11 shows the resulting left and right side matrices along with the display of the expression **row_reduce (#1,#2)**.

Then, we can simplify the entire block of columns all at once to examine the solution possibilities for all three systems. Figure 6.12 illustrates the result of simplifying the **row_reduce** expression in the exact precision mode. By reading down each of the three right-hand side columns in the reduced matrix, we have the corresponding solutions for the three given systems.

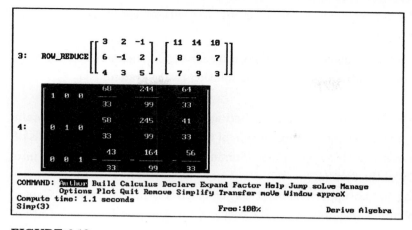

FIGURE 6.12
Simultaneous solution for three systems.

Exploration Exercises

6.1. In Example 6.24, suppose that we add the additional consideration that all of the variables of the problem must be nonnegative, that is, greater than or equal to zero. How does this affect the range of solutions for the system? What does this restriction do to the values of the free variable(s) present?

6.2. Suppose that, in addition to nonnegativity, the decision maker wants the solution in which the value of each variable is the smallest nonnegative value it can assume. How does this affect the solution and the free variable(s)?

6.3. Suppose that the decision maker wants the nonnegative solution that makes the expression $x_1 + x_2 + x_3 + x_4$ achieve its minimum value. Since this sum represents an objective specified by the decision maker, we call it an *objective function*. Is the solution that results unique? What is the minimum value that the objective function attains?

6.4. Suppose that the decision maker's objective changes. Now the decision maker wants a positive valued solution that minimizes the product $x_1 x_2 x_3 x_4$. A positive valued solution has all variables strictly greater than zero; none can take on the value zero.

6.4.7   Gauss-Jordan rules

These are three algebraic operations that `row_reduce` uses in applying Gauss-Jordan elimination:

1. Any individual row of the augmented matrix can be multiplied by a nonzero constant without changing the solution to the system.

2. The order of rows can be switched at any time without changing the solution to the system.

3. Any row of the augmented matrix can be added to another row of the augmented matrix without changing the solution to the system.

The Gauss-Jordan method is an organized application of these rules to obtain the identity matrix on the right-hand side of the reduced matrix. The details of how *Derive* executes these operations illuminate some interesting insights into the geometry of the system.

Starting in the upper left-hand corner of an augmented matrix, Gauss-Jordan elimination attempts to place a coefficient of 1 in that location by either multiplying the first row using a constant of $\pm 1/a_{11}$, or switching the first row with some other row below it that can accomplish this goal.

Next, focusing only on the first column of the augmented matrix, Gauss-Jordan elimination uses scalar multiples of the entire new first row to add to the rows below it, with the goal that all other components of the first column below the entry 1 become 0. The other entries of each row are appropriately changed by the addition of the component in their column from the multiplied first row, but these just go along for the ride while our attention is on the first column.

Once this initial goal is achieved, the technique, or *algorithm*, shifts its attention one position down the main diagonal and attempts to create a 1 in this next position, using the exact same strategy as before. All other entries below the 1 in this column are then changed to zero by adding appropriate multiples of the second row to the other rows.

The algorithm continues in this manner until it reaches a boundary of the matrix, either the bottom or the right side. The Gauss portion of the Gauss-Jordan algorithm stops at this point, since it is possible to simply back-substitute to solve for the values of the different variables.

The Jordan half of the algorithm, developed in 1873, picks up at this point. It starts back upward along the path of 1's that the Gauss algorithm created, attempting to create 0's above each 1. It again does this a single column at a time, using the exact same strategy as the Gauss algorithm did on the way downward through the matrix. It uses scalar multiples of each new row to add to the rows above it so that the components in each column above an entry of 1 become 0. It continues in this fashion until it reaches the upper left-hand corner of the matrix. The end result is the Gauss-Jordan reduced matrix that we see resulting from simplifying the **row_reduce** expression in *Derive*, equivalent to the initial augmented matrix, and yielding one of the three solution possibilities for a linear system of equations.

In a linear algebra course that focuses exclusively on linear systems, students usually go through the steps of Gauss-Jordan elimination by hand so that they understand all the details of the technique. A tool as powerful as *Derive* or a hand held calculator that has the algorithm encoded as part of its programming allows us to get at many of the same details without hand calculation.

The bottom line is that the steps used by Gauss-Jordan elimination are ones that leave the solution to the original system of linear equations *unchanged*. In terms of the geometric structure of the system of equations, the intersection point(s) of the original equations are exactly the same as the intersection point(s) of this row-reduced system. The two systems are called *equivalent*. The ability to interpret the results of Gauss-Jordan elimination in a geometric context of intersections of surfaces represented by the equations of the system is an important and useful insight.

EQUIVALENT SYSTEMS

Lastly, there is a correspondence between the form of the reduced matrix and the mathematical property of independence. In particular, notice that we can immediately identify both the rank of the system and which equations of the system are linearly independent. Any equation of the system that is linearly independent of the other equations in the system will allow Gauss-Jordan elimination to be successful in creating a 1 as the leftmost nonzero component of its corresponding row.

NOTE!

This position is called a *pivot* position of the row. The number of pivots in the reduced matrix is exactly equal to the rank of the matrix, which exactly equals the number of linearly independent equations in the system, which is exactly equal to the number of variables in the system that are not free in any solution. Any equation that completely disappears during the algorithm, having all zeros as components, is linearly dependent on some other equation.

HOT!

Exploration Exercises

6.1. Categorize each of the following systems as inconsistent, having a unique solution, or having multiple solutions. If the system is inconsistent, explain why.

Otherwise, specify a solution to the system of equations.

$$(a) \begin{bmatrix} 3 & 2 & -1 & | & 11 \\ 6 & -1 & 2 & | & 8 \\ 4 & 3 & 5 & | & 7 \end{bmatrix}$$

$$(b) \begin{bmatrix} 2 & -4 & -2 & -2 & | & 4 \\ 2 & -4 & 3 & -4 & | & -12 \\ 4 & -8 & 3 & -2 & | & 18 \\ 0 & 0 & -1 & 2 & | & 8 \end{bmatrix}$$

$$(c) \begin{bmatrix} 1 & 2 & | & 3 \\ 2 & 5 & | & 4 \\ 5 & 5 & | & 8 \end{bmatrix}$$

$$(d) \begin{bmatrix} -1 & -2 & 6 & 4 & -4 & | & 10 \\ -1 & 1 & -13 & 3 & -5 & | & 1 \\ -1 & -1 & 1 & 7 & -2 & | & 14 \\ -8 & -2 & 10 & 11 & 1 & | & -6 \\ 7 & 3 & 3 & 6 & 1 & | & 8 \end{bmatrix}$$

6.2. For one of the systems of equations in the previous exercise, specify two additional right-hand side column vectors, form a right-hand side matrix, and solve the combined system as in Example 6.26.

6.3. If we pick out one of the right-hand side values in an initial augmented matrix and make that component zero, will the corresponding component in the reduced matrix always be zero?

6.4. If we were to make all of the right-hand side components of an initial augmented matrix equal to zero, what happens to the original solution? If we keep the right-hand side values equal to zero, can this result ever change?

6.5. If we pick out one of the right-hand side values in an initial augmented matrix and increase or decrease that component by 1, will the corresponding component in the reduced matrix also increase or decrease respectively by the same amount?

6.6. How does a reduced matrix change if we switch the order in which columns appear in an original augmented matrix? Can you algebraically argue why this is so? Demonstrate with an example using *Derive*.

6.7. Develop an answer to the following questions in terms of either simultaneous solutions or intersection points of surfaces. Support your conclusion with a specific two-equation example.

(a) Can a two-equation inconsistent system of linear equations have all linearly independent equations?

(b) Can a two-equation inconsistent system of linear equations have any linearly dependent equations?

(c) Can a system of linear equations with dependent equations be inconsistent?

(d) Can a system of linear equations with independent equations be inconsistent?

(e) Can a system of linear equations that has zeros for all right-hand side values have a unique solution?

(f) Can a system of linear equations that has zeros for all right-hand side values be inconsistent?

6.4.8   The effect of near-dependency

The concepts of independence and dependence afford insights into the structure of systems of linear equations. We discovered that a dependent system has some left-hand side expressions that are linear combinations of other left-hand side expressions.

However, when equations are independent, but are very nearly the same, the solutions become very sensitive to the values of the coefficients. We can have wild swings in the solutions following very small changes in the problem—small changes such as those that can result from rounding or truncation error in our computer! **NEAR   DE-PENDENCY**

Example 6.27.   Consider the linear system of equations given by

$$x_1 + x_2 = 10$$
$$1.95x_1 + 2x_2 = 20$$

The left-hand side of the second equation is very close to being a multiple of 2 of the left-hand side of the first equation. These lines are very nearly the same, and very near to being dependent. The solution of this system has $x_1 = 0$ and $x_2 = 10$. Notice what happens when we alter the coefficients slightly, and solve the system

$$x_1 + x_2 = 10$$
$$2x_1 + 1.95x_2 = 20$$

The solution of this system has $x_1 = 10$ and $x_2 = 0$. For only a 2.5% change in the coefficients a_{21} and a_{22}, the solution changes significantly!

When the coefficient matrix for a system of linear equations has equations that are *near-dependent*, or very close to being parallel, it is called an *ill-conditioned* matrix. **NEAR DEPENDENT**

Ill-conditioned matrices are problematic for computer calculations because computers must work with floating point arithmetic, and the matrices are very sensitive to small changes in the component values. The solution is also very sensitive to the small changes imposed by rounding and truncation. A very simple experiment can provide some insight into why this happens.

Example 6.28.   Take two pieces of string about 8 inches in length, and lay them across each other on a table, stretched tight, forming an "×." Notice how distinct the point of intersection is for this case. Now, adjust the top string so that it becomes very nearly parallel to the bottom string, but still overlaps at the same point of intersection. The intersection point is less distinct for this case, and, depending upon the accuracy of the instrument we use to identify it (a pin, a finger, an eraser), our answer may not coincide with that of earlier; we may have to estimate the intersection point.

By placing the top string directly on top of the bottom one, and altering the alignment slightly, we can observe the intersection point rapidly changing locations for small changes in alignment. This is the same effect near-dependency has on the determining a solution in an ill-conditioned matrix.

Exploration Exercises

6.1. We can use *Derive* to examine why a computer has difficulty, with near-dependency by interpreting this condition in its geometric sense: near-parallel lines.

   (*a*) Plot each system of equations for Example 6.27 in a separate 2-D plot window of *Derive*. Use the *Derive* cross hairs to approximate the intersection point that represents the solution to each system.

   (*b*) Now, make the equations even closer to being parallel. For the first system of equations, change the system to

$$x_1 + x_2 = 10$$

$$1.99x_1 + 2.01x_2 = 20$$

Then, slightly change the system to create a second system

$$x_1 + x_2 = 10$$

$$1.99x_1 + 2.0x_2 = 20$$

Plot each of these systems in a different *Derive* window. Notice how slight the change is. Again, using the *Derive* cross hairs, approximate the solutions to both of these systems. Is it easier, or harder to determine the intersection points? Why?

   (*c*) For the last two systems, use the `row_reduce` command to find the actual intersection point, and determine the percent change in coefficients.

6.2. Someone offers the suggestion that by multiplying one near-dependent equation by a large enough number, we can eliminate the observed sensitivity to changes in coefficients. Is this correct? Why?

6.4.9   Discovering matrix algebra

Remember how variables were first introduced in algebra as place holders for numerical values? Matrices can likewise be thought of as higher-dimensional variables that can be manipulated algebraically in a manner similar to normal algebra, with only minor rule changes. An example is a 1×1 matrix, which is the same as a single variable or number. In matrix algebra, we will use the

LAR

term *scalar* when refering to a single number. In this section we are going to experiment with matrices, using *Derive*, to try to deduce the rules of matrix algebra.

Algebraic operations must be written into the computer code to manipulate expressions in applications such as *Derive*. For algebraic operations involving matrices such as Gauss-Jordan elimination, matrix addition, scalar multiplication of a matrix, and matrix multiplication, we typically input numerical entries for the components and let the software generate a numerical result. The values that we initially enter into the software are combined and simplified as the software applies the appropriate algorithm. By specifying matrix components in a clever way, the displayed result can reveal the underlying definitions used by the software. And, if we are *really* clever, we can pick each variable name to coincide with its original matrix location so that the final result displayed by *Derive* records the manipulations it performed.

To accomplish this detective work with *Derive*, we want to use alphanumerical variable names that are more like words than variables. To be sure *Derive* recognizes that an entry such as $a12$ represents the variable a_{12}, and not the multiplication $a \cdot 1 \cdot 2$, we set **Options**, **Input** to **Word**, as opposed to **Character**. We can then use the **Build** menu option to accomplish the construction of expressions involving matrices. As an example, let's examine one instance of scalar multiplication of a matrix.

Example 6.29. To discover how scalar multiplication of a matrix is defined by *Derive*, let's use a 2×2 matrix A, and a scalar p. To enter the proposed operation

$$p * \begin{bmatrix} a_{11} & a_{22} \\ a_{21} & a_{22} \end{bmatrix}$$

into *Derive*, we first **Declare** the **Matrix** having 2 rows and 2 columns. Next, we **Build** the appropriate expression, entering p directly as the **Build** first expression. Since p is a scalar, we select the scalar multiplication symbol "*" as the **Build** operator, and #1 as the **Build** second expression. The **Build** operator "." is the symbol for matrix multiplication in *Derive*. Simplifying the resulting expression yields the screen shown in Figure 6.13.

It appears as if multiplication of a scalar and a matrix simply distributes the multiplication to each component of the matrix. Of course, we should select several other examples of varying sizes to confirm that our detective work is correct.

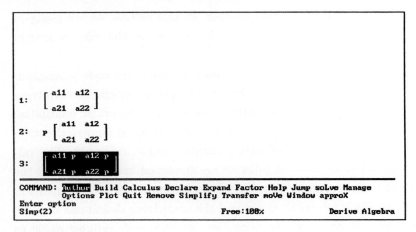

FIGURE 6.13
Scalar multiplication of a matrix.

Exploration Exercises

Develop a definition for each valid matrix operation using the technique shown in Example 6.29. Once the proper definitions are identified based on the routines programmed into the software, explain why those operations that are invalid cannot be accomplished.

6.1. If A and B are two matrices of the same size (e.g. 2×2), is the operation $A + B$ valid?

6.2. If A and B are two matrices of differing sizes (e.g. a 2×4 and a 2×3), is the operation $A + B$ valid?

6.3. If A and B and C are three matrices, under what conditions is the operation $A + B + C$ valid?

6.4. Complete the following definition of matrix addition:

> **Definition 6.4.   Matrix Addition.** If A and B are two matrices, then the operation $A + B$ is defined as
>
>
> and is valid under the condition(s):

6.5. Develop a rule for identifying the dimensions of the matrix resulting from matrix addition.

6.6. If A and B are two matrices of the same size (e.g. 2×2), is the operation $A \cdot B$ valid?

6.7. If A and B are two matrices of differing sizes, under what conditions is the operation $A \cdot B$ valid?

6.8. If A and B and C are three matrices, under what conditions is the operation $A \cdot B \cdot C$ valid?

6.9. Complete the following definition of matrix multiplication:

> **Definition 6.5.** **Matrix Multiplication.** If A and B are two matrices, then the operation $A \cdot B$ is defined as
>
> and is valid under the condition(s):

6.10. Develop a rule for identifying the dimensions of the matrix resulting from matrix multiplication.

6.11. Based upon the results of your exploration of matrix operations so far, do you consider it necessary to specify a definition of matrix subtraction? Support your answer with an explanation.

6.12. Using the augmented matrices that follow, identify the general procedure for performing Gauss-Jordan elimination on augmented matrices as discussed in Section 6.4.4.

$$(a) \left[\begin{array}{cc|c} a_{11} & a_{12} & b_1 \end{array} \right] \qquad (b) \left[\begin{array}{c|c} a_{11} & b_1 \\ a_{21} & b_2 \end{array} \right]$$

$$(c) \left[\begin{array}{cc|c} a_{11} & a_{12} & b_1 \\ a_{21} & a_{22} & b_2 \end{array} \right] \qquad (d) \left[\begin{array}{cc|c} a_{11} & a_{12} & b_1 \\ a_{21} & a_{22} & b_2 \\ a_{31} & a_{32} & b_3 \end{array} \right]$$

$$(e) \left[\begin{array}{ccc|c} a_{11} & a_{12} & a_{13} & b_1 \\ a_{21} & a_{22} & a_{23} & b_2 \end{array} \right] \qquad (f) \left[\begin{array}{cc|c} a_{11} & a_{12} & b_1 \\ a_{21} & a_{22} & b_2 \\ a_{31} & a_{32} & b_3 \\ a_{41} & a_{42} & b_4 \end{array} \right]$$

6.13. The previous exercise presented several varying sizes of augmented matrix representations for linear systems of equations. Letting $m =$ the number of equations, and $n =$ the number of variables, three cases are possible: (1) $m > n$, (2) $m = n$, and (3) $m < n$. Based upon the results of your symbolic exploration, which relationship between m and n would you usually suspect to yield the case of
(a) No solution?
(b) A unique solution?
(c) Multiple solutions?

6.14. Consider the augmented matrix given by

$$\left[\begin{array}{ccc|c} 1 & 3 & 3 & 2 & b_1 \\ 2 & 6 & 9 & 5 & b_2 \\ -1 & -3 & 3 & 0 & b_3 \end{array}\right]$$

Using the row_reduce command in *Derive*, determine for what values of b_1, b_2, and b_3 the system will be consistent, undetermined, or inconsistent.

6.15. Repeat the previous exercise for the following augmented matrices.

$$(a) \left[\begin{array}{cccc|c} 1 & 1 & 1 & 0 & a_1 \\ 1 & 1 & 0 & 1 & a_2 \\ 1 & 0 & 1 & 1 & a_3 \\ 0 & 1 & 1 & 1 & a_4 \end{array}\right] \qquad (b) \left[\begin{array}{ccc|c} -3 & 1 & 4 & d_1 \\ 1 & 1 & 1 & d_2 \\ -2 & 0 & 1 & d_3 \\ 1 & 1 & -2 & d_4 \end{array}\right]$$

$$(c) \left[\begin{array}{cccc|c} -4 & 1 & 1 & 0 & a_1 \\ 1 & 3 & 0 & 1 & a_2 \end{array}\right] \qquad (d) \left[\begin{array}{cc|c} -5 & 7 & d_1 \\ 3 & 1 & d_2 \\ -2 & 0 & d_3 \\ 1 & 11 & d_4 \end{array}\right]$$

6.5 SUMMARY

In this chapter, we have developed methods for solving systems of linear equations. Such systems arise when the predictors must satisfy several linear functions simultaneously.

A system of linear equations can have zero, one, or and infinite number of solutions, depending on the rank of the system and the number of variables.

Computer solution methods for systems of equations use basic multiplication and addition. The most famous, Gauss-Jordan, manipulates the equations to isolate the maximum number of independent variables on the left-hand side.

Solutions of systems of linear equations can be very sensitive to changes in the data if the equations are near-dependent.

Systems of equations can be represented by matrices, and solved using matrix methods. We derived some of the properties of operations with matrices by experimenting using *Derive*.

Systems of equations can also be solved by spreadsheets.

6.6 COMPLEMENTS

1. There are several excellent references on linear algebra and matrix methods. We recommend two

   - *Linear Algebra and its Applications*, 3rd Edition, by Gilbert Strang. (Harcourt Brace Jovanovich, San Diego, California, 1988.)
   - *A Unified Introduction to Linear Algebra: Models, Methods, and Theory*, by Alan Tucker. (MacMillan, New York, 1988).

2. Short biographies of Sylvester, Cayley, Gauss, and Jordan can be found at the Web site http://www-groups.dcs.st-and.ac.uk/ history/BiogIndex.html. These short biographies contain lists of additional print references. In all, there are biographies on over 1100 other mathematicians located at this Web site.

3. *The History of Mathematics*, Vols. I and II, by D. E. Smith. (Dover, New York, 1953.) Every good history of mathematics discusses the development of solution methods for systems of linear equations, but this is a particularly good reference. Volume II, page 432, starts his discussion of the solution of linear equations. He also gives background biographical data on the contributing mathematicians. Smith takes care to cite the contributions of other civilizations to mathematics, including the Chinese, Babylonian, Hindu, and Arabic in addition to the usual Greek and European threads.

4. *A Concise History of Mathematics*, by Dirk J. Struik. (Dover, New York, 1967.) At 195 pages, this is a concise but well written book that contains a great deal of information on the development of mathematics since the Renaissance, as well as a sketch of earlier developments.

CHAPTER 7

LINEAR INEQUALITIES

The mind contains furniture into which the guests must fit.

Morris Kline

Chapter Goals

⇒ Understand the difference between solutions to equations and solutions to inequalities.

⇒ Understand the effect of predictor constraints on the domain of the response-predictor function.

⇒ Understand the concept of optimization.

⇒ Specify a linear programming formulation of a modeling problem.

⇒ Solve a linear program both graphically and with a spreadsheet.

In this chapter, we explore relationships between predictor variables, as opposed to between the response and predictors.

Constraints are expressions that represent relationships between predictor variables. Constraints restrict the domain of the response-predictor function, limiting the allowable predictor values. As a result, the response variable, which is dependent upon the set of predictors, is limited in the values it can attain.

If a particular modeling objective seeks to make the response as large as possible (maximize), as in the case of profit, or as small as possible (minimize), as in the case of costs, the constraints on the predictor domain will act as a barrier to the response. We introduce a mathematical modeling technique called *linear programming* to explore some of the ideas associated with this type of environment.

7.1   SOLUTIONS TO INEQUALITIES

In the last chapter, we saw that a linear system of equations can yield multiple solutions when free independent variables are present. We made the claim that we're seeing the most interesting solution case when this happens.

Part of the reason for our claim lies in the flexibility that a multiple solution gives us. Rather than being limited to a single, unique solution (or no solution), we have a choice of any simultaneous solution that lies on the intersecting line or surface defining by the system. However, given such a choice is like being a kid in a candy store: Everything looks good, so which do we pick?

With a system of linear equations, we are concerned about restricting the domain when a multiple-solution case arises. With a system of linear *inequalities*, this concern is always present, due to the difference between solutions of linear equations and of linear inequalities. Let's examine this difference from both a geometric and algebraic perspective.

Any points satisfying an equation are forced to lie exactly on the line or surface that the equation defines. An inequality does not impose this restriction. It allows the value of the left-hand side of the expression to be less than ($<$), less than or equal to ($\leq$), greater than ($>$), or greater than or equal to ($\geq$) the value or expression specified on the right-hand side. These relationships are called the *sense* of the inequality.

From a geometric perspective, a linear inequality separates the response-predictor function's domain into two areas called *halfspaces*; one that contains the   HALFSPACE solutions to the inequality, and one that does not. The border between between halfspaces is defined by the equation obtained by replacing the inequality sign with an equality.

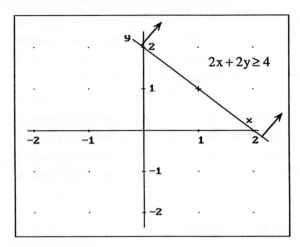

FIGURE 7.1
Greater than or equal to inequality.

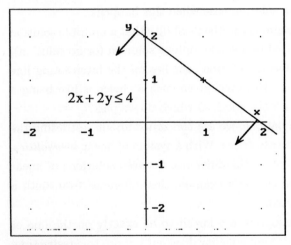

FIGURE 7.2
Less than or equal to inequality.

A algebraic solution to a linear equation is specified as a point. The algebraic solution to a linear inequality is specified as an *interval* of values for a particular variable. For example, a solution might look like $3 \leq x_1 \leq 14$. Let's examine a few of the possibilities graphically.

Assuming that x and y are both predictors, Figure 7.1 illustrates two half-spaces defined by the linear inequality $2x + 2y \geq 4$. This inequality allows the lefthand side to be greater than or equal to the righthand side. The points that

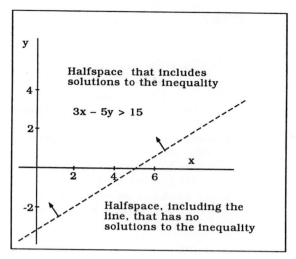

FIGURE 7.3
Strictly greater than inequality.

satisfy this inequality can lie exactly on the line $2x + 2y = 4$, or in the halfspace lying above the line.

By convention, the line $2x + 2y = 4$ is shown with a solid line when the points on the line are members of the restricted domain, and a dashed line when they are not. We also use small arrows to point into the halfspace where other possible solutions could exist. Figure 7.2 shows the case of the same expression with the sense of the inequality reversed. The halfspace containing solutions to this inequality is indicated by the arrows shown.

When an inequality is *strict*, the lefthand side is not allowed to be equal to the righthand side. Figure 7.3 shows the case of the strict inequality $3x - 5y > 15$. The dashed line represents the border $3x - 5y = 15$. The points lying exactly on this line are not part of the response-predictor function's domain. We again use arrows to indicate which halfspace contains possible solutions to the inequality.

Here is a really easy idea to determine which halfspace contains possible solutions to an inequality: one of the halfspaces *must* contain the origin. If the point $(0, 0)$ satisfies the inequality, then the halfspace containing the origin must be the region of the domain that holds solutions to the inequality. If the origin violates the inequality, then the region without the origin contains all the possible solutions. You could pick any point to test the halfspaces. We use the origin because it's a fast check.

7.2 SYSTEMS OF INEQUALITIES

Frequently, the response-predictor function's domain is restricted by more than a single inequality. The next example illustrates how this can happen.

> **Example 7.1.** Karen's Sweet Shop makes two of the greatest jellies on the planet: raspberry and blackberry. They are the only types of jelly the Sweet Shop makes.
>
> She asked us to help her decide how much of each type she should make so that the Sweet Shop makes the most profit. This would be our modeling objective. The raspberry jelly sells for \$4.80 a pint, and the blackberry, \$4.50 a pint.
>
> We can select our response as p = profit (dollars) the Sweet Shop will make from the sales of these two jellies. The predictors we will select are r = the pints of raspberry jelly made, and b = pints of blackberry jelly made. The response-predictor function is then
>
> $$p = f(r, b) = 4.8r + 4.5b \tag{7.1}$$
>
> The domain of $f(r, b)$ is currently the set of all nonnegative real numbers, since the Sweet Shop either makes this jelly or it doesn't. Our modeling objective seeks to make the value of p as large as possible. If the domain of $f(r, b)$ is not restricted, the answer is easy: Make an infinite number of both types of jellies to make an infinite profit! Clearly this isn't possible. Something must be restricting how much jelly the Sweet Shop can make. Let's look closer.
>
> Both of these jellies are made at the Sweet Shop using an automatic mixer. The mixer can process a total 300 pints of jelly per day. This restriction produces the constraint
>
> $$r + b \le 300 \tag{7.2}$$
>
> Karen also said that the labels for each jelly are made by hand by an artist who works for the Sweet Shop. The raspberry jelly label takes about 8 minutes to make, whereas the blackberry jelly label takes about 10 minutes. The artist can only work 8 hours (480 minutes) a day. This time restriction produces the constraint
>
> $$8r + 10b \le 480 \tag{7.3}$$
>
> These two constraints, in addition to the nonnegativity restriction on r and b, restrict the domain of $f(r, b)$, and yield the system of inequalities
>
> $$\begin{aligned} r + b &\le 300 \\ 8r + 10b &\le 480 \\ r &\ge 0 \\ b &\ge 0 \end{aligned}$$

Solutions to systems of linear inequalities are defined by the intersection of the individual constraint halfspaces. Any points satisfying all of the inequalities of a system simultaneously must also satisfy each individual inequality. If we can identify the restricted domain for each individual inequality, then determine the intersection of these halfspaces (the area in which all overlap), we can identify the restricted domain for the response-predictor function. This restricted domain is commonly called the *region of feasible solutions*, or the *feasible region*. We use the terminology "feasible region" and "restricted domain of the response-predictor function" interchangeably.

FEASIBLE REGION

Definition 7.1. Feasible Solutions. A *feasible solution* is one that simultaneously satisfies all of the predictor relationships of a system.

A feasible solution is not the same thing as the best solution for a particular problem. We'll deal with that issue in a moment.

Theorem 7.1. Consider a linear system of inequalities involving n variables and m equations

$$a_1 x_1 + b_1 x_2 + \cdots + n_1 x_n \; \triangle_1 \; c_1$$

$$a_2 x_1 + b_2 x_2 + \cdots + n_2 x_n \; \triangle_2 \; c_2$$

$$\vdots$$

$$a_m x_1 + b_m x_2 + \cdots + n_m x_n \; \triangle_m \; c_m$$

where each $\triangle$ represents one of the inequality relationships $>$, $<$, $\geq$, or $\leq$, and at least one of the coefficients $a_1, \ldots, a_m$, $b_1, \ldots, b_m$, $\ldots$, $n_1, \ldots, n_m$ is different from zero. Then, there exist only three possible outcomes for the simultaneous solution to this system:

1. No such solution exists. The restricted domain of the response-predictor function f defined by an intersection of constraint halfspaces that is empty. This system is called *inconsistent*.

   INCONSISTENT

2. A unique solution exists. The restricted domain of the response-predictor function f defined by the intersection of constraint halfspaces contains a single point. This system is called *consistent*.

   CONSISTENT

3. Multiple solutions exist. The restricted domain of the response-predictor function f defined by the intersection of constraint halfspaces contains more than one point. This system has an infinite number of solutions, and is called *undetermined*.

   UNDETERMINED

This theorem is a *generalization* of Theorem 6.1. It addresses more cases than does Theorem 6.1. The case when all $\triangle$ relationships are "$=$" is just one special case of a number of possibilities that can occur.

To illustrate Theorem 7.1, consider the following examples. Each of the three examples is a variation on the first. By making slight changes to one of the inequalities, we can create each of the three solution possibilities.

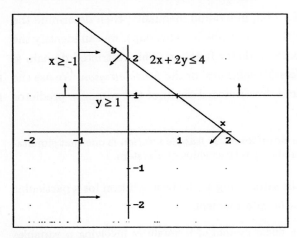

FIGURE 7.4
A region of feasible solutions.

Example 7.2. Assuming that x and y are predictors, Figure 7.4 illustrates the restricted domain of a response-predictor function $f(x, y)$ defined by the intersection of constraint halfspaces given by the system

$$2x + 2y \leq 4$$
$$x \geq -1$$
$$y \geq 1$$

The origin $(x, y) = (0, 0)$ satisfies the first two inequalities, and is contained in the halfspace of solutions for the first three constraints (indicated by arrows). The origin does not satisfy the last inequality, since $0 \not\geq 1$. The restricted domain of f that we want cannot contain the origin. All the points contained in the triangular feasible region, including the boundaries defining it, are solutions to this system of linear inequalities. This is the multiple solution case for linear inequalities.

The next example illustrates how we can end up working with a system of equations when trying to solve a system of inequalities. Frequently, we seek solutions that occur at *corner points* on the boundary of the feasible region. This returns us to solving systems of equations using the method of equating.

Example 7.3. Find the coordinates for each of the corners of the feasible region in Figure 7.4.

$$2x + 2y \leq 4$$
$$x \geq -1$$
$$y \geq 1$$

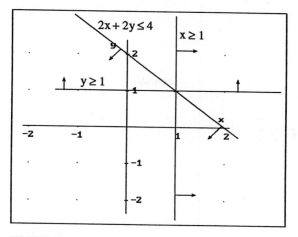

FIGURE 7.5
A unique solution case.

Using the method of equating, we can find the corner formed by the first and second inequalities

$$x = 2 - y \quad \text{and} \quad x = -1$$
$$\implies \quad 2 - y = -1 \implies y = 3$$

So, the corner is given by $(-1, 3)$. The corner defined by the 2nd and 3rd is obvious. Since it is defined by equalities, we have $x = -1$ and $y = 1$, or $(-1, 1)$. The corner defined by the first and third:

$$y = 2 - x \quad \text{and} \quad y = 1$$
$$\implies \quad 2 - x = 1 \implies x = 1$$

And, so, the corner is given by $(1, 1)$.

Example 7.4. Assuming that x and y are predictors, Figure 7.5 illustrates the feasible region defined by the intersection of halfspaces given by the system

$$2x + 2y \leq 4$$
$$x \geq 1$$
$$y \geq 1$$

in which we have changed the right-hand side value of the second inequality from -1 to 1. The feasible region is a single point that is a unique solution to this system.

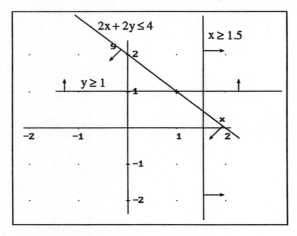

FIGURE 7.6
An inconsistent system of inequalities.

Example 7.5. By changing the second inequality in the last example to $x \geq 1.5$, we can see from Figure 7.6 that the feasible region becomes empty. There are no points that can simultaneously satisfy all three inequalities. Thus, the system of inequalities given by

$$2x + 2y \leq 4$$
$$x \geq 1.5$$
$$y \geq 1$$

has no solution.

For a number of modeling applications, our modeling objective is not simply to find a value of the response, but to find the "best" value of the response that satisfies all the constraints of the model.

In the next section, we'll examine one very popular modeling use for inequalities called *optimization*. Although a complete coverage of the material is a course by itself, we can cover enough material to give you a good understanding of the differences between equalities and inequalities, and how these differences affect solutions to problems.

Exploration Exercises_____

7.1. For each of the systems below, assume that the variables represent predictors for a mathematical model. Using arrows, draw and label the halfspace of solutions to each inequality on a Cartesian coordinate system. Then, determine the feasible region for each system, and identify what solution case you are dealing with. Finally, identify and label all corner points present.

(a) $3x + 4y \leq 12$
$x \geq -3$
$y \geq 1$

(b) $x - 2y \leq 0$
$x \geq -3$
$y \leq 0.5$

(c) $x + y \leq 10$
$x + y \geq 10$
$2x - y \leq 10$
$x + 3y \geq -15$
$y \geq 1$

(d) $x + 2y \geq 4$
$x + y \leq 6$
$x \geq 1$
$y \geq 1$

(e) $2x - 5y \leq 14$
$x - y \geq 1$
$5x + 2y \leq 10$

(f) $6y - 3x \leq 12$
$4x - y \leq 5$
$x \geq 0$
$4y \geq 4$

(g) $x + 2y \geq 4$
$x + y \leq 6$
$x \geq 1$
$y \geq 1$

7.3 OPTIMIZATION

When our modeling objective is to pick the "best" response value that satisfies all of the constraints present in our model, we are performing an *optimization*. For instance, our modeling objective might be to find the cheapest plane fare, the best-tasting chocolates, the loudest stereo system, or the most fuel efficient car.

In this section, our goal is to identify best solutions for linear optimization models graphically. The problems that we are going to examine will be restricted to having two predictors, but the principles remain the same for larger problems involving many more predictors.

An assumption included in every optimization model is that the predictors can be controlled. Optimization models are generally not used as descriptive models, but as tools to help people make good decisions. The solution(s) of an optimization model tells us what the values of the predictors should be to achieve the best response value.

Let's introduce the idea of optimization with an example with two predictors. This allows us to draw the response-predictor function on the same set of axes as the predictor relationship inequalities, even though the response-predictor function does not lie in this domain.

Example 7.6. Assuming that x_1 and x_2 represent predictors in a model, the system of inequalities given by

$$x_2 \leq 4$$
$$\frac{1}{2}x_1 + \frac{1}{3}x_2 \leq 2$$
$$x_1 \geq 0$$
$$x_2 \geq 0 \tag{7.4}$$

has the multiple solutions indicated by the shaded restricted domain in Figure 7.7. Which solution should we pick? One on the inside of the boundaries? Or, one on the boundaries? Perhaps one of the corners? What should guide us in our selection?

The answer is the response-predictor function! Let's see how it interacts with the predictor constraints.

Example 7.7. Suppose that the response-predictor function of the previous example is given by $v = f(x_1, x_2) = 2x_1 + 2x_2$. When $f(x_1, x_2) = 0$, we have $x_1 = 0$ and $x_2 = 0$, and the function is a straight line going through the origin, shown by the dashed line in Figure 7.8.

Predictors used in many optimization models represent amounts, or levels, of some resource that needs to be used efficiently. For example, they could represent the

- Number of rental automobiles to maintain at a specific location
- Amount of a fuel component to be used in a mixture
- Number of ambulances to assign to a specific area of a city
- Number of seats at a specific fare to allocate for a flight between New York and Paris

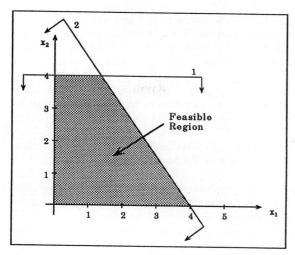

FIGURE 7.7
Feasible region for system of inequalities.

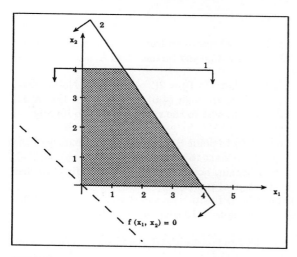

FIGURE 7.8
Feasible region with guiding objective function contour where $f(x_1, x_2) = 0$.

For this type of quantities, negative predictor values do not make sense. Nonnegativity restrictions on the domain of the response-predictor function then appear as part of the constraint set.

Let's pretend that the response-predictor function used in the previous example represents the output volume from a car stereo by adjusting two different knobs: knob 1 and knob 2. The response is given by v = volume, and the predictors for our model would be x_1 = setting on knob 1, and x_2 = setting on knob 2. We'll assume that neither of the knobs has a setting lower than 0, so we'll restrict the domain of f at the onset with the constraints $x_1 \geq 0$ and $x_2 \geq 0$.

The feasible region can then represent all the nonnegative knob settings that keep the stereo output from becoming distorted. This is a domain restriction on volume function. If we wanted the highest nondistorted volume possible, what settings should we pick?

Since both of the variables in $f(x_1, x_2)$ have positive coefficients, we know that we can increase either, or both, of the variables to increase the volume. In what order?

Definition 7.2.   Solution Location. A "best" solution to a linear optimization problem always lies on the boundary of the feasible region.

Knowing that we need to check predictor values that define the boundary of the restricted domain of $f(x_1, x_2)$, we impose the rule that we have to move along the boundary of the feasible region[t] to find the best solution.

First we draw the restricted domain. Next, we superimpose $f(x_1, x_2)$ on this graph, passing through the feasible region.

Starting at the current point (0, 0), we have two options for movement:

(a) Hold x_2 constant, and increase x_1
(b) Hold x_1 constant, and increase x_2

In Figure 7.9, following strategy (a) moves us from (0, 0) to point A along the lower boundary (Figure 7.9. We cannot go any further than A, since we would then leave the feasible region.

At point **A**, $(x_1, x_2) = (4, 0)$ so that $f(4, 0) = 2(2) + 2(0) = 8$. Notice that, when we draw a plot of $f(x_1, x_2)$ going through $(4,0)$, and leave in the initial position of $f(x_1, x_2)$, the function has moved to the right, parallel to its original position.

Strategy (b) moves us from (0, 0) to point B along the left boundary of the feasible region (Figure 7.10). Again, we want to stop at B, with $(x_1, x_2) = (0, 4)$, so that $f(0, 4) = 2(0) + 2(4) = 8$. Again, notice that the volume function has moved to the right, parallel to its original position.

Increasing the value of the volume function causes it to move to the right. We can see from either Figure 7.9 or Figure 7.10 that we can still move $f(x_1, x_2)$ further to the right.

In strategy (a), we can now hold x_2 constant and increase x_1, moving along the top boundary to point C (Figure 7.11).

Calculating the coordinates of point C:

$$x_2 = 4 \qquad \Longrightarrow \qquad x_1 = 2(2 - \frac{1}{3}(4)) = \frac{4}{3} \tag{7.5}$$

---

[t]The Simplex method, which this section is based on, is restricted to moving along boundaries of the feasible region. It is known as an *exterior point* method. Karmarkar's method of finding the best solution, is an *interior point method*. It allows our search to go directly through the feasible region.

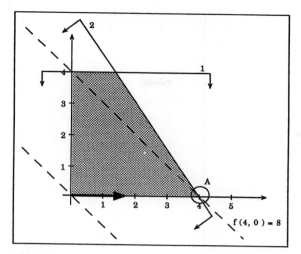

FIGURE 7.9
Direction of movement: Hold x_2 constant, increase x_1.

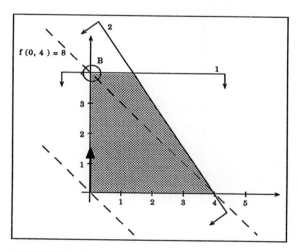

FIGURE 7.10
Direction of movement: Hold x_1 constant, increase x_2.

At point C, the value of the volume function is $f(4/3, 4) = 102/3$.

We could have also moved from point B along the right boundary to point C (Figure 7.12).

Notice that x_1 has to decrease at the same time x_2 increases, so it appears that going to point B will cause us to backtrack a little with the value of x_1.

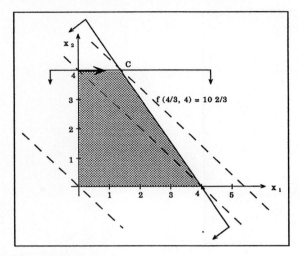

FIGURE 7.11
Moving to a better solution by increasing x_1.

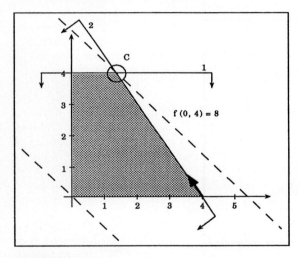

FIGURE 7.12
Moving to a better solution by increasing x_2 and decreasing x_1.

7.3.1 Finding a best solution

The big questions remaining unanswered are: (1) How do we know which direction to move in? and (2) How do we know we have the best solution? We've seen the answer to the first question an earlier chapter: We move in the direction of the gradient. To illustrate, we will briefly use vector terminology because of its compatibility with our graphical approach.

VECTOR

NOTATION

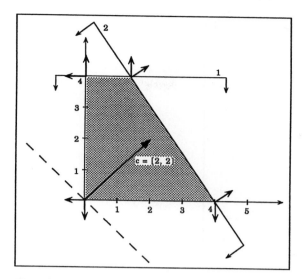

FIGURE 7.13
Labeling the gradient of the response-predictor modeling objective function.

Example 7.8. Suppose that we were back at the start point (0,0). Take the two predictor coefficients from the volume function, in order, and place them in the *vector* $\vec{c} = [c_1, c_2] = [2, 2]$. The notation c_n is used to represent the nth coefficient of the response-predictor function.

Now, place your pencil anywhere on the volume function. Starting from this location, move in the positive x_1 direction 2 units, and in the positive x_2 direction 2 units. Connect your start point with this point, and draw an arrow at the finish point end (Figure 7.13). This arrow represents the vector $\vec{c} = [2, 2]$. If the volume function was $v = f(x_1, x_2) = 4.1x_1 - 2x_2$, then $\vec{c} = [c_1, c_2] = [4.1, -2]$, and we would draw this vector by going to the right 4.1 units and down 2 units.

This vector $\vec{c}$ is called a *normal* vector. It is perpendicular to the surface of NORMAL the volume function. For linear functions like $f(x_1, x_2)$, this vector is also called VECTOR the *gradient* vector of $f(x_1, x_2)$.

The plot of the function $f(x_1, x_2)$ must move to the right for the response v to increase its value. Point C = (4/3, 4) is the last point in the feasible region that this function can take on. You can verify this by laying a pencil on the volume function and rolling it across the feasible region in the direction of increase.

Definition 7.3.   Gradient Vector. The *gradient* vector always points in the direction of greatest increase for a function.

This definition is just a vector restatement of the gradient information we introduced in Chapter 5.

The second question is still to be answered: How do we know we have the best solution?

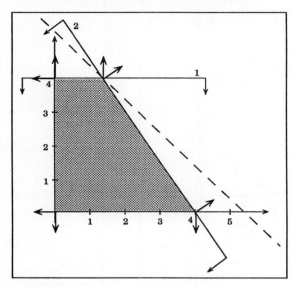

FIGURE 7.14
Labeling the rejected halfspaces.

Remember how we drew little arrows on each inequality to indicate the halfspace we were interested in, and to identify the feasible region? We'll use the same idea, but let's do something slightly different with the constraints. At each corner of the feasible region, we can draw straight arrows pointing toward the halfspaces we *don't* want (see Figure 7.14) for these constraints. Don't forget the corners defined by $x_1 \geq 0$ and $x_2 \geq 0$!

Here's how we know that we have found a "best" corner solution. A best corner solution is the *only* one in which the gradient vector lies inside the cone of the acute angle created by the constraint arrows drawn pointing into the halfspaces we don't want. A corner solution that meets this criteria is called an *optimal* solution.

ACUTE CONE

> **Example 7.9.** For the stereo volume problem, the optimal solution occurs at corner C. Figure 7.15 shows that this is the only corner where the gradient vector $\vec{c}$ lies inside an acute cone.

Discussion Ideas_____

⇒ Refer to the linear programming problem illustrated in Figure 7.15, and

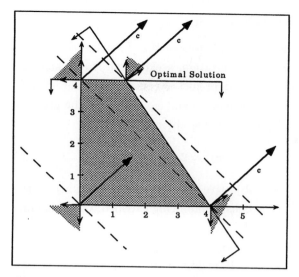

FIGURE 7.15
Acute cones and the optimal corner solution.

consider the following situation. Suppose that the two constraints defining the optimal solution location were nonlinear, each having some degree of bending associated with them. Perhaps they were 2nd degree or 3rd degree polynomial functions that restricted the objective function's domain in a similar manner as the linear constraints. The resulting problem would then be known as a *nonlinear programming* problem with a linear objective function. Could the same optimality condition involving an acute cone and the gradient of the objective function hold? Sketch a couple of cases using the outward gradients and the gradient of the objective function.

⇒ Suppose that we were to isolate a tiny amount of area circling the point where the two nonlinear constraints intersect and replace them with two linear constraints that intersect at the same point. If we applied the optimality condition to this this *local linear approximation* instead of the nonlinear constraints, would we always get the same result as the nonlinear constraints would yield?

7.4 LINEAR PROGRAMMING

As we have seen from the stereo volume example of the previous section, the response-predictor function drives an optimization, seeking the "best" solution from its restricted domain defined by the predictor constraints. Our goal in that example was to find the predictor values x_1 and x_2 that yield the greatest nondistorted volume. We can state this modeling objective as

$$\textit{Maximize} \quad v = f(x_1, x_2) = 2x_1 + 2x_2 \tag{7.6}$$

In another situation, a modeling objective function could be looking for the smallest response value subject to the constraints being satisfied. Our modeling objective would have a *minimizing* goal.

MATH PRO-
GRAM

The combination of a response-predictor function (like the volume function) and a set of constraints defining a feasible region is known as a mathematical *program.*

The volume problem is an example of a *linear program.*[‡] Using the volume problem as an example, the standard format for writing a complete linear programming optimization model is

$$\text{Maximize} \quad v = f(x_1, x_2) = 2x_1 + 2x_2$$

$$\begin{aligned} \text{Constraints:} \quad & x_2 \leq 4 \\ & \tfrac{1}{2}x_1 + \tfrac{1}{3}x_2 \leq 2 \\ & x_1 \geq 0 \\ & x_2 \geq 0 \end{aligned}$$

Linear programming is perhaps the most widely used math modeling technique in optimization today. We can easily solve problems with thousands of variables and thousands of constraints on a desktop computer.

Exploration Exercises

For the linear programs that follow, draw and label each constraint, identify the halfspace of solutions for each constraint, identify the feasible region, draw the response-predictor function , label the gradient vector of the response-predictor function, and graphically determine the optimal solution(s), if they exist.

[‡]Professor Emeritus George Dantzig of Stanford University is credited with inventing the field of linear programming in 1947, and is often called the father of linear programming.

7.1.   Maximize $z = f(x_1, x_2) = 2x_1 + 4x_2$

Constraints: $x_1 \leq 4$

$5x_1 + 5x_2 \leq 25$

$x_1 + 0.5x_2 \leq 1$

$x_1 \geq 0$

$x_2 \geq 0$

7.2.   Minimize $z = f(x_1, x_2) = -5x_1 + 5x_2$

Constraints: $x_1 \frac{1}{2}x_2 \leq \frac{3}{2}$

$\frac{1}{2}x_1 + x_2 \geq -2$

7.3.   Maximize $z = f(x_1, x_2) = x_1 + x_2$

Constraints: $-x_1 + 2x_2 \leq -2$

$x_1 \leq 6$

$x_1 \geq 0$

$x_2 \geq 0$

7.4. In the linear program of the previous exercise, how would you describe the effect of the constraint $x_1 \geq 0$? Is it actively doing anything for the problem? (Remember that the constraints are present to define the shape of the restricted domain of the response-predictor function.)

7.5.   Maximize $z = f(x_1, x_2) = x_1 + x_2$

Constraints: $-\frac{4}{6}x_1 + x_2 \leq 4$

$-3x_1 + \frac{9}{7}x_2 \geq 9$

$x_1 + x_2 \leq 8$

$x_1 \geq 0$

7.6.   Minimize $z = f(x_1, x_2) = 3x_1 + 3x_2$

Constraints: $x_1 - 2x_2 \leq -1$

$2x_1 - \frac{4}{3}x_2 \geq 1$

$2x_1 - \frac{6}{5} \leq 6$

$2x_1 + 2x_2 \geq 4$

$x_1 + 2x_2 \leq 11$

7.7.   Maximize $z = f(x_1, x_2) = 11x_2$

Constraints: $\frac{1}{2}x_1 + \frac{1}{3}x_2 \leq -2$

$x_1 \geq -2$

7.8. What happens to the solution of the previous exercise if we change the response-predictor function to read:

$$\text{Minimize}   z = f(x_1, x_2) = -11x_2$$

Do you think that this is a coincidence, or are we seeing some sort of relationship between minimizing and maximizing?

7.9.   Maximize $z = f(x_1, x_2) = x_1 + x_2$

Constraints: $x_1 + x_2 \geq 4$

$$x_1 + \tfrac{1}{3}x_2 \leq 1$$

$$x_1 \leq 3$$

$$x_2 \geq 0$$

7.10.   Maximize $z = f(x_1, x_2) = \tfrac{1}{2}x_1 + x_2$

Constraints: $x_1 - x_2 \geq 1$

$$\tfrac{1}{3}x_1 - \tfrac{1}{3}x_2 \leq 1$$

$$x_1 \geq 0$$

$$x_2 \geq 0$$

7.11. Describe what is happening to the solution to the previous problem. Would it matter if the response-predictor function read:

$$\text{Minimize } z = f(x_1, x_2) = \frac{1}{2}x_1 + x_2$$

Add a constraint to the formulation to fix this problem.

7.12.   Maximize $z = f(x_1, x_2) = 2x_1 + 4x_2$

Constraints: $x_1 - x_2 \geq 1$

$$4x_1 + 4x_2 \geq 16$$

$$x_1 + x_2 \leq 10$$

$$\tfrac{1}{3}x_1 - \tfrac{1}{3}x_2 \leq 1$$

$$x_1 \geq 0$$

$$x_2 \geq 0$$

7.13.   Maximize $z = f(x_1, x_2) = 2x_1 + \tfrac{2}{3}x_2$

Constraints: $x_1 - 2x_2 \geq -1$

$$-x_1 + x_2 = 3$$

$$x_1 \leq 0$$

$$x_2 \geq 0$$

7.14. What is the effect of the equality constraint on the feasible region of the previous problem? If you could change the equality constraint to an inequality constraint, what type of inequality constraint would you pick to guarantee that a solution exists?

7.15.   Maximize $z = f(x_1, x_2) = x_1 + x_2$

Constraints: $x_1 + x_2 \geq 4$

$x_1 + \frac{1}{3}x_2 \leq 1$

$x_1 - x_2 = -1$

$x_1 \leq 3$

$x_2 \geq 0$

7.16.   What is the effect of the equality constraint on the feasible region of the previous problem? Comment on how restrictive these types of constraints are on the domain of the response-predictor function's domain.

7.17.   Minimize $z = f(x_1, x_2) = 2x_1 - 4x_2$

Constraints: $\frac{1}{3}x_1 - \frac{1}{10}x_2 \geq \frac{1}{2}$

$x_1 + \frac{1}{4}x_2 \leq 3$

$x_1 \geq 0$

$x_2 \geq 0$

7.18.   Using several of the linear programs above that have solutions, explore the following questions.

(*a*)   Suppose that we allow the constant on the right-hand side of one inequality in a constraint set to change. How will this effect the shape of the feasible region? What effect will it have on possible solutions? Try increasing and decreasing the right-hand side constants for both greater than or equal to and less than or equal to constraints.

(*b*)   How is the feasible region affected by changes in the predictor coefficients of individual constraints in the constraint set?

(*c*)   If we were to allow the coefficients of the response-predictor function to change, what effect does this have on possible solutions?

7.5   SPREADSHEET SOLVERS

Most commercial spreadsheets, such as Excel and QuattroPro can solve reasonably sized linear programs. For example, QuattroPro can solve problems with hundreds of constraints and variables. Excel has a limit of 200 predictors, specifying two constraints for each predictor (an upper and lower bound), plus an additional 100 predictor constraints. Let's rework the volume problem using QuattroPro.

We set up the spreadsheet with cells representing the response variable, the predictor variables, and the left-hand sides of the constraint equations (Figure 7.16). The starting values of the predictors $x_1 = 0$ and $x_2 = 0$ are entered in cells B2 and B3. The response-predictor function is entered in cell B4, with the equation $= (2*B2) + (2*B3)$. We have also defined the right-hand side of the

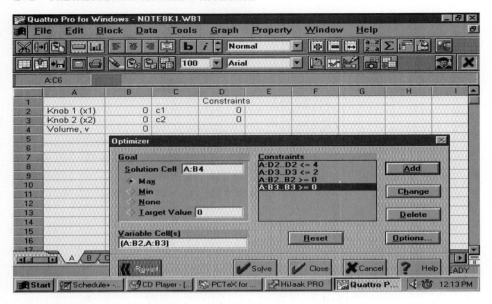

FIGURE 7.16
Setting up a QuattroPro spreadsheet for the radio volume problem.

constraints to be the values in cells D2 and D3. We also labeled these cells with entries in columns A and C.

To solve this linear program, we open the optimizer dialog box, which is also shown in Figure 7.16. Making the appropriate entries, we then select **soLve**.

The optimizer overwrites the predictor cells with the knob settings necessary for the response to achieve the maximum non-distorted volume. This solution is shown in Figure 7.17.

We obtain the same solution ($x_1 = 1.33\overline{3}$, $x_2 = 4$, $v = 10.66\overline{6}$) using the spreadsheet as we obtained using our graphical approach. The spreadsheet allows us to tackle larger problems that would be impractical to solve using a graphical approach. We introduced the graphical approach to give you a mental picture of what a solver such as QuattroPro is doing.

The optimizer in both Excel and QuattroPro will also solve some nonlinear problems, where the response-predictor function and the predictor constraints are not necessarily linear functions.

As you may have concluded by now, solving linear programs is relatively easy. The challenging part is in the modeling itself: identifying the proper response-predictor function and constraints, and interpreting the results of the model. This is where practice and creativity come into play, and where we add value to the

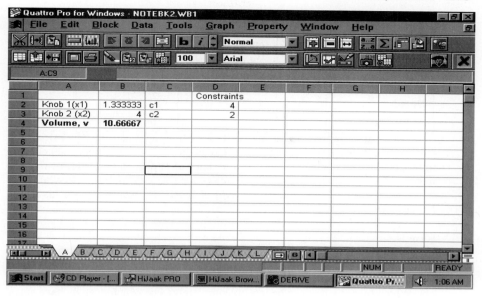

FIGURE 7.17
QuattroPro solution for the radio volume problem.

mathematics.

Exploration Exercises

7.1. Solve the following three linear programs using a spreadsheet solver. Compare your results to the answers you obtained in the previous exercise set.

(a)   Maximize $z = f(x_1, x_2) = 2x_1 + 4x_2$
$$\text{Constraints:}\quad x_1 \leq 4r$$
$$5x_1 + 5x_2 \leq 25$$
$$x_1 + 0.5x_2 \leq 1$$
$$x_1 \geq 0$$
$$x_2 \geq 0$$

(b)   Minimize $z = f(x_1, x_2) = -5x_1 + 5x_2$
$$\text{Constraints:}\quad x_1 + \tfrac{1}{2}x_2 \leq \tfrac{3}{2}$$
$$\tfrac{1}{2}x_1 + x_2 \geq -2$$

(c)   Maximize $z = f(x_1, x_2) = x_1 + x_2$
$$\text{Constraints:}\quad -x_1 + 2x_2 \leq -2$$
$$x_1 \leq 6$$
$$x_1 \geq 0$$
$$x_2 \geq 0$$

7.2. Jimmy's Bakery makes bread, cakes, doughnuts, and apple pies. For each of these products, Jimmy uses ingredient combinations and sells the items according to the following data:

294 PRECALCULUS: A MODELING APPROACH

	Flour (cups)	Milk (cups)	Sugar (cups)	Eggs (each)	Apples (cups)	Price (dollars)
Cake	2.25	1	1.5	4	0	3.00
Doughnuts (box)	3.5	0.75	1	4	0	4.00
Bread	5	1.75	0.25	0	0	1.50
Apple Pie	2	0	1	0	6	4.00

Let's assume that Jimmy can sell everything he makes for the price indicated in the table. Let's also suppose that he has 200 cups of flour, 100 cups of milk, 200 cups of sugar, 300 eggs, and 40 cups of apples on hand today. He also must make at least 4 batches of doughnuts for the local police officer, at least 2 cakes for display, and at least 4 loaves of bread. He also promised his mom, Karen (the owner of Karen's Sweet Shop), an apple pie.

Set this problem up as a linear program, and then use a spreadsheet to solve it.

(a) What should Jimmy bake today to maximize the amount of money he can make? (*Hint*: He should make approximately $246.33, according to our estimates.)

(b) Which ingredients does he use up completely? For which does he have extra left over?

(c) What recommendations can you give to Jimmy to help run his business, based on your linear program?

7.3. Jimmy's friend, Sergeant Murphy, has a problem. She has to develop a work schedule for her 38 officers that will cover the entire precinct and meet certain staffing requirements. A day of work is broken into six 4 hour shifts. An officer can start a duty day (which runs for 8 hours) at the start of any one of the six shift periods. However, due to traffic and crime, each period has a minimum number of officers that must be on duty, as shown in the following table.

Start time	Number required
0300	4
0700	12
1100	6
1500	12
1900	6
2300	8

(a) What is the fewest number of officers needed each day to meet the shift requirements, and how should they be scheduled? Notice that the number of officers on duty during any time period is the sum of those who started in the previous period and those who started in the current period.

(b) What are the response and predictors?

(c) What is the response-predictor function (modeling objective function)?

(d) What are the constraints?

(e) What is the solution?

(f) How should the officers be scheduled?

(g) During what periods are there excess officers? Can you suggest a weekly schedule that might be able to take care of this excess?

7.4. The bank you run has up to $100,000 to lend this month. Your bank offers two types of loans: car loans, which have an annual interest rate of 9%, and signature loans, which have an 11% annual interest rate. Both loans have an life of 36 months. We'll learn how to find the total amount of interest paid over the life of the loan later in the text—for now, we will use the financial functions built into a spreadsheet.

The QuattroPro function for calculating the accumulated interest over the life of a loan is `@amint( amt, int, term, term)`, where amt is the amount of the loan, `int` in the interest rate per period, and `term` is the number of periods. For a 36-month car loan, the accumulated interest would be calculated as `@amint(amt, 0.09/12, 36, 36)`. Excel has a similar function, called `cumipmt`.

As a bank manager, you want to maximize your profit, which is defined as the accumulated interest your bank receives over the 36-month life of loans, minus any losses. There is a 2% bad-debt cost for personal loans, and a 0.5% bad-debt cost for car loans. Your board of directors considers personal loans risky, and requires you to lend at least twice as much money for car loans as for personal loans.

(*a*) What loans should you make this month? How much profit can you make using this *optimal* strategy? (*Hint*: Ignore reinvesting the money as it is paid back to your bank, and the time value of money.)

(*b*) What assumptions would you change to make this a more realistic problem?

7.6 SUMMARY

This chapter focused on linear inequalities, highlighting the difference between the solutions of linear equations and linear inequalities.

The solution to either a single inequality or a set of inequalities is typically an interval or region, as opposed to a single point.

We examined a relationship between predictors called a *constraint*, and explored in depth the effects of predictor constraints on the domain of the response-predictor function.

We introduced the mathematical modeling technique known as *linear programming*. A linear program is defined as a combination of a linear response-predictor function, called the *modeling objective function*, and a set of predictor constraints.

Linear programming is a technique from an area of mathematics called *optimization*, in which either the maximum or minimum value of the response variable is sought.

The modeling objective function, also known simply as the *objective function*, drives the solution to a linear program. The greatest increase in the value of the response-predictor function is in the direction of this function's gradient.

We examined how to solve a linear program graphically and by using a spreadsheet.

7.7   PROJECT: COUCH POTATO OR HEALTH NUT?

This goal of this project is to give you the opportunity to develop, solve, and analyze a practical linear programming optimization model for a familiar subject: the food you choose to eat. You can use the model you develop as a tool to make nutritional decisions[§] in the future, as your level of activity, interests, and your tastes change.

Here is the setting:

We're constantly bombarded with advertisements telling us to eat less fat, less cholesterol, less sodium, and seemingly less of all the things that taste good, while other advertisements encourage us to "Get our own bag," and eat more "junk food." How can we sort out this mess?

⇒ What's the problem we're faced with?

Every school cafeteria is required to meet either state-specified or self-imposed Minimum Daily Allowance (MDA) nutritional standards for each meal. Although cafeterias are criticized for serving delicacies known as "mystery meat," "blah burgers," and "BRV's (barely recognizable vegetables)," assuming that a person eats an entire meal, the nutritional standards are usually met.

Your task is to develop two models that can assist you in choosing healthful foods, yet allow you to eat junk food. The first model we'll call the Couch Potato Model. Its modeling objective is to maximize the number of servings of junk food. The second model we'll call the Health Nut Model. Its modeling objective is to minimize the number of servings of healthful, but less tasty, food served in the cafeteria.

[§]The original setting of the Couch Potato or Health Nut problem is called the diet problem. A discussion of it can be found in most introductory textbooks on linear programming. The diet problem first appeared in "The Cost of Subsistence," by G. Stigler. *Journal of Farm Economics*, Volume 27, 1945.

Required Analysis

1. Develop a linear programming optimization model that determines the maximum number of servings of junk food that you can eat while staying below the MDA or national nutrition standards for dietary measures such as fats, cholesterol, etc.

2. Identify and include at least four predictors and 4 dietary measures. The predictors should represent individual servings of the junk food that you identify. Each dietary measure should generate a single constraint whose left-hand side is composed of the contributions that single servings of each junk food add to the dietary measure. The right-hand side of each dietary measure constraint should represent a specified limiting amount of that measure. You might consider using a table such as the one that follows for each model. Don't forget nonnegativity restrictions on the predictors, if they apply. The response-predictor modeling objective function should follow naturally.

	pred 1	pred 2	pred 3	pred 4	relation	limit
dietary measure					$\leq$	amount
dietary measure					$\leq$	amount
dietary measure					$\geq$	amount
dietary measure					$\geq$	amount

3. Develop a second linear programming optimization model that determines the minimum number of servings of the healthful (but less tasty) cafeteria food you would need to eat to meet the standards for nutrition in your school. Identify and include at least four predictors and four dietary measures in this model also.

4. Solve both models using a spreadsheet solver.

5. Analyze the results you obtain for both models, proposing a single eating strategy that combines both models' recommendations.

6. Write a project report, modifying the report format introduced in Chapter 5, Section 5.5.

7.8 COMPLEMENTS

1. A phenomenal Web site collection of resources and information on optimization and a host of other operations research topics was recently launched by the Institute for Operations Research and the Management Sciences (IN-FORMS). It is dedicated to providing the latest academic and professional practice information to students and young professionals. The top page is located at http://www.isr.umd.edu/ jwh2/iol/.

2. A second Web site written by John W. Gregory at the Optimization Techology Center of Argonne National Laboratory and Northwestern University that contains a very nice collection of frequently asked questions concerning linear and nonlinear programming can be found at

http://www.mcs.anl.gov/home/otc/Guide/faq/

3. This book contains two nice chapters on linear programming that go into more depth on the Simplex method and its uses.

   - *Finite Mathematics*, by Daniel P. Maki and Maynard Thompson. McGraw Hill, New York, 1989.

4. This is a great textbook that is used throughout the United States for undergraduate introductory courses in operations research. Chapters 3–7 have an extensive treatment of linear programming that examines additional topics such as the sensitivity of solutions and network applications that will allow you to extend the material covered in this book to suit classroom needs. The nice aspect of Winston's book is the manner in which he keeps looking at the same problems as examples, and adds complications to introduce the various topics. This approach has seemed to work very well with students, since they can develop a familiarity with a base set of problems. Additionally, Duxbury includes linear programming software called LINDO, which allows students to solve larger problems involving more than two variables.

   - *Operations Research: Applications and Algorithms*, 3rd Edition, by Wayne Winston. Duxbury Press, Belmont, California, 1994.

5. These classroom modules are available from the Consortium for Mathematics and its Applications (COMAP) Inc., Suite 210, 57 Bedford Street, Lexington, MA, 02173.

   - *The Graphical Simplex*, UMAP Modules: Tools for Teaching, Numbers 453 and 454.

CHAPTER
8

NONLINEAR MODELS I: POLYNOMIAL FUNCTIONS

Every body continues in its state of rest, or of uniform motion in a right straight line, unless it is compelled to change that state by forces impressed upon it.

Isaac Newton

Chapter Goals

⇒ Understand why linear models can fail to be valid if the rate of change of the response depends on the values of the predictor.

⇒ Understand the definition and properties of a polynomial function of one variable.

⇒ Understand the definition and properties of a polynomial function of several variables.

⇒ Understand the definition of a rational function, and when vertical asymptotes are useful for modeling.

⇒ Fit polynomial and rational models from data sets, and perform simple diagnostics.

In the previous chapters, we examined several properties and uses of linear models. One way that we can conveniently characterize this class of models is by stating that the change in the response is proportional to the change in predictor, no matter what starting value we pick. For example, when we modeled the height and weight for young males using a linear model, we saw that the slope of the line remained constant. Consequently, we expected a weight gain of 4.8 pounds (output) for every inch increase in height (fixed, incremental input), no matter what the person's starting height was.

These linear models have much to recommend them. They are straightforward to construct and simple to understand. For many applications, they provide good descriptions of observed behavior and/or decent predictions of future performance, especially if one considers a narrow range of inputs. Additionally, they are easy to analyze because of their uncomplicated algebraic form.

Simplicity, however, turns out to be a two-edged sword, because, unfortunately, many phenomena exhibit behavior that can not be well described by lines or surfaces with constant slopes. Their change in behavior (response) for a given fixed, incremental change in input depends on the initial value of the predictor. This more complicated behavior requires us to use *nonlinear* models that are better able to capture and mimic the characteristics we observe. In addition to possessing more complicated algebraic forms, nonlinear models also possess important and interesting properties. As we shall see.

NONLINEAR
MODEL

In this chapter, we begin our exploration of nonlinear models. Our primary focus will be on *polynomials*, a powerful class of nonlinear models that serve nicely as our starting point for this exploration. We begin by presenting several examples of nonlinear behavior, introducing some standard definitions, and then move on to visually identify some of the underlying properties of polynomial models. These properties allow us to construct polynomial models in which the marginal rates of change vary, and to examine data sets that support these kind of nonlinear models.

All along, keep in mind that we are not changing our approach to creating models; We are simply adding a new mathematical tool to use in our modeling efforts.

Iteration	y (in-lbs)	x (in)	Δy (in-lbs)	Δx (in)	$\Delta y/\Delta x$ (lb)
Start	0	0			
1	1	1	1	1	1
2	4	2	3	1	3
3	9	3	5	1	5

TABLE 8.1
Spring data (hypothetical).

8.1 NONLINEAR BEHAVIOR

Let's revisit the idea of varying rates of change. We'll keep things simple initially. Let's begin with a single predictor (independent variable) and a single response (dependent variable) case.

First, we need to recall some terminology. As in previous chapters, we let y denote a response, and a change in the response is then given by Δy. Similarly, a change in the predictor, from changing the value of the independent variable x, is denoted by Δx.

With a linear model, we know that the rate of change is constant. Thus, starting at the point (x_0, y_0), and measuring the rate of change of the model as we arrive at a new point (x, y), we have

$$\frac{\Delta y}{\Delta x} = \frac{(y - y_0)}{(x - x_0)} = m$$

where m is some constant value. This expression forms the basis for the point-slope formula of a line. No matter what point we pick for (x_0, y_0), the slope remains the same, and the ratio of change in output over change in input remains constant.

As mentioned earlier, linear models are not always an appropriate choice for modeling a given situation. Consider the case of a simple spring. The amount of tension in the spring depends upon the materials used in its manufacturing. However, we can describe its behavior in general: The more the spring is stretched, the more energy is stored in the spring.

Example 8.1. Suppose we were to attach a spring to the ceiling of a room. Then, to stretch it 1 inch may require work of, say, 1 inch-pound. To stretch it a second inch requires adding 3 more inch-pounds of energy. To stretch it yet another inch, we must add 5 more inch-pounds, so that the total amount of energy added to the spring is 9 inch-pounds.

The important point to make is that more energy is stored in the string as the spring is stretched, and the amount of additional energy depends on the length of the spring In other words, the ratio of change in outputs over change in inputs is not constant. Let x_n, $n = 1, 2, 3$, represent the length of the spring for each of the n measurements, and y_n represent the amount of energy in the spring. Then, starting at $(x_0, y_0) = (0, 0)$, the results of our experiment are shown in Table 8.1.

From the table, we see that the values of $\Delta y / \Delta x$ grow linearly, and are not a constant m. This tells us that $y = f(x)$ should not be modeled with a linear function.

Of course, there is also a *limit* on the value of the predictor, or how far the spring will stretch. At some length, the spring will deform or break, and the model will no longer be valid.

In this model, the domain of x is restricted by the physical properties of the spring.

Let's consider another example.

Example 8.2. Consider a model of a falling ball. We will let the time the ball has been falling be the predictor, and the height of the ball be the response. We want to predict the location of the ball at any given time.

We first decide to ignore air resistance. We also set our coordinates so that when $t = 0$, $h = 0$. We release the ball.

One second later, $h = -16$ feet. The average rate of fall is

$$r = \frac{d}{t} = \frac{-16 \text{ feet}}{1 \text{ second}}$$

One second later, when $t = 2$, $h = -64$ feet. For the time between $t = 1$ and $t = 2$, the average rate of fall is

$$\frac{-48 \text{ feet}}{1 \text{ second}}$$

We see again that a one second change in the predictor, time, gives different changes in the response, depending on the level of the predictor. Again, this is nonlinear behavior, because changes in the response are not strictly proportional to changes in the predictor.

Here is a third example.

Example 8.3. If you have a personal wealth of $1000, you would value finding $1000 a great deal. We say that the $1000 has a great deal of utility for you. Now obviously, more money is better. However, you can reach a state of wealth where another $1000 doesn't mean that much to you. In other words, after you have made your first billion dollars, then next thousand dollars is not as important to you as your first thousand dollars was. The change in utility due to a change in wealth is affected by the level of wealth. The utility of money is a nonlinear function.

8.2 POLYNOMIAL FUNCTIONS OF ONE VARIABLE.

We have already seen instances of polynomials. In Example 5.27 of Section 5.4.6, we examined a parabola with equation $w = h^2$, noting then that it was not appropriate to try to fit a line to points that lay on a parabola.

A polynomial function has a special form. It can be written as the sum of multiples of nonnegative integer powers of the predictor. The function $f(x) = 1 + x + 3x^2$ is a polynomial. We can write $f(x)$ as $1x^0 + 1x + 3x^2$, which is a sum of multiples of nonnegative integer powers of the independent variable. In contrast, $g(x) = 1 + x^{-1}$ is not a polynomial, because the term x^{-1} has an exponent that is not a non-negative integer. We capture this idea with a definition.

> **Definition 8.1. Polynomial Function.** A polynomial function of degree n is a function of the form $f(x) = a_0 x^0 + a_1 x^1 + \cdots + a_n x^n$, where $a_i, i = 0, 1, 2, \ldots, n$ are real numbers, and $a_n \neq 0$.

Linear functions are special cases of polynomial functions of degree 0 or 1. A nonzero constant function is a polynomial function of degree 0. A linear function can be written as a polynomial of degree 1: $f(x) = a_0 + a_1 x$. We do not define the degree of the function $f(x) = 0$. A polynomial function of degree 2 is often called a *quadratic function*, and one of degree 3 a *cubic function*.

Polynomials can be written in another form, that emphasizes the roots of the polynomial. The general function expression for this form is

$$f(x) = c_0 (x - c_1)(x - c_2) \cdots (x - c_n) \qquad (8.1)$$

where the c_i values are the roots of the equation—the values of the predictors when the response is zero. The values of the c_i's need not be unique, since just like the roots of a polynomial, they may be repeated.

Example 8.4. The quadratic polynomial function

$$f(x) = 1 + 2x + x^2$$

can be written in the alternative form (8.1) as

$$f(x) = (x + 1)(x + 1)$$

where c_1 and c_2 both equal -1. This alternative form is useful for modeling, since it clearly reveals predictor intercept information.

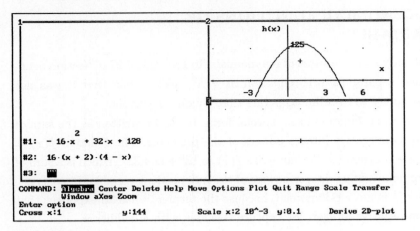

FIGURE 8.1
$h(x) = 128 + 32x - 16x^2$ plotted in windows 2 and 3. Note scale in window 3.

As in the case of finding roots of polynomials, some or all of the values of c_i can be complex numbers. When this happens, it means that there is not a COMPLEX
real-valued root associated with that factor.   ROOTS

Example 8.5. Expressing the function $f(x) = x^2 + 1$ in alternative form (8.1) results in the function

$$f(x) = (x - i)(x + i)$$

since $f(x)$ does not have a real-valued x-intercept. The function has the two complex roots $i = +\sqrt{-1}$ and $i = -\sqrt{-1}$, where $i^2 = -1$.

8.2.1 Graphs

Let's plot some polynomial functions, using *Derive* and begin our exploration graphically.

Example 8.6. We start with $h(x) = 128 + 32x - 16x^2$. We see this function plotted in Figure 8.1. This *quadratic* function is interesting. First, it clearly has a maximum value, which we can find graphically at $(x = 1, y = 144)$. This also means that the range of the function is $(-\infty, 144]$. Second, the function slopes upward until $x = 1$, and then slopes downward.

We also see that the roots that we found by factoring the function in expression #2 into our alternate form are verified on the graph. The graph also appears to open downward.

We are inspired to ask more questions: What is the relation between the x value where the maximum occurs and the x values of the two roots? What is the relation between the degree of the equation and the number of roots?

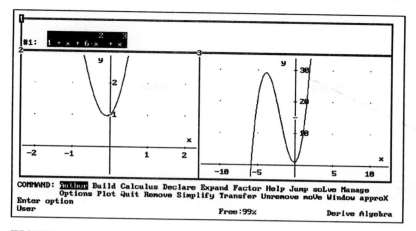

FIGURE 8.2
$f(x) = 1 + x + 6x^2 + x^3$, plotted in windows 2 and 3.

We will look at quadratic functions in detail in the next section. They are very useful for modeling situations with curvature, and are often a good first model to try after the linear model. With quadratic models, the rate of change of the behavior depends on the independent variable, but the rate of change is a *linear* function of the independent variable. This property can be utilized for modeling.

In our next example, we will examine a higher-order polynomial.

Example 8.7. Consider the cubic function given by $f(x) = 1 + x + 6x^2 + x^3$. The function is plotted in Figure 8.2. In window 2, we see only a portion of this *cubic* function. By changing the scale in window 3, we see the full behavior of the function. This cubic has a local maximum and a local minimum. Its range is the set of all real numbers, so it has no global maximum or minimum. Notice also that the function "opens down" until $x = -2$, and then it "opens up." We shall define terms for these properties shortly.

When we analyze graphs of polynomials, we routinely look for the intercepts and roots of the function. As in the case of linear functions, the y-intercept is the point where the graph of the function crosses the y-axis, and it is found by evaluating $f(0)$. The x-intercepts are found by finding those values of x such that $f(x) = 0$. INTERCEPTS

We also determine the values of x for which the function is increasing. At these points, the graph of the function has positive slope: A small increase in x yields an increase in y. The graph is decreasing at those points where a small increase in x results in a decrease in y. INCREASING, DECREAS- ING

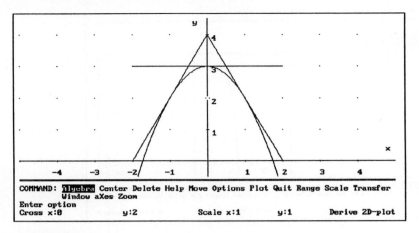

COMMAND: **Algebra** Center Delete Help Move Options Plot Quit Range Scale Transfer
         Window aXes Zoom
Enter option
Cross x:0   y:2   Scale x:1   y:1   Derive 2D-plot

FIGURE 8.3
The graph of $f(x) = 3 - x^2$, with three tangents superimposed. Notice that the curve is below the tangent lines, which means the curve is concave down.

EXTREMA   The maximums and minimums of the polynomial functions are also of interest. These extreme values are called *extrema*. For polynomials, a local maximum occurs when the function changes from increasing to decreasing. A local minimum occurs when a polynomial changes from decreasing to increasing. We can find these extreme points by examining the plot of the function. In calculus, we will learn analytical methods to supplement the graphical methods.

CONCAVITY   We also look to see if the function is concave up or down. A function is *concave down* over an interval if the graph of the function lies below the tangent to the curve at each point in the interval. In other words, the curve is bending downward. A function is *concave up* if the curve is above the tangent line for each point in the interval. Again, we can determine the concavity of the function by examining the graph. We will also learn analytical techniques in calculus.

Let's analyze a few more graphs and determine the intercepts, intervals where the function is increasing and decreasing, extrema, and concavity.

Example 8.8. The parabola shown in Figure 8.3 is opening downward, and we see that the curve is below the indicated tangents. This means the curve is *concave down*.

We also see that the curve is increasing when $x < 0$ and decreasing when $x > 0$. The slope of the tangents helps us to see where the function is increasing. There is a maximum when $x = 0$, which is where the curve changes from increasing to decreasing and the tangent line is horizontal.

For a quadratic, it is easy to find the x-intercepts. We can use the quadratic

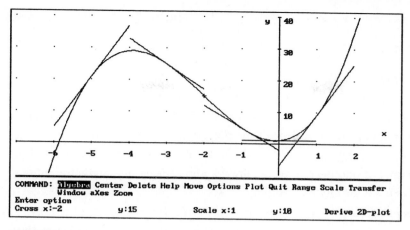

FIGURE 8.4
The function $f(x) = 1 + x + 6x^2 + x^3$ with its tangents superimposed.

formula

$$x = \frac{-b \pm \sqrt{b^2 - 4ac}}{2a}$$

or use the *Derive* soLve command to find the values of x where $f(x) = 0$. We obtain the values $x = \pm\sqrt{3}$, after simplification. Since $f(0) = 3$, we see that the y-intercept is 3.

The next example analyzes a cubic function. The approach we use is similar to that used for the quadratic function.

Example 8.9. Consider the cubic polynomial function $f(x) = 1 + x + 6x^2 + x^3$ shown in Figure 8.4. By drawing tangent lines to the graph at various points, we can see that the graph is concave down until about $x = 2$, since the curve lies below the tangents. After the predictor value $x = 2$, the curve lies above the tangent lines. The tangent line that passes through $(x = 2, y = 35)$ lies above the curve to the left of the point and below the curve to the right of the point. The point $(x = 2, y = 35)$ is called an *inflection point*, which is a point where the graph changes concavity. INFLECTION
POINT

We also see that the function is increasing until about $x = -3.91$, then decreases until about $x = -0.08$, and then increases again. There is a local maximum at about $(-3.91, 29)$ and a local minimum at about $(-0.08, 0.96)$. EXTREMA

The function has only one x-intercept, at about $x = -5.8$. The y-intercept is found at $f(0) = 1$. We can estimate the values of these points by using the *Derive* crosshair. We could also find their exact values using analytical techniques.

8.2.2   Properties

We have seen that polynomial functions can be analyzed graphically to determine several properties, such as intervals where the function is increasing, concavity, intercepts, etc. Now we look at some more general properties of polynomial functions.

8.2.2.1 DOMAIN AND RANGE.

What is the domain of a polynomial? Since we can evaluate a polynomial function for any value of the predictor, the domain is the set of all real numbers. The range is a bit more difficult. If the degree of the polynomial is odd, the range is the set of all real numbers. An odd polynomial can assume any value. In other words, for a polynomial of odd degree we can always find at least one predictor value x such that $f(x) = r$ for any real number r.

This is not true for polynomials of even degree. If the degree of the polynomial is even, the function will have either a global maximum or minimum (but not both, unless the degree is 0). In any case, the range of a polynomial of even degree is *not* all real numbers, but a subset of the real numbers.

A moment's experimentation with graphing polynomials of even and odd degree will convince you of the truth of the preceding paragraphs.

Why do we care about the range of polynomials? Imagine that you have modeled the profit of your business with a quadratic function of production, and that the graph is concave down. Knowing the range will tell you the maximum profit you can obtain. More important, knowing that the range is bounded above, you will not expect to continue to increase profit indefinitely by increasing production.

8.2.2.2 ONE-TO-ONE, INCREASING AND INVERSE.

Polynomials in general are not one-to-one functions, unless they are of degree 1. Every even polynomial is clearly not one-to-one or monotonic, since it will fail the horizontal line test. Not every polynomial of odd degree is one-to-one, either, as we saw in Figure 8.4.

Since polynomial functions are not always one-to-one, they will not necessarily have inverses. Some will: We have to check. However, by restricting their domain, we can often find inverses for polynomial functions that are not one-to-one if we allow the entire domain to be valid input to the polynomial.

8.2.2.3 OPERATIONS WITH POLYNOMIALS.

One of the more interesting operations we can perform with polynomial functions is constructing new polynomials using algebraic operations on other polynomials.

Definition 8.2. **Operations on Polynomials.** The sum or product of polynomial functions is another polynomial function.

Example 8.10. Using the functions $g(x) = 1 + 3x^3$, $h(x) = 2 + x^2$, and $f(x) = 3 + x + x^3$, we can create a new polynomial function $s(x)$ with addition:

$$
\begin{aligned}
g(x) &= 1 + 3x^3 \\
h(x) &= 2 + x^2 \\
f(x) &= 3 + x + x^3 \\
\hline
& 6 + x + x^2 + 4x^3 = s(x)
\end{aligned}
$$

Notice that the degree of the resulting polynomial $s(x)$ cannot be more than the highest degree of the polynomials involved in the addition.

Similarly, we can create a new polynomial function using multiplication.

$$
\begin{aligned}
g(x) \times h(x) &= (1 + 3x^3)(2 + x^2) \\
&= 2 + x^2 + 6x^3 + 3x^5 = p(x)
\end{aligned}
$$

Here, the resulting polynomial function $p(x)$ is of a higher degree than those we started with.

We can also construct polynomials using a composition of functions, the operation we examined in Section 4.7.1. We define the composition of two functions f and g, written $(f \circ g)(x)$ as $f(g(x))$. The second function $g(x)$ becomes the argument for the first, $f(x)$. Since the range of the second polynomial must be a real number, the output of the second function is an acceptable input for the first function.

Definition 8.3. **Composition of Polynomials.** The composition of polynomials is another polynomial.

Example 8.11. The composition $g(h(x))$, where $g(x) = 1 + 3x^3$ and $h(x) = 2 + x^2$ is given by

$$
\begin{aligned}
g(h(x)) &= 1 + 3(2 + x^2)^3 \\
&= 25 + 36x^2 + 18x^4 + 3x^6 = v(x)
\end{aligned}
$$

produces another polynomial function $v(x)$.

We have seen that the sum, product, and composition of polynomials produces polynomials. How about other operations? Does the ratio of two polynomials produce a polynomial? Let's consider a simple example.

Example 8.12. Let $f(x) = 1$, and $g(x) = x$. Then

$$(\frac{f}{g})(x) = \frac{1}{x} = x^{-1} = z(x)$$

Notice that $z(x)$ is not a polynomial, since the exponent (-1) is not a nonnegative integer.

RATIONAL FUNCTIONS

In general, the ratio of two polynomials is *not* necessarily a polynomial. We define the ratio of two polynomials as a *rational* (from *ratio*) function, and we will revisit them later in this chapter.

8.2.3 Modeling polynomials functions of one variable

When we decide to model behavior using a polynomial function, we must first decide what degree polynomial to use. There are two approaches to selecting the degree of the polynomial model. The first determines the degree from an analysis of the context of the problem. The second is a statistical approach that fits polynomials of increasing degree until some criteria indicates a best-fitting model. We will look extensively at the first approach, and briefly survey the second.

The decision to model with one independent variable assumes that we have already done our triage of possible predictors, and that we were left with one. In the next section we will look at polynomial models with more than one predictor.

In Chapter 5, we used the *Derive* `Fit` command to obtain the equation of the best fitting line through a set of points, using ordinary least squares (OLS). We also used the `Fit` command to fit a quadratic function to a data set in Example 5.28. Once we have determined the degree of the polynomial, we can fit other polynomial functions to data sets.

For a change, we will use a spreadsheet to fit the next models.

Let's return to the height and weight example of Section 5.4.4.1. Recall that we were trying to predict a young adult male's weight from his height. We determined that the best fitting line for predicting height from weight was $\hat{w} = 4.74991h - 165.010$. This line was fairly accurate for predicting weight over the range of heights. However, a close examination of the residuals from this plot indicates pronounced curvature, as seen in Figure 8.5.

Since there is curvature in this plot, a line is not a good choice for a model. Let's see if we can reason as to what degree of polynomial would be appropriate.

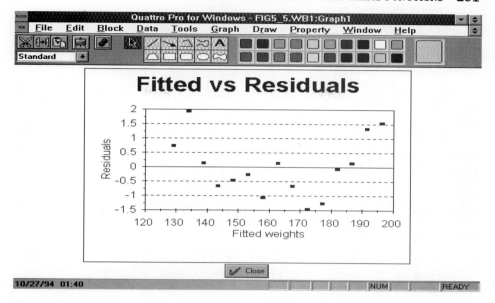

FIGURE 8.5
Residual plot from the height-weight example of Section 5.4.4.1

An alternative approach would be to say that the residual plot looks like a parabola, and to try to fit a quadratic model based on that observation. We'll try that approach after we try some reasoning using first principles.

A person's weight is probably tied closer to body volume than to height. We can think of a person's body as a cylinder of constant density, and we can further assume that the radius of the cylinder is proportional to the person's height. These assumptions imply that the weight is proportional the height cubed. Using the notation "$\propto$" to represent "proportional to," we have

FIRST PRIN-CIPLES

NOTATION

$$
\begin{aligned}
\text{weight} \ &= \ \text{density} \times \text{volume} \\
&\propto \ \text{volume} \\
&\propto \ \text{height} \times \pi \times \text{radius}^2 \\
&\propto \ \text{height}^3
\end{aligned}
$$

Accordingly, we will try a cubic model using the *Derive* `Fit` command to determine the cubic function that best fits the data. We see from Figure 8.6 that the cubic function does seem to have a better fit. The plot of residuals versus fitted values confirms this, as we see in Figure 8.7. The total magnitude of the residuals in the cubic model is about half that in the linear model, and there is no pattern in the residuals that might suggest a bad fit.

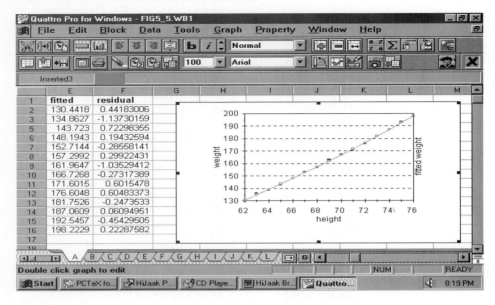

FIGURE 8.6
Plot of the best-fitting line and cubic function over the height-weight data points. Notice that it is hard to tell the two functions apart.

Three implications of this cubic model are significant. First, the marginal gain in weight associated with a gain in height *depends* on the person's height. It is not constant. Second, there is still an intercept in this model. That means that a person who has no height still has weight, which disagrees with our experience. Accordingly, we should not glibly extrapolate with this model outside the range of the data we are given. Last, the curve is concave up in this region. That means that the marginal gain of height against weight as a function of weight is itself increasing. In other words, if we gain 4 pounds per inch at a height of 65 inches, we will gain more than 4 pounds per inch at a greater height. The marginal rate of gain for the cubic polynomial is a *quadratic* function of the x-value. (A proof of this fact will have to wait until calculus).

We mentioned earlier that there are two ways to choose an appropriate degree for the polynomial used to model behavior. The first was to reason from first principles, using known properties of the modeled phenomena. The second is to use statistical techniques to find a model that fits well, although there may be no theoretical justification for the form of the model. We now will reexamine the height-weight data from that perspective.

A principle we want to adhere to when building models with statistics is the

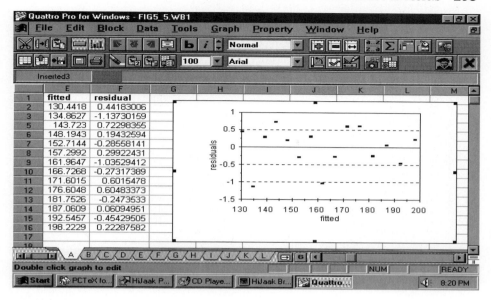

FIGURE 8.7
Plot of the residual versus fitted values for the cubic model of height-weight data. The residuals show no obvious pattern, suggesting that the model is not inappropriate. Also, notice the vertical scale of this graph.

principle of *parsimony*. This means that we want to create the simplest model that fits well to the data. [†] With this principle in mind, if we can fit the data well with a quadratic model, we would prefer it over a cubic. Let us examine fitting a quadratic model to the height-weight data.

> **Example 8.13.** When we looked at the plot of residuals versus fitted values for the linear height-weight model, we observed the pattern in Figure 8.5. It appears to be quadratic. Accordingly, let's fit a quadratic model to the data.
> The model we obtain, $w(h) = 0.048013h^2 - 1.82574h + 59.3565$, is a good fit. Note the lack of any pattern or obvious curvature in the residual plot, Figure 8.8. Note also, however, that the magnitude of the residuals is larger in this plot than in Figure 8.7, the residual plot from the cubic model. Our model is simpler, but fits a little less well.
> This is a common problem. We can usually improve the fit of a model by increasing the degree of the polynomial, but there is a point at which this doesn't make sense. The tradeoffs between increasing complexity and decreasing

---

[†] This principle is called *Occam's razor*. Its origin is from the Franciscan monk William of Occam (1285–1349), an English scholastic philosopher, who is quoted as having said "What can be done with fewer [assumptions] is done in vain with more."

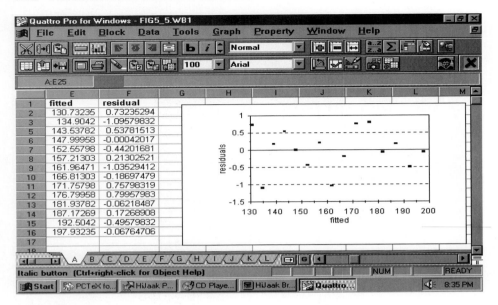

FIGURE 8.8
Plot of residuals versus fitted values for the quadratic model with intercept, height-weight data.
Note the size of the residuals compared to the cubic model of height-weight data

error require judgment and skill, and we skirt the issue by adopting the simplest model with a patternless residual plot.

There is a second question besides the degree of polynomial to use. The model with intercepts still suffers from the same logical problem that all models with intercepts face for this data: According to this model, a male with no height would still weigh 59.3565 pounds. We can interpret this one of two ways. Either we should not use the model to predict so far away from the data (extrapolation), or we should construct a model without an intercept.

NO

INTERCEPT

Constructing a model without an intercept is straightforward. The *Derive* command is Fit([h, bh + ch²], *data*. The equation that we obtain is $w(h) = 0.0355361h^2 - 0.101233h$. How good of a fit does this new model provide? A check of residual versus fitted values in Figure 8.9 shows that there is still no visible pattern, but that the magnitude of the residuals is larger than in the model with an intercept. For our purposes, either model is acceptable.[‡]

Exploration Exercises

[‡]To apply *Occam's razor*, we could use statistical tools to choose among these competing models. One such tool is *Mallow's C_p*, which is discussed in most introductory linear regression courses. This tool allows us to balance simplicity versus goodness of fit. If you are interested in this topic, a course in linear regression should appeal to you.

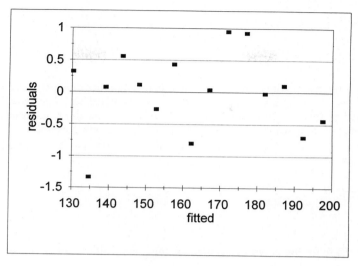

FIGURE 8.9
Plot of residuals versus fitted values for the quadratic, no intercept model. Compare the size of these residuals with those from the model with an intercept in Figure 8.8.

8.1. Is the utility of money always increasing? Is it concave up or down? Why? Could the answer be different for different people?

8.2. Identify which of the following expressions are polynomials. For those that are polynomials, identify the degree.
(*a*) $1 + x$
(*b*) $1 + \frac{1}{x}$
(*c*) $x^3 - 3x^2 + 1$
(*d*) $(x + 10)^{15}$
(*e*) $(x + 10)^{-15}$
(*f*) $\sin(x^2 + 1)$

8.3. For the following data set, find the best fitting linear, quadratic, and cubic function for y as a response to x. Plot the residuals for each model. Which model would you choose to represent the data? Why?

x	y	x	y	x	y
1	1	5	15	9	75
2	3	6	25	10	89
3	6	7	37		
4	10	8	49		

8.4. Plot each of the following quadratic expressions using *Derive*. Factor them using *Derive*. Identify the roots (if any). Estimate the intercepts, extrema, and inflection points from the graph. Identify where the expressions are concave up and concave down. Do you see a relationship between the sign of the coefficients and the concavity?

(a) $1 + x + x^2$

(b) $1 + 2x + x^2$

(c) $1 + 3x + x^2$

(d) $1 - x - 3x^2$

(e) $2 + 4x + x^2$

(f) $1 + x - x^2$

8.5. Consider the quadratic formula, which finds the roots of a quadratic expression $ax^2 + bx + c$. The expression $b^2 - 4ac$ is called the *discriminant*. Find a relationship between the sign of the discriminant and the number of real roots. Then test your result on the quadratics in the preceding exercise.

8.6. For the following functions, estimate the roots, extrema (if any), and inflection points.

(a) $(x - 3)^3$

(b) $x + y^3$

(c) $(x + 3)(x - 2)(x + 1)$

(d) $\frac{(x-3)^3}{(x-2)(x-1)}$

(e) $(1 + x + x^2)^3$

8.7. For the following polynomials of more than one variable, identify the degree and the number of cross terms.

(a) $(x + y)^3$

(b) $x + y^3$

(c) $(xy)^3$

8.8. Show that the maximum (or minimum) of a quadratic function of one predictor occurs when the dependent variable is at the midpoint of the roots.

8.9. Show that a polynomial function of even degree must have a global maximum or minimum.

8.3 POLYNOMIALS OF MORE THAN ONE VARIABLE

8.3.1 General

Frequently, we will have more than one predictor in our model. When this happens, our model should allow each of the predictors to contribute to the response value. We do this by constructing a model that depends on more than one independent variable. Polynomials of several variables are a natural starting place, just as polynomials of one variable are a natural starting place when we have only one variable of interest.

> **Definition 8.4. Polynomial of Several Variables.** Any expression that can be written as the sum of terms, each of which is the product of a constant and various nonnegative integer powers of the variables, is called a *polynomial of several variables.*

Example 8.14. The function $f(x,y) = 3xy + 6x^3y^2 + x - 1$ is a polynomial of two variables, x and y.

Example 8.15. The function $g(x,v) = xv + 2$ is a polynomial of two variables, x and v. This type of nonlinear function is also called a *multilinear* function, a generalization of linear functions. We'll avoid using this terminology in our exploration of polynomial functions because of the danger of misinterpretation.

For our purposes, we will consider the *degree* of each term as the sum of the exponents of the variables in that term; the degree of the polynomial is the largest degree of its several terms. In Example 8.14, the function $f(x,y)$ has terms of degree 2, 5, 1, and 0, respectively. The polynomial itself is of degree 5, the degree of its largest term.

Polynomials of several variables are classified by their degree and by the number of variables they contain. As before, a polynomial of several variables is *linear, quadratic, cubic, quartic* or *quintic*, according to whether its degree is 1, 2, 3, 4, or 5, respectively.

A term with more than one variable is also called a *cross term*.

CROSS TERM

Example 8.16. The multivariable term $6x^2y$ is a cross term, since it has the two variables x and y in it. The term $36z^4$ is not, since it involves only the variable z.

A polynomial model without cross terms is simpler to analyze than one with cross terms, because the response to changes in one of the variables is not affected by the level of the other variables. For this reason, cross terms typically arise in modeling situations in which there exists a level of *interaction* occuring between predictors. By this we mean that changes to one predictor affect the contribution that another predictor makes to the value of the response.

Example 8.17. Suppose that a particular polynomial model was given by $g(x,y) = P = 2x^2 + xy - y^3$, where P represents the response, and x and y represent predictors. A 1-unit increase in the value of the predictor x will contribute 2 to the value of the response because of the term $2x^2$, regardless of the value of the predictor y. However, the 1-unit change in x will affect P differently through the term xy, depending upon the value of y. For instance, if $y = 3$, then the 1-unit increase in x will cause the term xy add 3 to the value of P. The term xy captures this predictor interaction.

The initial models we will examine will not include crossterms. Our analysis will reveal whether we need to include them in a revised model.

8.3.2 Review of linear functions of several predictors

Let's review what we have learned about linear functions of several predictors:

- Our functional form is $f(x_1, x_2, \ldots, x_n) = m_1 x_1 + m_2 x_2 + \cdots + m_n x_n + b$.

- The rate of increase for changes in x_i is independent of the value of x_i

- There is a direction of maximum increase for changes in the predictors. Changes that are proportional to the gradient have the maximum increase; the maximum rate of increase is the length of the gradient.

- The level curves for the plane, corresponding to constant values of y, are perpendicular to the lines of maximum increase.

- Extrema occur on the boundary of a plane region.

8.3.3 Extending the linear model

You are probably wondering why we went into such detail about linear models. Here is the reason: Every first model should be a linear model when dealing with multiple predictors, unless there are compelling reasons from the context of the problem to start with a nonlinear model.

If we have a data set with *two* predictors and one response, corresponding to two independent (input) variables and one dependent (output) variable, we can find the best-fitting plane using the *Derive* Fit command or using a spreadsheet, just as we found the best-fitting line in the case of one predictor variable. Then we can apply what we learned about the direction of maximum increase to adjust our inputs optimally to get improved outputs.

Often, we fit a linear function and then find that the plot of residuals versus fitted values indicates that there is curvature in the model. This alerts us that we must extend the linear model to include nonlinear terms. We usually start with simple polynomial models.

8.4 NONLINEAR POLYNOMIALS OF SEVERAL VARIABLES

We now turn to the more general case of nonlinear polynomials of several variables. We will first consider the case when there are no cross terms in the model. These simpler models are easier to analyze, because the various levels of the

| Height, Age, Gender and Weight Data | | | | | | | |
| Males | | | | Females | | | |
Height	Age	Gender	Weight	Height	Age	Gender	Weight
62	22	0	130	58	22	1	105
62	27	0	134	58	27	1	110
62	35	0	138	58	35	1	113
62	45	0	140	58	45	1	118
62	55	0	141	58	55	1	121
62	65	0	140	58	65	1	123
63	22	0	136	59	22	1	110
63	27	0	140	59	27	1	112
63	35	0	143	59	35	1	115
63	45	0	144	59	45	1	121
63	55	0	145	59	45	1	125
63	65	0	144	59	65	1	127
64	22	0	139	60	22	1	112
64	27	0	143	60	27	1	114
64	35	0	147	60	35	1	118
64	45	0	149	60	45	1	123
64	55	0	150	60	55	1	127
64	65	0	149	60	65	1	130

TABLE 8.2
Data for weight, height, gender, and age example. Source: 1993 World Almanac.

factors independently affect the rates of change of the response. These nonlinear models can incorporate curvature, and often better represent the data.

When we have data that is from a relatively small region, we often can model the data with quadratic polynomials. This is particularly true if we are looking for maximums or minimums from our data analysis. Planes will always have their extrema on their boundaries (if our inputs are bounded), whereas quadratic functions can have extrema located in the interior of the region of INTERIOR possible inputs. Even if the behavior we are modeling is better modeled by a EXTREMA different nonlinear function, a quadratic model often gives a useful approximation that helps to locate these extrema.

Let's look at the height and weight data again and A partial listing the data is shown in Table 8.2. The full data set is available from our Web site. A

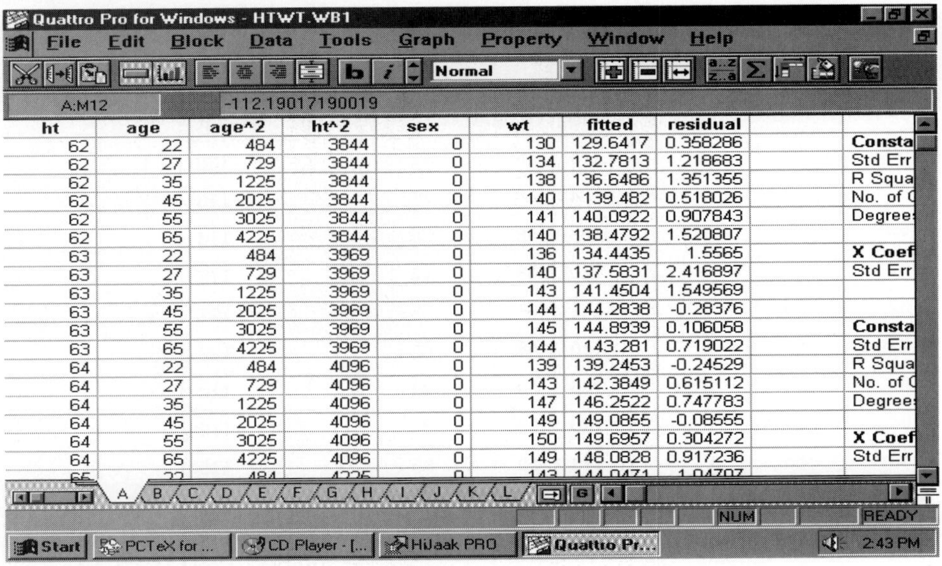

FIGURE 8.10
Data for the height and weight model. We have added columns for $(age)^2$ and $(ht)^2$. We will use additional columns for the fitted values and residuals, as we compute them.

cursory examination of the data shows that for males, the data appears to be concave down with respect to age. That is, males appear to gain weight as they get older, but the rate of increase slows. For females, the rate of increase appears to be constant, or at least to slow less than for males.

Let's try to develop a two-predictor model for each gender that captures weight (wt) as a response to predictors height (ht) and age (age):

$$wt = a\,(ht) + b\,(age) + c\,(age)^2 + d$$

where a, b, c, and d are model coefficients that we have to determine. To distinguish between genders, we will use a variable called sex, with $sex = 0$ for males and $sex = 1$ for females.

We have added columns for the non-linear terms in our spreadsheet, and organized that data as shown in Figure 8.10.

The QuattroPro output of these models is found in Figure 8.11. The quadratic model for males' weight as a function of their height and age is given by:

$$wt = f(ht, age) = 4.801786ht + 1.1725914age - 0.01112age^2 - 188.486 \quad (8.2)$$

If we fix the value of height, we see that the model is a parabola opening

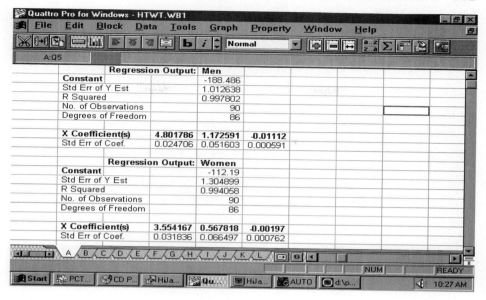

FIGURE 8.11

Fitting separate quadratic models to the weight data for males and females. The coefficients match the order the predictors were entered into the regression dialog; in this case, height, age, and age squared.

downward for the variable *age*, since the sign of the age^2 term is negative. This supports our observation that the data appeared to be concave down.

The quadratic model for female weight as a function of height is given by

$$wt = f(ht, age) = 3.554167ht + 0.5678181age - 0.00197age^2 - 112.1902 \quad (8.3)$$

Again, if we fix height we see that this is a parabola opening downward for age. The coefficient of the age^2 term is about 5 times smaller in the female model, which means that the parabola is wider. This supports our observation that the female data is less concave down.

As usual, we construct the residual plot to check for the appropriateness of our model. We leave the analysis of the residual plots for the two models to you as an exercise. You see the plots in Figure 8.12.

As our analysis of the residual plots still indicate curvature, we could add additional terms to the model until we had a better fit. One good model to try would be to introduce a quadratic term involving the height variable:

$$wt = a\,(ht) + b\,(ht)^2 + c\,(age) + d\,(age)^2 + e \quad (8.4)$$

This is an especially good candidate, since we earlier saw that weight was mod-

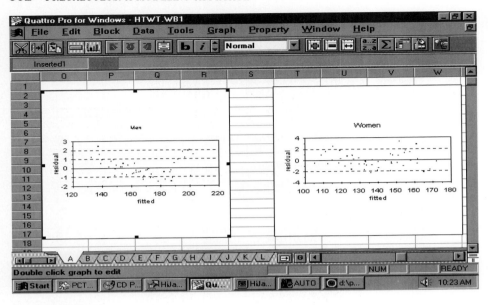

FIGURE 8.12
Fitted versus residuals plot for the models in Figure 8.11.

eled nicely as a quadratic function of height for 22-year-old males. It is not unreasonable to test whether this generalizes to all persons.

8.4.0.1 AN ADVANCED CONCEPT.

It is worth mentioning that there is another convenient characteristic associated with models that do not contain interactive terms. If we are looking for extrema for such multivariable models with no constraints, we can decompose SUBMODELS the function expression into *submodels* involving only single predictors, and examine for maximums and minimums of the submodels. This approach is truly exploratory and should be used only to guide your search for extrema. However, we introduce the idea here for you to add it to the mathematical techniques you have at your disposal.

Example 8.18. Suppose that we are looking for the global maximum for the model

$$y = f(x_1, x_2) = 3 - x_1^2 - x_2 - 2x_2^2$$

where x_1 and x_2 represent predictors for the response y. Because there are no interactive crossterms, we can decompose the model as

$$y = f(x_1, x_2) = \left[3 - x_1^2\right] + \left[-x_2 - 2x_2^2\right]$$
$$= s(x_1) + s(x_2)$$

and look for the x_1 value which maximizes $s(x_1) = 3 - x_1^2$ and the x_2 value which maximizes $s(x_2) = 3 - x_2 - 2x_2^2$. Because both of these submodels are quadratic models, and quadratic models have unique global extrema (negative quadratic— unique global maximum; positive quadratic—unique global minimum), if there is a global maximum in the two variables, it will occur at some combination of the maxima for the one variable models.

Here, $s(x_1)$ achieves a maximum when $x_1 = 0$, and $s(x_2)$ achieves its maximum when $x_2 = -0.25$. In this case, we see that this candidate for a global maximum is the global maximum that is found by plotting the function and graphically confirming a maximum in the area of that point.

Discussion Ideas

This is an idea worth discussing that will extend the way you think about functions. Even if you don't see it straight away, just wrestling with the idea will help your ability to visualize mathematical objects.

⇒ From another perspective, decomposing a function in the manner just described is equivalent to *projection* operation: The function $s(x_1)$ is the same as $f(x_1, x_2)$ when the value of the predictor x_2 is fixed at $x_2 = 0$. Likewise, $s(x_2)$ is the same as $f(x_1, x_2)$ when $x_1 = 0$. Examining the extrema of $s(x_1)$ is the same as examining the extrema of $f(x_1, 0)$, which is surface defined by the function $f(x_1, x_2)$ when it is traced out on the vertical plane $x_2 = 0$. The result is just a one-predictor function. Similarly, $s(x_2)$ is equivalent to $f(0, x_2)$ projected onto the vertical plane $x_1 = 0$. Conveniently, the planes $x_1 = 0$ and $x_2 = 0$ come together in exactly the same way as the walls of the room you are sitting in. Think of the surface $f(x_1, x_2)$ as a blanket floating in the room that touches the two walls. Can you see what this projection operation is doing, and why the global extrema of $s(x_1)$ and $s(x_2)$ will correspond to the global extrema of $f(x_1, x_2)$ only in a very limited number of cases?

⇒ How would fixing x_1 and x_2 at values other than 0 effect the projections?

For the height-weight model given by Equations 8.2 and 8.3, we see there is not a global maximum inside of the function's domain because we have strong linear terms (ones possessing large coefficients) that dominate the quadratic terms. For this particular domain, maximum and minimums will be located on the boundaries. If we extended the domain sufficiently, the domain values of the pre-

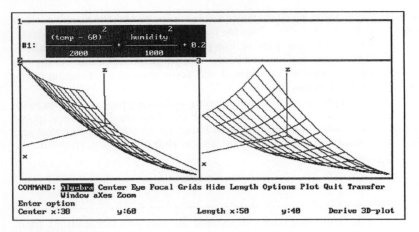

FIGURE 8.13
A plot of the quadratic model without interactions in the left window, and a quadratic model with interactions in the right window, as seen from the same viewpoint. Note how the response surface has changed.

dictors *ht* and *age* will permit the quadratic terms to assume much larger values than the linear terms could achieve. The quadratic terms would then have a greater influence on what the surface of the function would look like, and there would be a maximum or minimum on the interior of the domain.

In the exercises, you will be asked to analyze several different height-weight models.

8.5 QUADRATIC MODELS AND INTERACTIONS

Imagine a process that has two inputs of interest and one output, say, a machine that makes electronics. Let the two inputs be temperature and humidity, and the output be the failure rate. (Of course, there are many other possible predictors that we will ignore in this example.) Let's assume that there is an ideal temperature that gives minimum failures, and that failures go up as you move away from this temperature (up or down). Let's also assume that there is an ideal humidity setting (0%) and that failures go up as you move away from this ideal humidity level. The ideal temperature will be 60°, and the ideal humidity will be 0%. We will restrict our temperature inputs between 40° and 80° and our humidity inputs between 0% and 50%. We will model the increase in failure rates for both variables as quadratics.

If there is no interaction, there will be no cross terms. Say then that we have the model

$$\text{rate} = \frac{(\text{temp} - 60)^2}{2000} + \frac{\text{humidity}^2}{1000} + 0.02$$

We know that for this model a change in the temperature will result in the RESPONSE same change in failure rate for any humidity. A plot of this *response surface* is SURFACE shown in Figure 8.13.

Common experience tells us that the effects of temperature and humidity often interact, and that high temperature accompanied by high humidity is probably worse for electronics. Accordingly, a better model might take that interaction into effect. To do so, we will add a cross term of the form

$$a\,(\text{temp} - 60)(\text{humidity})$$

Different choices for a result in different shapes for our response surface. This is similar to the situation from conic sections, where if $ax^2 + bxy + cy^2 + d = 0$, the sign of the *discriminant* $(b^2 - 4ac)$ determines whether we obtain a parabola, ellipse, or hyperbola.

If we were building a model from a real data set, we would find the coefficient for our cross term by adding the cross term when we fit the model. In this hypothetical example, we add a term that does not dramatically change the shape of the response surface. By adding a crossterm of the form

$$(\text{temp} - 60)(\text{humidity})/1000$$

we see from the right window of Figure 8.13 that now the combination of high humidity and high temperature is much more serious than a high setting of either one alone. This is the key idea behind interactions: A change in one of the variables can have dramatically different effects on the response, depending on the settings of the other variables.

One of the main tasks of industrial experimentation and modeling is to determine whether these interactions exist, and to minimize their effect on the outputs. This can be done by setting the inputs at a "flat" part of the response surface, so changes in the inputs result in small changes in the outputs.

Exploration Exercises

8.1. For the following data set, assume that x and y represent predictors and z is the response. Fit a linear model to the data, estimate the maximum slope for this linear model, and the direction in which it occurs. Identify any points in the domain of $f(x, y)$ where the model fits especially poorly.

x	y	z	x	y	z
1	1	5.9	−1	−2	−6.1
1	2	8.1	−1	1	0.1
2	1	8.8	−2	−2	−7.1
2	2	10.9	−2	−2	−8.0
0	0	1.1	1	−1	1.9
−1	−1	−6.9			

8.2. Now fit a quadratic surface to the data in the table in the preceding exercise. Include both x^2 and y^2 terms. Does the fit improve? How can you tell?

8.3. Construct and analyze the residual plots from Figure 8.12.

8.4. For the following exercises, use the height-weight data from our Web site.
   (a) Find a linear function (plane) that fits weight as the response to age and height just for males, and find direction of greatest increase. Plot the residuals for this plane. Comment on the fit.
   (b) Repeat the preceding exercise for females. Does a linear fit appear better for females? What are the implications if one does?
   (c) Fit Equation 8.4 to the height-weight data, and analyze the resulting model.
   (d) Add a cross-term for the interaction between age and height to Equation 8.4, fit the new model, and analyze it.

8.6   RATIONAL FUNCTIONS

While polynomials are useful for many modeling situations, there are cases for which they are not appropriate.

For example, polynomials are unbounded (except the constant polynomials, which we will ignore for now). If our response is always between two values for all values of the inputs, a polynomial might not be appropriate. This situation arises when we build models that represent probabilities, which must be between 0 and 1. It also arises in the context of decay: We start with an amount of substance, and it is reduced over time to 0. Here again the response is bounded between the initial value and 0.

A second situation occurs when the value of the response becomes arbitrarily large as we approach a certain value of the predictor. These vertical asymptotes can not be modeled by polynomials.

One possible model for both these situations is to use *rational functions*. A rational function is defined as the ratio of two polynomials. The rational **RATIONAL** functions include polynomial functions as a special case (where the denominator **FUNCTION** is the polynomial $f(x) = 1$). We will explore some of the properties of rational functions in this section. Fitting rational functions with *Derive* or a spreadsheet is often awkward, but we will be able to fit some special cases.

8.6.1   General

We will begin our analysis by looking at an example, and find most of the properties of rational functions through exploration. Our first example will be the ratio of two quadratic polynomials

$$h(x) = \frac{(x-1)(x-3)}{(x-2)(x-4)}$$

We know a quotient is 0 only when the numerator is 0, so this rational expression has roots at $x = 1$ and $x = 3$. What happens when $x = 2$ or $x = 4$? The denominator is 0, and the fraction is therefore not defined. However, as $x \to 2$ (read "x approaches 2"), the response gets very large and positive or large and negative, depending on which side we approach 2 from. It looks like the graph gets very close to a vertical line. This vertical line is called a *vertical asymptote*. The same behavior occurs as $x \to 4$.

VERTICAL
ASYMPTOTE

We can write our expression as

$$1 + \frac{1}{2(x-2)} + \frac{3}{2(x-4)}$$

using *Derive's* **Expand** command. This form is called *partial fractions*. Now we see that as x gets large, the two fractions approach 0, and the value of the expression gets closer and closer to 1. The line $y = 1$ is called a *horizontal asymptote*. This **HORIZONTAL** behavior can be seen in Figure 8.14. **ASYMPTOTE**

Earlier we learned that the product, sum, and difference of polynomials were polynomials, but that the ratio of polynomials was not. The rational functions are more pleasing

Definition 8.5.   Rational Function. The product, sum, difference, and ratio of two rational functions are called *rational functions*.

Modeling with rational functions can often be done by determining the asymptotic responses we want to capture in the model.

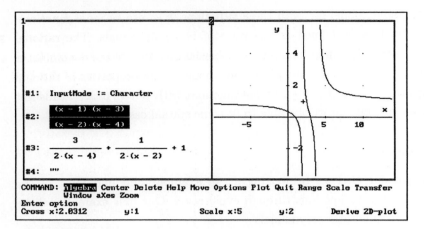

FIGURE 8.14
A plot of the rational function $f(x) = ((x-1)(x-3))/((x-2)(x-4))$ with its partial fraction equivalent listed below it in the algebra window. Note the vertical asymptotes at $x = 2$ and $x = 4$, and horizontal asymptote at $y = 1$.

Example 8.19. Suppose we want to model a process we are observing (response) y of a single predictor x that has the horizontal asymptote $y = 1$, no vertical asymptotes, and is never negative. Since there are no vertical asymptotes, the denominator must never be 0. Two possible models might be given by

$$y = f_1(x) = \frac{x^2}{1+x^2}$$

$$f_2(x) = 1 + \frac{1}{1+x^2}$$

Another context for modeling with rational functions occurs when we naturally have a quotient for our response. For example, we could be modeling speed, and have polynomial models for distance and time in terms of some third variable. We could then get a rational model for speed by the natural construction of

$$\text{speed} = \frac{\text{distance}}{\text{time}} = \frac{d(x)}{t(x)}$$

8.6.2 Graphical analysis

As with polynomial functions, we are interested in where rational functions are increasing and decreasing, concave up and concave down, and what the intercepts are. Additionally, we are interested in the asymptotes. If we put the rational expression in the appropriate form, we can find much of the information without

graphing the expression. Writing the numerator and denominator in their factored form enables us to read the roots and vertical asymptotes directly from the
zeros of the numerator and denominator, respectively. Writing a rational function expanded into partial fractions using the **Expand** command, we can directly
see the asymptotes. We still determine concavity by examining the graph of the
rational function.

It often occurs that when we expand a rational function into partial fractions, we obtain an expression in the form a a polynomial plus several terms that
are fractions that have constants in the numerator. The polynomial portion is
called an *oblique* asymptote, because the graph of the rational function will get
very close to the graph of the polynomial as $|x|$ gets large. This oblique asymtote
acts in the same manner as a vertical or horizontal asymptote, except that the
oblique asymptote acts as a curved wall instead of a plane, as the usual vertical
or horizontal asymptote does.

Example 8.20. Consider the rational function

$$f(x) = \frac{(x+1)(x-1)(x-2)}{x+2} = x^2 - 4x + 7 - \frac{12}{x+2}$$

The graph of this rational function gets very close to the graph of the quadratic
polynomial $x^2 - 4x + 7$ as $|x|$ gets large, since the term $12/(x+2) \to 0$ as x is
allowed to increase to larger and larger values. The polynomial portion of $f(x)$
$x^2 - 4x + 7$ is an oblique asymptote.

In the days before computer algebra systems, we would find oblique asymptotes by synthetic division of the polynomials. Now we can do it by computer.
It is useful to remember one rule from the days of hand analysis, which is easy
to verify.

Definition 8.6. Asymptotic Analysis. Consider the rational expression
given by

$$f(x) = \frac{r(x)}{s(x)}$$

where $r(x)$ and $s(x)$ are nonzero polynomials. If the degree of $r(x)$ is greater than
the degree of $s(x)$, the rational function $f(x)$ will have an oblique asymptote. If
the degree of $r(x)$ equals the degree of $s(x)$ the rational function $f(x)$ will have
a nonzero horizontal asymptote. If the degree of $r(x)$ is less than the degree of
$s(x)$, the rational function $f(x)$ will have the horizontal asymptote $f(x) = 0$.

Percent removed	Cost (in $1000)
5	85
10	100
20	160
30	200
45	300
60	600
65	700
70	800
80	1000

TABLE 8.3
Data for the pollution abatement example.

8.6.3   Fitting

Derive allows only certain forms of expressions to be found using the `Fit` command. The coefficients we determine must be linear combinations of functions of the data. As a result, we can fit a/x to determine a, but we can not fit $1/(x-c)$ to find c: The second expression is not linear in c. This makes fitting rational expressions using *Derive* impossible unless one knows or assumes the roots of the denominator ahead of time. We can still fit some rational expressions, however.

> **Example 8.21.** It is increasingly expensive to remove pollutants from a process, and the cost of removing the last 5% of the pollutants can be much more expensive than removing the first 95%. In this example, we have a small table (Table 8.3) of the estimated costs of removing the percentage of pollutants from an emissions stream. Because we believe that the cost grows prohibitively as we get closer to removing 100% of the pollutants, we decide to model this response as having a vertical asymptote at percent $= 100$. We will try to fit a model of the form
>
> $$f(x) = \frac{a}{x - 100} + b$$
>
> We use the *Derive* commands as usual. The result is pictured in Figure 8.15.
>   Compare this model with a quadratic function. A quadratic model would not capture the essential feature of the data: The cost gets prohibitively higher the closer one gets to 100% abatement.

Very few software packages can directly fit arbitrary rational functions. However, let's think about how we would do such a fit. Using the least squares criteria, we would want to minimize the sum of the squares of the residuals. Returning to our pollution abatement example, say we did not know where the vertical asymptote would be. Then we would want to find a, b, and c to minimize

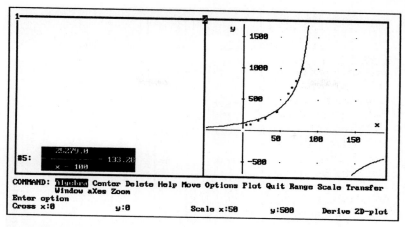

FIGURE 8.15
Fitted pollution abatement data.

the sum of the squared residuals, or the sum of the terms

$$\text{residual}^2 = \left(y - \left(\frac{a}{x - c} + b\right)\right)^2$$

We could set up a spreadsheet that found that sum for different choices of a, b, and c, and vary the coefficients until we convinced ourselves we had found a minimum. This is a search strategy. A sample spreadsheet showing this approach is in Figure 8.16.

In Figure 8.16, we have included a plot of the data and the fitted values. By varying the values in the cells F2, G2, and H2, we vary the values of a, b, and c. As we do, the plot of the fitted values changes, and the sum of the residuals, in cell E12, also changes. The formula for the first fitted value is displayed in the editing window: $+\$F\$2/(A2 - \$H\$2) + \$G\$2$. (Recall that the "$\$$" sign mean that the value of that cell doesn't change when the formula is copied to other cells. It establishes an absolute reference to the cell.)

We ask you to try to fit a rational expression to the pollution data in the exercises. We want you to get feel for how the curve changes as you vary the values of a, b, and c.

In your calculus course, you will learn how to find the arguments a, b, and c that minimize the sum of the squared residuals and provide the least squares fit. You will be able to do this for any form of model, as long as there are as least as many data points as unknown coefficients.

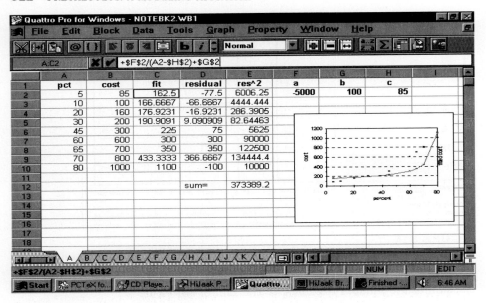

FIGURE 8.16
A spreadsheet approach to finding the coefficients to minimize the sum of squared residuals for the pollution abatement model.

Exploration Exercises

8.1. Identify the vertical, horizontal, and/or oblique asymptotes of the following rational functions:

(a) $(x^2 + 2x + 1)/(x - 1)$

(b) $(x^4 + x^3 + x + 1)/((x - 2)^3)$

(c) $(x^4 + x^3 + x + 1)/((x - 2)^3(x - 3))$

(d) $(x^4 + x^3 + x + 1)/((x - 2)^3(x - 3)(x - 4))$

8.2. Using a spreadsheet such as in Figure 8.16, fit a model of the form

$$\frac{a}{x - c} + b$$

to the pollution abatement data in Table 8.3. Comment on the pattern of residuals versus fitted values. If your fitted value for c is greater than 100, what does that mean in this context? (*Hint:* Try these initial values: $a = -90,500$, $b = -600$, $c = 125$. We eventually got the sum of squared residuals to be less than 11,000. How about you?)

8.3. Would a rational function be a natural choice for a model of the height–weight data? Why or why not?

8.4. Compare Equations 8.5 and 8.6. Can you think of a "mess" that goes with each model? What could be modeled with these equations?

8.5. Show that the definition of a rational function holds. (*Hint:* For the sum and difference, obtain a common denominator, and use the property that the product of polynomials is a polynomial. For the product and quotient, rewrite the expressions as a single fraction, and use the property that the product of polynomials is a polynomial.)

8.7 SUMMARY

Creating and analyzing polynomial models is a very broad subject. We have only introduced a select number of ideas and a few of the techniques associated with polynomial models. However, the ability to fit and analyze even these simple models provides you with a very powerful set of tools. These tools are useful in calculus, where you will expand and refine them, and in almost every other class that uses numerical data. We hope that you will find that they are useful in your other life activities, such as real estate! (At least one of the authors did.)

You should feel you understand the following topics:

- The definition of a polynomial function of one or more predictor
- How to plot and graphically analyze a polynomial function of one predictor
- Why we use polynomial models to extend linear models, and how to tell when we should
- How to fit polynomial models to data using *Derive* and/or a spreadsheet
- How to interpret a plot of residual versus fitted values
- How to model asymptotic behavior using rational functions

8.8 PROJECT: ESTIMATING THE PRICE OF A HOUSE

One of the authors moved from the Midwest to the East coast in the summer of 1995. As part of the process, he attempted to sell his house.

Around Christmas 1994, he interviewed two real estate agents to select one to list the house. They gave him very different estimates of the listing price of the house. Intrigued, he decided to see if he could gather some data and model real estate prices for his neighborhood.

He gathered information on all the houses offered for sale within 1 mile of his house within the previous 6 months. His source was the local Multiple Listing Service (MLS). For each house, he determined 11 variables: central air conditioning (ac); age (age); number of bathrooms (ba); number of bedrooms (br); whether the house was located in Edinborough, a prestigious local subdivision (eb); number of fireplaces (fp); number of finished square feet (fsf);

ac	age	ba	br	eb	fp	fsf	gar	h20	tax	cost
1	4	1	3	0	0	1100	2	0	1033	89,900
0	4	2	4	0	0	2000	2	0	1172	103,889
1	6	2	3	0	0	1959	2	0	1689	124,500
1	8	3	4	1	1	2412	2	0	1807	125,900
1	14	3	4	0	2	2323	2	0	2200	136,900
1	8	3	3	0	1	2013	2	0	2077	137,900
0	0	2	3	1	1	1610	3	0	1000	138,900
0	0	2	3	1	1	1808	3	0	1000	149,900
1	63	2	4	0	1	2712	4	1	3693	190,000
0	0	2	3	1	0	1168	2	0	1000	116,900
0	0	2	3	0	1	1808	3	0	1000	152,900
1	6	3	4	0	1	2387	2	0	2955	150,000
0	0	2	3	1	1	1808	3	0	1000	152,900
1	8	1	3	0	0	1166	2	0	1418	114,500
1	8	2	3	0	2	1935	2	0	1911	122,900
1	8	3	3	0	1	2013	2	0	2077	135,000
1	8	3	4	0	2	2301	3	0	2022	147,900
1	7	3	4	0	1	2862	2	0	2536	159,000
0	9	2	3	0	1	1800	2	0	1500	104,490
0	0	2	3	1	0	1164	2	0	1000	117,500
1	40	2	4	0	2	2301	3	1	2999	149,900
1	6	3	4	0	1	2387	2	0	2955	150,000

TABLE 8.4
Real estate data for the project.

number of cars the garage could hold (*gar*); whether the house was listed as view or waterfront property (*h20*); the current annual property taxes (*tax*); and the listed cost of the house (*cost*). The data is shown in Table 8.4, and is also contained on our Web site in the files **house.mth** and **house.wb1**.

The author's house had central air-conditioning, was 5 years old, had 2 baths, 4 bedrooms, was not in Edinborough, had one fireplace, 2184 finished square feet, a 3 car garage, no view or waterfront, and he paid $1688 in real estate taxes.

Required Analysis

1. How much should he list his house for?

2. How good do you feel your estimate is? Provide supporting *Derive* or QuattroPro output and graphs.

3. If you could only use one or two predictors, which would you use, and why?

4. Summarize your findings in a one page memorandum.

8.9 COMPLEMENTS

1. For a student-friendly introduction to linear regression, you might enjoy
   - "Curve fitting via the criteria of least squares," ,UMAP Modules: Tools for Teaching, Numbers 321. These classroom modules are available from the Consortium for Mathematics and its Applications (COMAP) Inc., Suite 210, 57 Bedford Street, Lexington, MA, 02173.

2. An excellent textbook for fitting models to data is
   - *Applied Linear Regression,* by Sanford Weisberg, John Wiley and Sons, New York, 1985.

3. Sanford Weisberg and Dennis Cook have written a good text on graphical methods for fitting models to data, called
   - *An Introduction to Regression Graphics,* by Sanford Weisberg and Dennis Cook, John Wiley and Sons, New York, 1994.

4. The real estate data for the project was provided by Counselor Realty in Minneapolis. The variables were taken from listings of comparable houses, obtained by the realtors from the Minneapolis Multiple Listing Service. The author's house was in Brooklyn Park, Minnesota.

CHAPTER 9

NONLINEAR MODELS II: EXPONENTIAL FUNCTIONS

Population, when unchecked, increases in a geometric ratio.
Subsistence increases only in an arithmetical ratio.

Thomas Malthus

Chapter Goals

⇒ Understand how exponential models arise in applications.

⇒ Understand and apply the laws of exponents.

⇒ Build and solve discrete and continuous exponential models.

⇒ Understand how logarithmic models arise.

⇒ Understand the relationship between exponential and logarithmic models.

⇒ Understand and apply exponential and logarithmic transformations.

9.1 EXPONENTIAL GROWTH AND DECAY

In the last chapter, we examined functions whose marginal rate of change depended on the level of the predictor. This chapter examines models in which the marginal rate of change depends on the *level of the response*. These models are called *exponential* models. When a response value increases proportional to the current value of the response, this type of behavior is called *exponential growth*; decreases or loss proportional to the current value of the response is called *exponential decay*.

EXPONENTIAL MODELS

In going from a mess to a model, how do we tell when an exponential model might be appropriate?

The bottom line up front: Whenever the response changes in proportion to the amount of response present, an exponential relationship is suspected. Problems described by statements such as:

- "We lose 3% of our total income each pay period."
- "My account balance doubles every 6 years."
- "The company extracts 10% of the remaining crude oil from the wells each year."
- "The human body eliminates 2% of the remaining chemical in the body each hour."
- "The amplitude of the output drops one tenth each second."

provide us with a clue that the response behavior might be exponential.

In this chapter, we'll focus our attention on several exponential response-predictor relationships. We'll also examine the inverse function for exponentials: the logarithmic function. This logarithm function also provides us with another class of powerful models.

Let's begin our exploration by examining a familiar topic to us all: money.

9.2 COMPOUNDING

When you put money in the bank, the bank doesn't leave your money sitting in an account collecting dust. They take your money, pool it together with everyone elses, and invest it in other businesses, stocks, land developments, etc. Because you really are letting the bank do what they will with your money, the bank

pays you *interest* for the use of the money. The amount of interest you receive
is a percentage of the amount that you have on deposit.

When a *simple interest* rate is used, the interest that you receive is directly
proportional to the deposit that you made. The model for predicting the amount
SIMPLE IN- of interest I that you will receive is a linear function through the origin:
TEREST

$$I = DrN$$

where D represents the amount of money that you deposit, r is the interest rate
per period (usually an annual interest rate), and N represents the number of
interest periods.

If you buy a bond, the interest is paid periodically, and you receive coupons
that entitle you to the interest payments. If your money is in a savings account,
the interest is credited directly to your account, increasing the amount of money
you have in your account even if you don't make any further deposits. From the
time you deposit your initial amount into the bank, you then earn interest on
both your original deposit and the interest paid to you.

The process of paying interest on a deposit plus interest is called *compounding*. This is an important idea to understand if you are going to start investing
for some future goal such as purchasing a house, buying a boat, starting your
own business, retiring, etc.

The fascinating aspect of compounding is that how often the bank calcu-
lates and makes interest payments affects the total amount you earn, as we shall
see.

Example 9.1. Yesterday was your lucky day, and you won $1000 in a contest at
school. Suppose that you decide to put all $1000 into a bank account on January
1st. This initial amount is called the *principal* amount, to distinguish it from
interest payments. As is typical, the bank quotes you an annual interest rate on
deposits. Let's say it's 10% . Although the bank advertises a 10% annual interest
rate, they offer you two different options to choose from:

- The first option is *coupons*. The bank will pay you your principal ($1000) at
  the end of the year, and monthly interest payments at the rate of one-twelfth
  of 10% of the amount you have on deposit. Using ordinary simple interest,
  the annual interest rate is divided into 12 monthly interest payments.
- The second option is *compounding*. At the end of the year, the bank will
  give you back your original amount plus 10% interest *compounded* monthly.
  Using this option, the bank now pays you interest each month on both your
  principal deposit and the accruing interest in your account.

The difference between the two options is interesting and significant. We can observe this difference by examining the monthly pattern of adjustments to your account's total balance. First, let's take a look at Option 1.

Time period	principal + interest on principal = total
Initial amount:	$1000 + 0 = 1000$
End of month 1:	$1000 + \frac{0.10}{12}(1000) = 1008.33$
End of month 2:	$1008.33 + \frac{0.10}{12}(1000) = 1016.67$
$\vdots$	$\vdots$
End of month 12:	$1091.67 + \frac{0.10}{12}(1000) = 1100.00$

Does the total of $1100 seem fair enough? They are, after all, paying you 10% as advertised. This is simple interest. Now, let's look at Option 2.

With Option 2, the bank is saying that, at the end of each month, it will first check the balance in your account, and then pay you the advertised amount of interest *based on the amount they see each month.* This interest payment is the change in your account balance, and it now is a multiple of the amount in your account. *The rate of change is proportional to the amount of the response!*

Time period	account total + interest on total = total
Initial amount:	$1000 + 0 = 1000$
End of month 1:	$1000 + \frac{0.10}{12}(1000) = 1008.33$
End of month 2:	$1008.33 + \frac{0.10}{12}(1008.33) = 1016.73$
$\vdots$	$\vdots$
End of month 12:	$1095.58 + \frac{0.10}{12}(1095.58) = 1104.71$

Basing interest payments on the individual monthly amount produces a greater final value. This effect is *compound interest,* or simply compounding.   COMPOUND

Instead of explicitly writing the balances out for each month in a table, we'd   INTEREST like to find a model that can represent the amount of money in our account as a function of time. Our search for this general model will lead us to exponential functions.

We begin with a more general notation.

Example 9.2. Suppose that we let P_t equal the amount of money in your account at time t. Let r equal the annual interest rate, and N equal the number of interest periods per year that you are considering. Now, let's look at how the monthly amount changes under Option 1 and Option 2. We will let P_0 be the amount you deposit at the start.

For Option 1, in which the amount in your account receives simple interest, we have:

$$\begin{aligned} &\text{At the start}(t=0): &&P_0 \\ &\text{At the end of month } 1(t=1): &&P_1 = P_0 + 1\tfrac{r}{N}(P_0) \\ &\text{At the end of month } 2(t=2): &&P_2 = P_0 + 2\tfrac{r}{N}(P_0) \\ &\qquad\qquad\qquad\qquad\vdots \\ &\text{At the end of month } 12(t=12): &&P_{12} = P_0 + 12\tfrac{r}{N}(P_0) \end{aligned}$$

The marginal rate of change in the account is a constant: your balance goes up by $\tfrac{r}{N}P_0$ each month:

$$P_t - P_{t-1} = \frac{r}{N}P_0$$

If we let I represent the interest earned, we can see that it follows the linear proportional relationship introduced earlier:

$$I(t) = kP_0 = \left(\frac{r}{N}\right)t$$

where $k = r/N$ is a constant of proportionality. When $t = 0$, the function passes through the origin, a requirement for proportional models.

For Option 2, compounding monthly has an different effect on the marginal rate of change:

$$\begin{aligned} &\text{At the start } (t=0): &&P_0 \\ &\text{At the end of month } 1 \ (t=1): &&P_1 = P_0 + \tfrac{r}{12}(P_0) \\ &\text{At the end of month } 2 \ (t=2): &&P_2 = P_1 + \tfrac{r}{12}(P_1) \\ &\text{At the end of month } 3 \ (t=3): &&P_3 = P_2 + \tfrac{r}{12}(P_2) \\ &\qquad\qquad\qquad\qquad\vdots \\ &\text{At the end of month } 12 \ (t=12): &&P_{12} = P_{11} + \tfrac{r}{12}(P_{11}) \end{aligned}$$

The difference between the two options is that with compounding the amount of monthly interest deposited into your account grows as time goes on. The marginal rate of change of the amount in your account is not constant. Interest is calculated on an increasing amount of money.

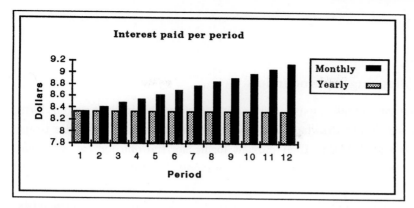

FIGURE 9.1
Compounding versus simple interest.

Period	Monthly Compounding	Simple Interest
1	8.33	8.33
2	8.40	8.33
3	8.47	8.33
4	8.54	8.33
5	8.61	8.33
6	8.69	8.33
7	8.76	8.33
8	8.83	8.33
9	8.91	8.33
10	8.98	8.33
11	9.05	8.33
12	9.13	8.33
Acct Balance:	1104.71	1100

Now, $4.71 might not seem worth the additional bookkeeping effort. It is, though—it represents a 4.71% increase in your rate of return. You can see this effect graphically in the chart in Figure 9.1, which shows a closer look at compounding each month versus not simple interest.

The effect of compounding is an example of a *recursive* relationship. The RECURSION distinguishing characteristic of recursion is that the output from one period is used as the input for a subsequent period. In this case, the recursive relationship takes the balance from the previous period and feeds it into the next period as input:

$$P_t = \left(1 + \frac{r}{N}\right) P_{t-1}$$

9.2.1 Collapsing the recursion

Although the compounding expressions are understandable in their current form, they have a significant drawback as they are currently written. In order to use any of these expressions in their current form, say the one for P_5, we would already have to know the previous periods' amounts; in this case: P_3, P_2, P_1 and P_0.

Ideally, we would like our expressions to depend only on knowing the initial deposit P_0, so that when we need to calculate how much money is in our account at the end of any time period t, we only need to know the time period, the annual interest rate r, the number of compounding periods per year N (in this case, 12 times a year), and the amount of our initial deposit.

We can accomplish this goal by collapsing the set of recursive equations into a single recursive equation by using substitutions beginning with month 1:

Amt at the end of month 1 $\quad=$ Amt at the start of month 1 $+$ interest paid

$$P_1 \quad = P_0 + \tfrac{r}{12} P_0$$

$$= (1 + \tfrac{r}{12}) P_0$$

Then, month 2:

Amt at the end of month 2 $\quad=$ Amt at the start of month 2 $+$ interest paid

$$P_2 \quad = P_1 + \tfrac{r}{12} P_1$$

$$= (1 + \tfrac{r}{12}) P_1$$

$$= (1 + \tfrac{r}{12}) \left((1 + \tfrac{r}{12}) P_0\right)$$

$$= (1 + \tfrac{r}{12})^2 P_0$$

Similarly, for month 3:

Amt at the end of month 3 $\quad=$ Amt at the start of month 3 $+$ interest paid

$$P_3 \quad = P_2 + \tfrac{r}{12}P_2$$

$$= (1 + \tfrac{r}{12})P_2$$

$$= (1 + \tfrac{r}{12})\left((1 + \tfrac{r}{12})^2 P_0\right)$$

$$= (1 + \tfrac{r}{12})^3 P_0$$

See the pattern developing? By the time that we make the last substitution into the expression for P_{12} and simplifying, we get

$$P_{12} = (1 + \frac{r}{12})^{12} P_0 \tag{9.1}$$

We actually could have stopped once we identified the trend, but we wanted to make sure that you saw the pattern emerging from the recursive equations.

The overall function expression for the amount of money in the account after t months using monthly compounding can be represented by the single recursive equation

$$P_t = (1 + \frac{r}{12})^t P_0 \tag{9.2}$$

The expression $(1+r/N)^t$, where N represents the number of compounding periods in one year, r is the annual interest rate, and t represents the time periods that have passed, is known as a *compounding factor*. Since we are typically COMPOUNDING working with annual interest rates and comparing investments on a yearly basis, FACTOR we frequently encounter this compounding factor written as

$$(1 + r/N)^N$$

The annual interest rate r used in this factor is known as the *nominal interest rate*.

Exploration Exercises

9.1. Consider each of the following compounding problems. For each problem, identify the compounding factor, write a set of recursive equations for each period until you are able to identify the emerging pattern, then collapse this set of recursive equations into a single recursive equation that expresses the account total being dependent upon the initial amount deposited.

(*a*) Initial deposit amount of $500; annual interest rate of 15%; total time period of 2 years; compounding occurring monthly.

(b) Initial deposit amount of $500; annual interest rate of 15%; total time period of 1 year; compounding occurring daily.

(c) Initial deposit amount of $1200; annual interest rate of 9.3%; total time period of 5 years; compounding occurring monthly.

(d) Initial deposit amount of $11,000; annual interest rate of 7.5 total time period of 10 years; compounding occurring every 6 months.

(e) Initial deposit amount of $11,000; annual interest rate of 5.5 total time period of 10 years; compounding occurring monthly.

9.2. Returning to the compounding example introduced earlier, suppose now that, instead of depositing $1000 as an initial amount and letting the bank compound this amount on a monthly basis, you also deposit $200 at the start of periods 1 through 12.

(a) Write out the recursive expressions for the first five periods to identify a pattern in the algebra.

(b) Find the single recursive equation that depends only on the initial deposit.

(c) Calculate the stream of interest payments for periods 1 through 12.

(d) What is the total amount of interest paid by the bank at the end of the year?

9.3. Suppose that you were considering taking out a 5-year personal loan to buy an $8000 new motorcycle. Bank A will give you the loan at a fixed annual rate of 9%. Bank B will give you the loan at an annual rate of 7% for the first 2 years, and then 11% for years 3 through 5. Both loans will be compounded monthly over the entire 5-year period.

(a) Which loan will cause you to pay out the greater amount interest by the end of the 5 years?

(b) During which of the 60 months is the total amount of interest paid to date for both loans approximately equal?

9.4. Show that the compounding factor is greater than the amount paid with nominal interest rate $(1 + r)$ when $N = 2$ by expanding out $(1 + r/2)^2$ and comparing it to $(1 + r)$. Is this also true for $N = 3$? Is it true for any positive integer value of N?

9.5. Convince yourself that with the annual interest rate r held constant the more compounding periods, the better. That is, demonstrate if $M > N$, then $(1 + r/M)^M > (1 + r/N)^N$ by experimenting with a few values of $r, M,$ and N.

9.6. Suppose that you have to make a choice between two different banks that you can deposit your money into. Both banks use the same interest rate r, but one bank uses M compounding periods and the other uses N, what does the relationship you just explored advise you to do?

MORE DIFFI-
CULT

9.7. Suppose that one bank uses interest rate r_1 with M compounding periods, and the other uses interest rate r_2 with N compounding periods, and assume that $r_1 > r_2$ and $M < N$. Now, in which bank should you deposit your money?

9.3 EXPONENTIAL FUNCTIONS

The expression

$$P_t = (1 + r/N)^t P_0$$

is an example of an *exponential* function. In comparison with the other models we have examined where a variable such as t would appear in an expression in places such as: $P_0 = 3t$, or $P_0 = 6t^2 + 15t$, the variable t appears in the position normally reserved for an *exponent*. Hence, the name *exponential* model. In the monthly interest example, the portion of the compounding factor given by $(1 + r/12)$ is called the *base* of the exponent.

EXPONENTIAL MODEL

Because we're considering 12 monthly compounding periods, we divide the annual interest rate r by $N = 12$ in the base of the compounding factor. If we had 20 compounding periods in a single year, the base of the compounding factor would have been $(1 + r/20)$.

Let's fix the general expression for the compounding factor as

$$\left(1 + \frac{r}{N}\right)^N$$

The law of exponents states that if we raise an exponential expression to a power, the exponents multiply:

$$((\text{base})^a)^b = (\text{base})^{ab} \tag{9.3}$$

We can apply Equation 9.3 to write

$$\left(1 + \frac{r}{N}\right)^N = \left(\left(1 + \frac{r}{N}\right)^{\frac{N}{r}}\right)^r$$

We now have an equivalent exponential expression for our compounding factor in which the interest rate r is included in the exponent. The base of this new expression is

$$\left(1 + \frac{r}{N}\right)^{\frac{N}{r}}$$

Let's examine the behavior of this base for different values of N.

Example 9.3. Using some values from earlier, $r = 0.10$ and $N = 12$, the value of the base is

$$\left(1 + \frac{0.10}{12}\right)^{\frac{12}{0.10}} = 2.707 \tag{9.4}$$

What happens if we increase the number of compounding periods in the year, say, to 20? Making this substitution yields

$$\left(1 + \frac{0.10}{20}\right)^{\frac{20}{0.10}} = 2.7115 \tag{9.5}$$

Something is happening here. The value of the base isn't changing much when we change the number of yearly compounding periods N, but it is *increasing*. Let's continue.

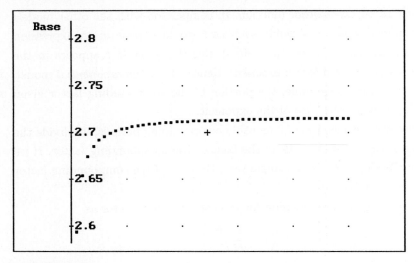

FIGURE 9.2
Discrete base values.

Example 9.4. Increasing the number of compounding periods to 40:

$$\left(1 + \frac{0.10}{40}\right)^{\frac{40}{0.1}} = 2.7149 \tag{9.6}$$

Now to 100:

$$\left(1 + \frac{0.10}{100}\right)^{\frac{100}{0.1}} = 2.7169 \tag{9.7}$$

Now to 150:

$$\left(1 + \frac{0.10}{150}\right)^{\frac{150}{0.1}} = 2.7174 \tag{9.8}$$

Now to 200:

$$\left(1 + \frac{0.10}{200}\right)^{\frac{200}{0.1}} = 2.7176 \tag{9.9}$$

It appears that some of the digits after the decimal place are locking in their values as we increase N.

Let's take a graphical look at this compounding factor to examine its performance for all values of N, while holding the value of r constant. We have the option of either plotting individual values of this base for specific values of N using a discrete plot of points, as in Figure 9.2, or, we can assume that the variable N can assume all real number values, not just integers. This means that

CONTINUOUS we are assuming that N is a *continuous variable*, and not a *discrete variable*.

VS. This is an assumption not to be taken lightly. Making this change is not

DISCRETE always appropriate. In this case, we're safe in making this assumption since we

VARIABLES

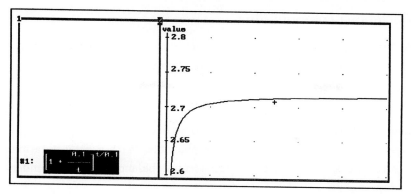

FIGURE 9.3
Continuous annual compounding.

want to look at a general graphical trend. If we want the integer values of the base we can identify them from the continuous plot.

> **Example 9.5.** We know that we will have at least one compounding period in a year, otherwise an annual interest rate does not make sense. The results of plotting the expression
>
> $$(1 + 0.10/N)^{N/0.1}$$
>
> for $1 \leq N \leq 50$ in *Derive* are shown in Figure 9.3, where we have adjusted the **Range** of the plot display to left $= -1$, right $= 50$, top $= 2.8$, and bottom $= 2.6$.
> As the value of N increases, the value of $(1 + 0.10/N)^{N/0.1}$ approaches some value ≈ 2.7183, but never quite seems to get there. You can confirm this by zooming in on a particular section of the plot. Increasing **Options Precision** to 20, you will notice that the digits do not repeat. Not even if we increase the **Precision** even further.

As the number of compounding periods N gets larger and larger, the value of the base approaches a very special number that appears frequently in exponential models. In fact, it occurs so often that many people mistakenly think of only this base when working with exponential models. Rather than writing an approximation for this base when we need it (because it never repeats or ends its series of digits after the decimal point; check it out), it has its own special symbol: e, called the Euler number, designated in honor of the great mathematician Leonard Euler (1707–1783).   THE NUMBER e.

A common notation used when working with exponential functions that have base e is to use the function notation $f(x) = \exp(x)$. This highlights the fact that we are working with a function expression.

9.3.1   Continuous compounding

If we let the bank compound our interest at rate r more and more frequently, the compounding factor gets closer and closer to the number

$$e^r$$

Without calculus, we don't have the tools to prove that this is true, but we can convince ourselves in the exercises that this is plausible. With a little notation change, we can write an expression for our account balance at time t under continuous compounding.

First, we will let $T = t/N$. In other words, we'll express the total time T in years elapsed as the number of time periods t divided by the number of compounding periods per year N. This means, equivalently, that $t = NT$.

Then our account balance function can be changed from

$$P_t = (1 + \frac{r}{N})^t P_0$$

$$= (1 + \frac{r}{N})^{NT} P_0$$

$$= ((1 + \frac{r}{N})^{N/r})^{rT} P_0 \tag{9.10}$$

$$= (e^r)^T P_0 \tag{9.11}$$

$$= e^{rT} P_0 \tag{9.12}$$

where the step from Equation 9.10 to 9.11 is justified by letting N get very large so that the base approaches e^r.

EFFECTIVE INTEREST RATE

Equation 9.12 allows us to find the effective rate for interest that is compounded continuously. If the annual interest rate for an account is r, continuous compounding increases the effective rate of interest to $e^r - 1$.

Example 9.6. A 9% annual interest rate means that $r = 0.09$. If a bank uses continuous compounding, increases the effective rate to

$$e^r - 1 = e^{.09} - 1 \approx 0.09417$$

Exploration Exercises_____

9.1. Fix the value of $r = 0.10$, and determine the value of the compounding factor using the format of the following table.

T	Factor value	T	Factor value
50		25000	
100		50000	
250		100000	
750		150000	
1000		500000	
5000		750000	
25000		1000000	
100000			

9.2. In the previous exercise, our exploration fixed the value of the interest rate r. Suppose that we now allow the interest rate to vary between $0.1 \le r \le 0.99$. Pick several new values of r and see if the compounding factors still approaches the value e as we increase the number of compounding periods, T.

9.3. Annual Percentage Rate. Suppose that you are going to apply for a personal loan for $1500 from a bank that advertises an annual rate of interest of 11%, without specifying how the bank is going to compound the amount that they are going to loan you. The $1500 is known as the *principal* amount of the loan. Let's assume that you are going to pay back this loan to the bank over 1 year using monthly payments. You have seen that the number of compounding periods that the bank uses has an effect on the amount of money that it will be paid. (Think of the bank as an investor; it's investing in you at a rate of 11%.) The question is: How do the number of compounding periods effect the rate you are supposedly paying? That is, if the number of compounding periods in the year increases, are you really paying 11% interest on the loan?

One way to answer this question is to calculate the Annual Percentage Rate (APR), which is given by the formula

$$\text{APR} = \frac{\text{total} - \text{principal}}{\text{principal}} \times 100 \tag{9.13}$$

Calculate the total amount paid back to the bank for 8 different choices of compounding: annually (once a year), semiannually (twice a year), bimonthly (every two months), monthly (once a month), weekly (once a week), daily (once a day), hourly (once an hour), and once every minute, and examine the effect of compounding on APR. What are your conclusions?

9.4. What is the effective interest rate if 6% interest is compounded continuously? What is the percentage change between the effective rate and 6%? Is the percent change bigger when $r = 0.09$ or when $r = 0.06$?

9.4 THE EXPONENTIAL FUNCTION

Models that use an exponential function with base e to capture the relationship between the response and predictor are called *natural* exponential models. The

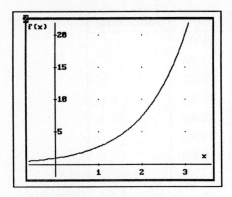

FIGURE 9.4
The graph of $f(x) = \exp(x)$.

function $f(x) = \exp(x)$ is referred to as a natural exponential function.

> **Definition 9.1. Natural Exponential Function.** The *natural exponential function* is defined as
>
> $$y = f(x) = \exp(x) \qquad (9.14)$$
>
> where x is a predictor variable that can assume any real number value.

Any value can serve as the base of an exponential function or model. Variables appearing in the exponent position can also have coefficients different from 1.

A more general definition of an exponential function is given next.

> **Definition 9.2. Exponential Function.** An *exponential function* is defined as
>
> $$y = f(x) = a^x \qquad (9.15)$$
>
> where x is a predictor variable that can assume any real number value.

The graph of the natural exponential function $f(x) = \exp(x)$ appears in Figure 9.4. From the figure, we see that this function is positive and increasing for all values of x.

9.4.1 Law of exponents

Exponential functions can be composed with other functions to obtain more complicated forms. If we let $f(x) = \exp(x)$ and $g(x) = 2x + 5$, we can write

$$f \circ g(x) = f(g(x)) = \exp(2x + 5)$$

This particular expression can be written as the product of two exponential functions: $e^{2x}e^5$, because of another law of exponents:

$$(\text{base})^a(\text{base})^b = (\text{base})^{a+b}$$

where a and b are any real numbers. Notice a very important point with this definition: *The bases are the same!* If the bases are different, the two exponential functions do not combine as shown. Here are a couple of examples that reinforce the definition.

Example 9.7.

$$2^{3x}2^{4x} \quad = 2^{3x+4x} = 2^{7x}$$

$$10^{-3x}5^{5x} = \text{cannot combine}$$

$$e^{12}e^{10} \quad = e^{12+10} = e^{22}$$

What happens if the exponent is negative? We have a law for that case also.

$$(\text{base})^{-a} = \frac{1}{(\text{base})^a} \tag{9.16}$$

where a is any real number.

These different laws allow us to algebraically simplify functions.

9.4.2 Properties

We have seen from the graph of $f(x) = \exp(x)$ that this function is increasing and positive for all values of x. As a result, $f(x) = \exp(x)$ does not have a maximum or minimum value if we don't somehow restrict the domain of $f(x)$. The domain of $f(x) = \exp(x)$ is the set of all real numbers; the range of $f(x) = \exp(x)$ is the set of positive real numbers. We also can observe from its graph that the exponential function is concave up.

Since $f(x) = \exp(x)$ is nonlinear, we know that its rate of change is not constant; it depends upon what value of x and $f(x)$ we are considering. However, one interesting feature of this particular exponential function is that the rate of change of $f(x)$ at *any instant,* or any fixed value of x, is equal to the value of the function at that point:

Instantaneous rate of change at $x_i = \exp(x_i)$ for all i

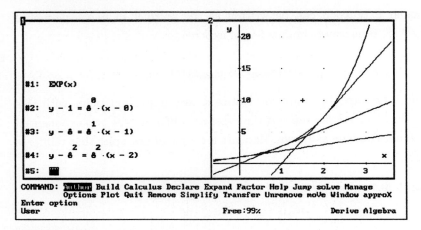

FIGURE 9.5
The graph of $f(x) = \exp(x)$ and the lines $y - 1 = e(x - 0)$, $y - e = e(x - 1)$, and $y - e^2 = e^2(x - 2)$.

An actual proof of this property requires calculus, but we can gain an understanding of what it means graphically by relating back to some information that we already have seen.

Figure 9.5 illustrates this property in this rather clever way. If the rate of change of $f(x_i)$ at any point x_i in the domain of $f(x)$ is the same as the value $\exp(x_i)$, then we should be able to construct a straight line that passes through the point $(x_i, \exp(x_i))$ with the value $\exp(x_i)$ as its slope. Then, by plotting this line, we should see it just touch the exponential curve at the point $(x_i, f(x_i))$; it will be a tangent line to the exponential curve.

Using the point-slope form of a line

$$y - y_0 = m(x - x_0)$$

with $y = f(x) = \exp(x)$, gives us the general form of the lines that we are looking for:

$$y - \exp(x_0) = \exp(x_0)(x - x_0)$$

Figure 9.5 shows a plot of the nonlinear function $f(x) = \exp(x)$, along with three lines passing through the exact points $[0, \exp(0)]$, $[1, \exp(1)]$, and $[2, \exp(2)]$. We can see that these three lines are tangent to the curve $f(x) = \exp(x)$, and the slopes of each tangent line are e^0, e^1, and e^2, respectively. In other words, the slopes of these tangent lines have the same values as the value of the function at the tangent points!

At the start of this chapter, we made the comment that when a response value y changes in a manner proportional to the current value of the response, an exponential model is suspected to be appropriate. We're now in a position to show you why this is so using a slightly more general exponential function form $y = f(x) = \exp(bx)$, where b is any real number.

The instantaneous rate of change for $y = f(x) = \exp(bx)$ is given by $b\exp(bx)$. From this, it follows that the instantaneous rate of change for an exponential function with a leading coefficient $y = g(x) = a\exp(bx)$ will be $a \cdot b\exp(bx)$.

Suppose that y represents the response and x represents the predictor, and we are observing some particular response value y_0 corresponding to the predictor value x_0. The marginal rate of change that exists at $x = x_0$ is given by the instantaneous rate of change of the response, which is $b\exp(bx_0)$, or $bf(x_0)$, or by_0! Thus, if we observe that the marginal rate of change for a response is proportional to the amount of the response (i.e., by_0), we can use an exponential model to capture the underlying behavior.

CRITICAL OBSERVATION!

The most general form of an exponential model we will be working with has the form

$$y = f(x) = a\exp(bx) \tag{9.17}$$

In many applications, the predictor variable is time t, yielding $f(t) = a\exp(bt)$. If $b < 0$, the response is decreasing with time, and we have a *decay* model. If $b > 0$, the response is increasing with time, and we have a *growth* model.

Example 9.8. The rate of change of the population of bacteria in a colony is proportional to the amount of bacteria currently in the population. This makes sense if one does not consider that the amount of resources available to the population (food, space, etc.) may be finite.

Let y represent the amount of bacteria, and t be measured in minutes. If the instantaneous rate of change is 2% of the population at any time, we have the model

$$y = f(t) = a\exp(0.02t)$$

where a is the population when $t = 0$. For example, if $a = 100$, then

$$f(60) = 100\exp(0.02 \cdot 60) = 100\exp(1.2) \approx 332.011$$

Recall the compounding example we began the chapter with. Remember how compound interest had a greater effect on the deposit than simple interest? Compound interest was an exponential relationship just like bacteria growth. Looking at the population of bacteria as a "deposit," and thinking of the percent change as interest rates, with $b = 0.02$ the compounding factor is $e^b = e^{0.02} = 1.02020$. This means that our equivalent rate of change per minute is about

334 PRECALCULUS: A MODELING APPROACH

2.02%, which is slightly greater than if we just multiplied the starting population by 2%. Bacteria growth is a compounding effect, which helps explain why their populations tend to grow so quickly.

Example 9.9. The classic exponential decay example ($b < 0$) is radioactive decay. The amount of material lost is proportional to the amount present. This is similar to a bank deposit experiencing negative interest (i.e., there is some amount of money lost during each period).

The decay of Radium-226 follows the model for exponential decay given by Equation 9.17 with $b = -0.000436$, and time represented in years. If we start with 100 grams of Radium-226, in 1000 years we will have

$$f(1000) = 100 \exp(-0.000436 \cdot 1000) = 100 \exp -0.436 \approx 66.64$$

grams of radium remaining.

After 1589.78 years, the amount of radium will drop to one-half the original amount:

$$y = f(1589.78) = 100 \exp(0.000436 \cdot 1598.78) = 50$$

The time it takes to decay to one half the original amount is called the *half-life* of the material.

Exploration Exercises

9.1. Use the laws of exponents to simplify the following expressions.
  (a) $e^{3x}e^{7x/3}$
  (b) $10^{24w}10^{5x}9^3$
  (c) $(x^3 + 9x + 13)^{15}(x^3 + 9x + 13)^{-15}$

9.2. For each set of functions that follow, rank the functions in an order that places the fastest changing response y for changes in the predictor x first. If this ranking only holds true for specific predictor values in the domain of the predictor, then identify these values using inequalities (i.e., $0 \le x \le 17$, etc.). If the functions cross, identify the points where the intersection occurs. For each set of functions, provide a plot of all three of the functions on the same plot.
  (a) $y = f(x) = 6^x$, $y = g(x) = 6x$, $y = h(x) = 6^{x^2}$
  (b) $y = f(x) = 3^x$, $y = g(x) = 9^x$, $y = h(x) = 7^x$
  (c) $y = f(x) = 3^{-2x}$, $y = g(x) = 9^{-\sqrt{x}}$, $y = h(x) = 1/3 \cdot 5^{-2.2x}$
  (d) $y = f(w) = 30 \exp(2w)$, $y = g(w) = 3 \exp(4w)$, $y = h(w) = 0.3 \exp(8w)$
  (e) $y = f(w) = 5 \exp(w)$, $y = g(w) = 5 \cdot 5^w$, $y = h(w) = 5 \cdot 2^w$
  (f) $y = f(x) = 1/10 \cdot \exp(x)$, $y = g(x) = 1/1000 \cdot \exp(10x)$, $y = h(x) = 1/100,000 \cdot \exp(100x)$

9.3. For each of the following exponential functions, determine the equation for the tangent line at each point listed, and estimate the instantaneous rate of change at that point using the slope of the tangent line. Plot both the function and the tangent lines on the same plot.
  (a) $y = f(x) = 0.5 \exp(3x)$; points: $x = 11$, $x = 25$, $x = 31$
  (b) $y = f(x) = 33 \exp(-0.25x)$; points: $x = 8.5$, $x = 18.5$, $x = 41.5$

    (c) $y = f(w) = \pi \exp(11w)$; points: $w = 3$, $w = 11$, $w = 17$

    (d) $y = f(x) = \exp(x) \cdot \exp(3x)$; points: $x = 1.2$, $x = 4.5$, $x = 9.1$

    (e) $y = g(w) = \exp(-3w)/\exp(-4w)$; points: $w = 4$, $w = 7$, $w = 11$

9.4. For each of the functions in the previous exercise:

    (a) Calculate the average rate of change ($\Delta y / \Delta x$) of the exponential functions that occurs between the first and second points, and the first and third points.

    (b) Find the average rate of change of the average rates of change that you just calculated. That is, how fast is the rate of change changing between the first and third points for each of these functions?

9.5. An *algorithm* is a stepwise calculation procedure that is used to find the solution to a mathematical problem. To anticipate how well a particular algorithm will perform, scientists frequently resort to counting the number of algebraic operations that the algorithm must perform. This total is typically expressed as a function of n, the number of independent variables involved in a problem. Suppose that one algorithm requires $100(n^3)$ steps to find a solution, and a second algorithm requires 3^n steps.

    (a) For what value of n do the two algorithms roughly perform the same, (i.e., for what value of n do the two algorithms require approximately the same number of steps to find a solution?) (Hint: Use a graphical analysis.)

    (b) If each step required 0.003 seconds to perform, is there a practical limit to the number of independent variables (n) for which you would recommend using these two algorithms on?

9.6. Suppose that we take a chessboard, and starting at one corner, we place a penny on the corner square. Working across the chessboard, we place 2 pennies on the next square, 4 pennies on the next, 8 pennies on the next, and so on, doubling the previous total each time we move to a new adjacent square. Suppose that we do this row by row until each square has pennies on it. If each penny weighs 0.5 gram, how heavy is the chessboard when all of the squares have pennies on them? How much money would be on the board at the finish?

9.7. While analyzing the products of a nuclear reaction, you discover a new and exciting radioactive element, Driscolite, which appears to decay exponentially. Driscolite loses 10% of its mass every minute. You initially have 1 gram before you run to get your trusty assistant, Igor, to show him the material.

    (a) Write the exponential model that applies to this situation, and plot the function for $0 \leq t \leq 60$ minutes.

    (b) If it takes you 10 minutes to find Igor, how much will left for him to see?

    (c) What is the instantaneous rate of change of this exponential function at the instant you show Igor the material?

    (d) After showing the material to Igor, you then run to show your boss, which takes an additional 15 minutes. How much will Driscolite will remain for her to see?

    (e) What is the instantaneous rate of change of this exponential function at the instant you show your boss the material?

    (f) What is the average rate of change of the material between the time you show Igor and your boss the material. (Hint: Remember that the average rate of change is given by $\Delta y / \Delta t$, which is a secant line.)

9.8. You inherit $1000 and decide to invest it in a tax-free account, reinvesting the dividends. Your teacher suggests the GrowWell Fund, which historically pays an annual interest rate of return of 15%. You model the value of your investment as $P = v(t) = 1000(1 + 0.15)^t$. A classmate says that the correct model to use is $P = w(t) = 1000\exp(0.139761t)$. Compare the two models when $t = 1$, $t = 5$, $t = 10$, and $t = 30$. Compare and comment on the differences between the two models, and about how fast your money is growing. Do you see any weaknesses in using either model?

9.5   LOGARITHMIC FUNCTIONS AND MODELS

The exponential function $f(x) = \exp(x)$ is positive and increasing for all values of x, and its range consists of the positive real numbers.

We recall from Chapter 4 that a function that is monotonically increasing is a one-to-one function, and therefore has an inverse. In this section, we study the inverse of the natural exponential function, the *natural logarithm*. We will briefly develop its properties, and then discuss how it is used for modeling certain nonlinear behavior. We will conclude with a few examples to illustrate the usefulness of this particular inverse function.

9.5.1   Definition and properties

Let's begin with a definition:

> **Definition 9.3.   Natural Logarithmic Function.**   Let $f(x) = \exp(x)$. The function given by $x = f^{-1}(y)$ is called the *natural logarithm* of y, and is written using the notation $x = \ln(y)$.

Here is a subtle point to make concerning notation. When we model a response-predictor relationship as a natural logarithmic function, we will write $y = \ln(x)$. When we use the logarithmic function in its role as an inverse, we'll write $x = \ln(y)$. Be watchful of the context in which we use this function.

NOTATION ALERT!

Figure 9.6 shows a graph of the function $y = f(x) = \ln(x)$. Notice from the graph that the $\ln(x)$ function is an increasing function. The domain of $y = f(x) = \ln(x)$ is the positive real numbers $0 < x$. This makes sense considering that this function is the inverse of the exponential function, and so the domain of the natural logarithm function is the same as the range of the exponential function, and vice-versa. We also have the following properties, which follow from Chapter 4 and the graph of $\ln(x)$:

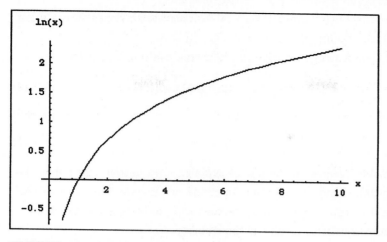

FIGURE 9.6
A plot of the function $y = f(x) = \ln(x)$.

Theorem 9.1.   Properties of the natural logarithm function.

- The range of the natural logarithm function is the set of all real numbers.
- The natural logarithm function is an increasing function over its domain.
- The natural logarithm function is one-to-one.
- The natural logarithm function does not have a maximum or minimum value without restricting its domain.
- The natural logarithm function is concave down everywhere on its domain.

Rather than leaving the proof of what follows as an exercise, let's develop one or two other properties of the natural logarithm function.

9.5.2   Law of logarithms

Recall that one of the properties of the exponential function is

$$\exp(a)\exp(b) = \exp(a + b)$$

This property was called the *law of exponents*.

Let's develop an analogous law of logarithms, using the properties of inverses. We want to show that

$$\ln(ab) = \ln(a) + \ln(b) \tag{9.18}$$

and justify our results using the law of exponents and the fact that the natural exponential function is a one-to-one function.

Since the natural logarithm and natural exponent are inverses of each other, their effects cancel: $\exp(\ln(x)) = x$ and $\ln(\exp(x)) = x$.

With this idea in mind, we have the following chain of equalities

$$\exp(\ln(a) + \ln(b)) = \exp(\ln(a))\exp(\ln(b)) \tag{9.19}$$

$$= ab \tag{9.20}$$

$$= \exp(\ln(ab)) \tag{9.21}$$

Equation 9.19 holds because of the law of exponents. Equation 9.20 follows because the logarithmic and exponential functions are inverse functions of each other. Equation 9.21 then follows from the definition of inverse functions.

This chain of equalities results in the equality

$$\exp(\ln(a) + \ln(b)) = \exp(\ln(ab))$$

Now, from a previous chapter we know that if $f(a) = f(b)$ for a one-to-one function, then $a = b$. Since the exponential function is a one-to-one function, this property implies that

$$\ln(a) + \ln(b) = \ln(ab)$$

which establishes Equation 9.18.

A similar argument shows that

$$\ln(a) - \ln(b) = \ln\left(\frac{a}{b}\right) \tag{9.22}$$

One of the major benefits of introducing the material in Chapter 4 is our ability to develop the law of logarithms in this section. Once we understand the properties of functions and inverses, many ideas such as those above become accessible. The moral of our story: The more mathematics we know, the easier mathematical concepts become!

The second property we wish to show is that *rate of increase* of the logarithm function gets very close to 0 as the predictor gets very large. This follows from the law of logarithms.

Example 9.10. Let's fix $\Delta x = 1$, and consider the points $x_0 = a$ and $x_1 = a+1$. Then, examining the rate of change of the function between these points, we see that

$$\frac{\Delta y}{\Delta x} = \frac{\ln(a+1) - \ln(a)}{1} = \ln(a+1) - ln(a) = \ln\left(\frac{a+1}{a}\right) \tag{9.23}$$

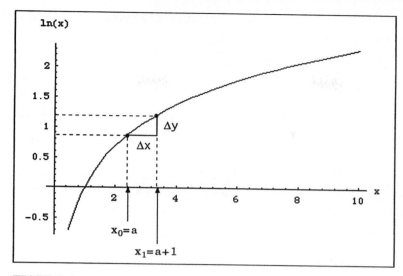

FIGURE 9.7
The rate of change of the function $y = f(x) = \ln(x)$.

As a gets very big, $(a+1)/a$ approaches one because the effect of adding 1 to the numerator gets overshadowed by the value of a. Looking at Figure 9.7, we see that as a gets close to 1, $\ln(a)$ gets close to 0.

What we can't see from Figure 9.7 is what we wish to assert in the next proposition.

Proposition 9.0. The instantaneous rate of change of the natural logarithm function at $x = x_0$ is equal to

$$\frac{1}{x_0}$$

While the proof of Proposition 9.0 must wait for calculus, we can use the same technique that we used earlier with the exponential function to at least graphically verify that the Proposition seems correct.

If the rate of change of $y = f(x_i) = \ln(x_i)$ at any point x_i in the domain of $f(x)$ is the same as the value $1/x_0$, then we should be able to construct a tangent line that passes through the point $(x_i, \ln(x_i))$ with the value $1/x_i$ as its slope. Then, by plotting this line, we should see it just touch the logarithm curve at the point $(x_i, f(x_i))$.

Example 9.11. Using the point-slope form of a line

$$y - y_0 = m(x - x_0)$$

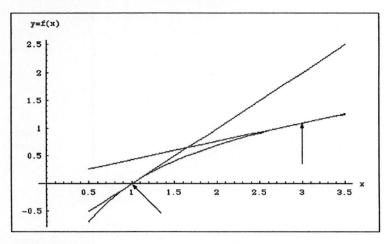

FIGURE 9.8
A plot of $f(x) = \ln(x)$ with tangent lines.

with $y = f(x) = \ln(x)$, we get the general form of the lines that we are looking for:

$$y - \ln(x_0) = \frac{1}{x_0}(x - x_0)$$

Figure 9.8 shows the graph of $f(x) = \ln(x)$ along with the tangent lines through $(x_0, f(x_0))$ with slope $1/x_0$ for the values of $x_0 = 1$ and $x = 3$. And, as we suspected, they touch the function just at the points $(x_0, f(x_0))$. In order for this to happen, the rates of change (slopes) of the tangent lines and the function $y = f(x) = \ln(x)$ must match, and we see the result we are looking for.

This property of deceasing rate of change motivates us into modeling with logarithms.

9.5.3 Modeling with the logarithm

If the rate of change of the response is proportional to the reciprocal of the predictor, Proposition 9.0 implies that we can model the response with a natural logarithm function.

When would such a situation arise? Well, remember the utility of money in our examples from Chapter 8? At that time, we said that the utility of money was an increasing function, but the rate of increase declined as the amount of money increased. That is, money is worth more when you have less of it. One possible (and classic) model represents the utility of money as a logarithmic function of the amount of money one has.

Example 9.12. Let $u = f(w) = \ln(w)$, where u is a response representing the utility of the amount of wealth we have, and $w = \$1000$ is the amount of wealth we currently possess. The change in utility for us when our wealth increases from \$1000 to \$2000 is

$$\Delta u = u(2000) - u(1000) = \ln(2000) - \ln(1000) = \ln(2) \approx 0.6931$$

This means that an extra \$1000 in our level of wealth results in a 0.6931 gain in utility.

Now, let's assume that our current level of wealth is significantly higher, with $w = \$1,000,000$. At this level of wealth, the gain in utility for the same increase in wealth of an additional \$1000 is

$$\Delta u = \ln(1001000) - \ln(1000000) = \ln(1.001) \approx 0.0000995$$

The quantity Δu is much smaller in this case: The change in utility is only about one-tenth of 1% as great at the higher level of wealth than it was at the lower level of wealth. In terms of utility, when our current level of wealth is small, the \$1000 increase is much more significant, as we would suspect.

9.5.4 Taxation and utility

Modeling utility with the natural logarithm function has interesting implications for taxation policy. If you are a firm supporter of the proposed flat tax systems, you may be surprised by what follows.

If a positive change in utility is good, then a negative change in utility is bad or "painful." This is why taxes are said to hurt. Taking any portion of FLAT TAX your wealth decreases your utility. But, since taxes are necessary to keep the government functioning, the question is: What taxation scheme is fair?

It's a reasonable idea that taxes should hurt everyone the same. One fair way to develop a tax strategy is to tax everyone using flat percentage of the UTILITY OF *utility of their wealth*, not their actual level of wealth. WEALTH

A graph of the function using utility of wealth versus the wealth is shown in Figure 9.9. Let's see what this model means.

If a person earns \$100,000 per year, her utility is 11.5129. If we tax 10% of that utility, she would have 10.3616 units of utility remaining. How much money remains? Here's where the inverse relationship comes in handy. Since $u = \ln(w)$, applying the natural exponential function to both sides of the equation yields

$$w = \exp(u)$$

which now allows us to calculate the amount of wealth given a fixed utility. In this case, the wealth remaining after this 10% tax on utility would be

$$w = \exp(10.3616) \approx 31,621$$

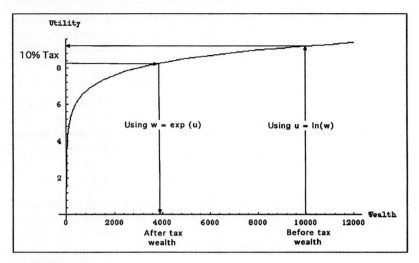

FIGURE 9.9
Utility versus wealth using the natural logarithm and its inverse, the exponential.

This is a pretty hefty tax bite: about 70%!

How about for someone earning, say, $30,000? Her current level of utility is 10.3089. After taking 10% of her utility, she has 9.27801 units of utility left. That translates back to $10,700. Ouch! That's is still about a 65% tax rate for a middle income earner—not a good idea.

And, for someone earning $10,000 a year, his current utility is 9.21034. The 10% tax on utility reduces his utility to 8.28931, which translates to leaving him with $3,981; a 60% tax rate. This effect is illustrated in Figure 9.9. Time to lower that tax rate on utility!

Let's try a 1% tax on utility. The following table shows the results for the three wealth levels that we are examining.

Before tax		After tax		Tax
Wealth	Utility	Wealth	Utility	Effect
$100,000	11.5129	$89,125	11.3978	11%
$30,000	10.309	$27,061	10.205	9.8%
$10,000	9.2103	$9,120	9.1182	8.8%

For the person earning $100,000, her tax bill would be $10,875. That is still about 11%. The percent is not too high, but it is still a lot of money. The woman earning $30,000 would pay $2,938—about 9.8%. Ouch: That is still a lot.

Lastly, the person earning \$10,000 would see about an 8.8% tax bill. However, although all three people are paying a different amount of money in taxes, the effect of that loss of money is the same; they all lose the same amount of utility.

The point here is that, to be a fair strategy, taxes should hurt every income earner equally. If the actual utility of wealth function is increasing and concave down, which most people would agree it is, a progressive tax scheme such as the one above results. Wealthier people pay higher tax amounts, because the impact of losing the same amount of money as someone with less wealth has a smaller effect on the wealthy person than it does on the person who has a lower income. A logarithm function provides a natural model in this situation.

9.6 LOGARITHM AS INVERSE

In this section, we use the property that the natural logarithm function is the inverse of the exponential function. This allows us to solve some new problems, and tie up some loose ends from earlier sections.

9.6.1 Effective interest rate versus simple interest rate

We have seen that a simple interest rate r that is compounded continuously gives an effective interest rate of $(e^r - 1)$. If we have an effective interest rate of p under continuous compounding, what is the equivalent simple interest rate?

We are interested in finding the value of r so that $p = e^r - 1$, or $1 + p = e^r$. To solve this equation, we take the natural logarithm of each side of the last equation, obtaining

$$\ln(1 + p) = \ln(\exp(r)) = r$$

This relationship allows us to make a major simplification in the growth models we introduced earlier. If our effective interest rate under continuous compounding is p, we have

$$
\begin{aligned}
P(t) \quad &= P_0 \exp(rt) && \text{original model} \\
&= P_0 \exp((\ln(1 + p)t) && \text{substitution} \\
&= P_0(\exp(\ln(1 + p)))^t && \text{because } \exp(at) = (\exp(a))^t \\
&= P_0(1 + p)^t && \text{new model}
\end{aligned}
$$

9.6.2   Half-life calculations

To find the half-life of a substance given that we know the decay rate r, we must solve the equation

$$\frac{I_0}{2} = I_0 \exp(rt_h)$$

to find t_h. We can do this in a very straightforward manner using logarithms:

$$\frac{I_0}{2} = i_0 \exp(rt_h)$$

$$\frac{1}{2} = \exp(rt_h)$$

$$\ln\left(\frac{1}{2}\right) = rt_h$$

$$t_h = \frac{\ln(1/2)}{r} \qquad (9.24)$$

So now, we can use Equation 9.24, which is a mathematical model, to determine half-lives.

Example 9.13. In the earlier radioactive decay example, radium had a decay rate of $r = -0.000436$. To find the half-life of this material, we solve

$$t_h = \frac{\ln(0.5)}{-0.000436} \approx 1589.78$$

We can also use Equation 9.24 to find r, given the half-life. If a substance has a half-life of 1000 years, then solving for r gives

$$r = \frac{\ln(1/2)}{t_h} = 0.0006931$$

This approach generalizes. If p is the fraction remaining at time t_p, then the following relation holds:

$$t_p = \frac{\ln(p)}{r} \qquad (9.25)$$

The model given by Equation 9.25 allows us to find any one of the three quantities t_p, r, or p if we know the other two.

Exploration Exercises

9.1. An isotope of Carbon, Carbon-14, has a half-life of 5770 years. It is produced naturally in the atmosphere by the action of cosmic rays. The age of a piece of wood or wood product can be determined by comparing the amount of Carbon-14 in the piece with the amount of Carbon-14 in a specimen of known age. (We can no longer use living trees for our benchmarks, because atmospheric testing of nuclear devices increased the amount of Carbon-14 in the atmosphere over the last 50 years.) The amount of Carbon-14 is proportional to the number of counts on detect on a Geiger counter. A portion of the Dead Sea scrolls contained 23% of the Carbon-14 of a normal piece of parchment. Estimate the age of the Dead Sea scrolls.

9.2. The half-life of Uranium-238 is $4.511 0^9$ years. Find r. How long would it take for a piece of Uranium-238 to decay to 10% of its original size?

9.3. Show graphically that the exponential and logarithm functions are inverses. (Hint: Remember that inverses reflect across the line $x = y$.)

9.4. Justify each part of Theorem 9.1.

9.5. Justify Equation 9.22.

9.6. The relationship $\ln(\exp(x)) = x$ is true for all x, but $\exp(\ln(x)) = x$ only for positive x. Why is this so?

9.7. Show that Equation 9.25 is true.

9.8. Taxation is a subject that affects everyone. What kind of factors and principles would constitute a fair tax system? Here are some issues:

(a) Current U.S. tax law has a top tax bracket of 38%. Compute the equivalent tax on utility for someone making $1,000,000$ and someone making $100,000$ per year by converting before and after tax wealth into utility and computing the percent change. Who pays less tax on their utility?

(b) Not counting tax credits, someone earning $10,000$ is taxed at a 14% rate. What is the equivalent tax rate on her utility?

(c) Most reasonable people agree that the utility of wealth is an increasing, concave down function, but there are folks that object to it being represented using the model $u(w) = \ln(w)$. Their proposed model is $u(w) = \sqrt{w}$. How does a tax scheme based on a percentage of this utility function compare with one based on the logarithmic utility function? Can you think of a better model? Why do you think it is better?

9.7 EXPONENTIAL PARAMETERS FROM DATA

When we know or suspect the *form* of the functional relationship between a response and predictor(s), we have a strong motivation to fit curves to try to model this relationship. In the case when we suspect the relationship to be linear, we saw how we can use regression to fit a model of the form $\hat{y} = ax + b$ to a set of data. What about the case when we suspect an exponential model? Do we still want to use a linear model just because its convenient? The answer is no.

But, suppose that the model form that we suspect is the single predictor model $y = a\exp(bx)$. Even if we have an extensive data set, the task of identifying the parameters a and b that are appropriate for our specific situation still remains.

We could simply plot the data and try to estimate the parameters through trial-and-error by guessing different values of a and b, plotting the resulting curve on top of the data, and then visually checking how well it fits. This approach might work fine for some applications, so don't discard the idea completely just because of its brute-force nature. We would still have to identify what we mean by a "visually good fit" in this case.

Regression provides a means of identifying a and b so that the best fit exponential curve that results is based on the least squares criteria. But, first, we have to do something special to the original data set that moves us away from having to work with nonlinear function expressions. There is a clever way of identifying the exponential model parameters by using a subtle observation to change the expression we are working with into a linear model. First, the observation.

9.7.1 Transforming predictors: $y = a \exp(x)$

Suppose that we are dealing with a modeling situation in which we know that the form of the applicable model is $y = a\exp(x)$, so that the only parameter we have to identify is the leading coefficient a. Suppose further that we have a table of data consisting of m data points representing the set of response values y_i along with their corresponding single predictor values x_i, for $i = 1, 2, \ldots, m$:

x	y
x_1	y_1
x_2	y_2
$\vdots$	$\vdots$
x_m	y_m

How can we identify an appropriate value for a?

Take a good look at the model

$$y_i = a\exp(x_i)$$

and watch closely the following observation. If we were to plot the data as it is listed, we would get a plot with the x-values on the horizontal axis and the y-values on the vertical axis. If an exponential model is appropriate to describe the relationship between the predictor and response, the plotted data should display a curved pattern indicating this kind of relationship. Practically speaking, we wouldn't expect the data to *exactly* follow an exponential pattern because we would expect some amount of error to be present in the data that would cause them to deviate from this exact pattern.

What if, instead of plotting y versus x, we plot y versus $\exp(x)$? In other words, we change, or *transform* the data set to be

CRITICAL OBSERVA-TION!

$\exp(x)$	y
$\exp(x_1)$	y_1
$\exp(x_2)$	y_2
$\vdots$	$\vdots$
$\exp(x_m)$	y_m

What would this *transformed* data set look like? It would look as if we just plotted data from the model

DATA TRANSFORMATION

$$y_i = aX_i$$

where $X_i = \exp(x_i)$. Nothing yet? Look at the above model once again. What kind of model is it? It's a *linear* model! The response y_i is a linear function of X_i. Plotting y versus $\exp(x)$ will cause our data set to look linear.

The parameter a from the exponential model has not changed in this new model: It's the same a as it was before. Only now, rather than being an unknown coefficient from an exponential model, it is the slope of a very simple linear function $y_i = aX_i$.

In statistics, a model of the type $y = a\exp(x)$ is known as an *intrinsically linear model* because it can be expressed in the linear form $y = aX$ by a suitable *transformation*. There are exponential models for which performing a linearizing transformation is not possible, such as $y = a\exp(bx) + c + \epsilon$, where ϵ represents an additional error term. However, we'll leave those for a course on statistics.

Once we have transformed the original data, we can obtain a value for a using several approaches:

- OK. Visually approximate the slope of a straight line,
- BETTER. Select a couple of data points, determine the equation of the line connecting them, and use the slope of this line to approximate a,
- BEST. Use linear regression to identify the best-fitting line for the transformed data set with y as the response and $\exp(x)$ as the predictor. Then, select the

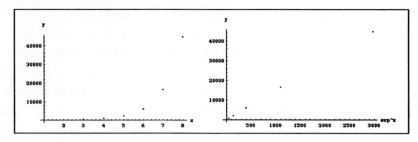

FIGURE 9.10
Plots of the original data set and the transformed data set.

slope of this line to use as the estimated value of a.

Example 9.14. Let's see if we can verify what we are claiming above using a contrived test problem. The following data set was generated using an exponential model of the form $y = a \exp(x)$ and rounded to the nearest whole number. Let's try to estimate a using the approach just introduced.

x	y	x	y
1	40	5	2226
2	110	6	6051
3	301	7	16,449
4	818	8	44,714

Suppose this was our starting point. We know the form of the underlying behavior reflected in the data shown. The challange is to determine the value of the leading coefficient a in the exponential model.

A plot of the x-values versus y-values is shown on the left side of Figure 9.10. Now, we *transform* the x-values as described above. This produces the following data set.

$\exp(x)$	y	$\exp(x)$	y
3	40	148	2226
7	110	403	6051
20	301	1097	16,449
55	818	2981	44,714

The right-hand plot in Figure 9.10 shows a plot of this data set with the original x-values now transformed into $X_i = \exp(x)$. Notice the linear pattern that results from this transformation of the predictor values.

Since the data was generated using an exponential function, all three of the techniques that we could use to identify the parameter a would work about the same. So, using points 6 and 7, we can calculate the slope of the line in the

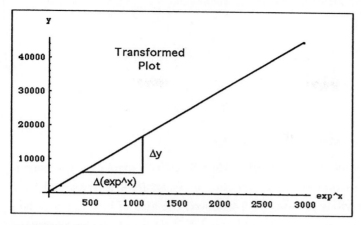

FIGURE 9.11
Approximating the slope of the linear fit line in the transformed plot.

transformed plot:

$$a = \frac{\Delta y}{\Delta(\exp(x))} = \frac{(y_7 - y_6)}{(\exp(x_7) - \exp(x_6))} = \frac{(16,449 - 6051)}{(1097 - 403)} = \frac{10,398}{694} = 14.98$$

This approximation technique is illustrated in Figure 9.11. Thus, the exponential model that we would use for this data set would be

$$y = f(x) = a \exp(x) = 14.98 \exp(x)$$

To generate the numbers in our original data set, we used the exponential function $y = f(x) = 15 \exp(x)$. The difference between the estimated value of $a = 14.98$ and the exact value used to generate the values $a = 15$ can be directly attributed to rounding error that we introduced by not working with exact values.

Exploration Exercise

9.1. Given the following data sets, estimate the value of the leading coefficient a in the exponential model $y = a \exp(x)$.

(a)

x	y	x	y
1	40	5	2226
2	110	6	6051
3	301	7	16,449
4	818	8	44,714

(b)

x	y	x	y
1	40	5	2226
2	110	6	6051
3	301	7	16,449
4	818	8	44,714

x	y	x	y
1	40	5	2226
2	110	6	6051
3	301	7	16,449
4	818	8	44,714

(c)

9.7.2 Using logarithms: $y = a \exp(bx)$

A more general form of an exponential model allows us control over the magnitude of the predictor exponent in the function $y = a \exp(bx)$, where a and b are constants. In the previous section, we introduced the idea of linearizing a data set using this more general model by fixing $b = 1$. This simplification permitted us to introduce the idea of linearizing a data set using a predictor transformation without the additional complication of identifying two parameters within model.

When $b = 1$, as in the previous section, we could directly transform the predictor values from $x \longrightarrow \exp(x)$. When $b \neq 1$, this approach is not possible immediately since the parameter b is unknown. What we need is some way to "open up" the exponent (bx). Enter the natural logarithm.

Starting with the exponential model

$$y_i = a \exp(bx_i)$$

we can take the natural logarithm of both sides of the equation

$$\ln(y_i) = \ln(a \exp(bx_i))$$

Applying the laws of logarithms and using the fact that the natural logarithm is the inverse function of the exponential, the right-hand side simplifies to

$$\ln(y_i) = \ln(a) + \ln(\exp(bx_i)) = \ln(a) + bx_i$$

Now, take a good look at the resulting model

$$\ln(y_i) = \ln(a) + bx_i$$

Rearranging the terms may make the critical observation more evident:

$$\ln(y_i) = bx_i + \ln(a)$$

What do we have here? Doesn't this model look suspiciously like

$$Y_i = bx_i + A$$

where $Y_i = \ln(y_i)$ and $A = \ln(a)$? We're dealing with another linear model! The parameter b is still unknown, but it is now the slope of a line whose intercept is $\ln(a)$. Remember that the intercept that we are talking about here is on the y-axis. And, if we change all the y_i-values to $\ln(y_i)$:

x	y		x	$\ln(y)$
x_1	y_1		x_1	$\ln(y_1)$
x_2	y_2	$\longrightarrow$	x_2	$\ln(y_2)$
$\vdots$	$\vdots$		$\vdots$	$\vdots$
x_m	y_m		x_m	$\ln(y_m)$

then the y-axis becomes the $\ln(y)$-axis in which all the values that you can read directly from the axis are natural logarithm values. This means that, if we suspected the underlying behavior to be exponential and we had no reason to believe that $b = 1$, we could transform the y-values as shown and then plot the new data set.

The resulting data should then be approximately linear: We're back to using one of the techniques suggested in the previous section to identify the equation of some fitting line in this transformed data set plot. The slope of this line, $\Delta(\ln(y))/\Delta x$, gives us our estimate for the parameter b. The intercept of this line is $\ln(a)$, where a is the leading coefficient in the exponential model we want to determine. So, by applying the exponential function to this intercept value we get $\exp(\ln(a)) = a$. Now, knowing both a and b, we can specify the exponential model that applies to our original data set: $y_i = a \exp(bx_i)$.

Example 9.15. Because the material used to generate power for satellites in geosynchronous orbit around Earth is radioactive, it is known that the power output in watts can be modeled using the exponential model

$$P = a \exp(bt)$$

where P is the power output, a and b are parameters of the model, and t represents time (days). For one particular power supply, the following data set was gathered.

t (days)	P (watts)	t (days)	P (watts)
100	34	600	5
200	23	700	3
300	15	800	2
400	10	900	1
500	7	1000	0.9

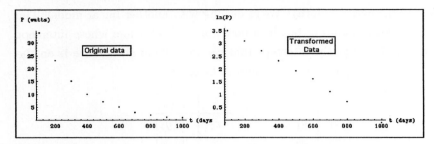

FIGURE 9.12
Satellite example: original and transformed data.

A plot of this discrete data set is shown in the left-hand illustration of Figure 9.12. Applying natural logarithms to both sides of the proposed model, we get

$$\ln(P) = \ln(a) + bt$$

To use this linear model to estimate a and b, we have to transform the response data $P_i \longrightarrow \ln(P_i)$, for $i = 1, 2, \ldots, 10$. This produces the transformed data set shown in the right-hand side of Figure 9.12:

t (days)	$\ln(P)$	t (days)	$\ln(P)$
100	3.5	600	1.6
200	3.1	700	1.1
300	2.7	800	0.7
400	2.3	900	0
500	1.9	1000	-0.1

For this example, rather than visually connecting several points and estimating a good fitting line for the transformed data, we'll use linear regression to produce the linear model for us. Using $\ln(P_i)$ as the response and t as the predictor produces the best-fitting line

$$\ln(P_i) = 3.95 - 0.004t$$

which is shown superimposed on the plot of the transformed data in Figure 9.13. From this line, we get $\ln(a) = 3.95$—Remember that we are working with transformed data, and the vertical axis shows natural logarithm values!—and $b = -0.004$. Solving for

$$a = \exp(\ln(a))) = \exp(3.95) \approx 52$$

we obtain our estimate for the parameters we need for our model:

$$P = 52\exp(-0.004t)$$

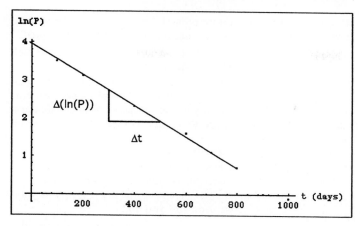

FIGURE 9.13
Best-fitting line in for the transformed data of the satellite example.

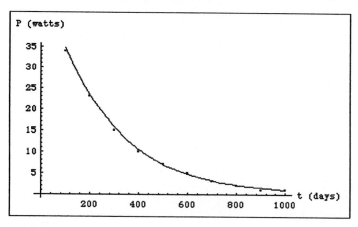

FIGURE 9.14
Exponential model versus the original satellite data.

Figure 9.14 shows our exponential model plotted against the original data to see how well it describes the pattern in the data.

There are numerous questions that we could answer using our working model, which we will leave for the next exercises.

Exploration Exercises

9.1. In the previous satellite example, use the exponential model that was developed to answer the following questions.
   (*a*) How much power will be available at the end of 1 year? 2 years?
   (*b*) How long will it take for the power supply to drop to half of its initial wattage?

(c) Assuming that the satellite needs a minimum of 8 watts of power to remain operational, how long will it be until the satellite is no longer operational?

9.2. Let's get some practice on estimating model parameters for the exponential model $\hat{y} = a \exp(bx)$. For each of the following data sets,

- Plot the original data, and see how well you can guess the appropriate parameters a and b by plotting your guess for the exponential model over the data. How many guesses did it take until you were satisfied with the model's fit? On what basis are you judging the fit of the model? (The number of points it actually passes through, etc.)
- State the associated linear natural logarithm model.
- Perform the necessary transformation and plot the transformed data.
- Using linear regression, identify the exponential model's parameters.
- State the resulting exponential model and plot it on the same graph as your original data set and your best guess. How did you do?

(a)

t	$f(t)$	t	$f(t)$
0	330	10	2
2	121	12	0.8
4	44	14	0.3
6	16	16	0.1
8	6	18	0.04

(b)

t	$f(t)$	t	$f(t)$
1	109	57	7
8	77	64	5
15	54	71	4
22	38	78	3
29	26	85	2
36	19	92	1
43	13	99	0.8
50	9		

(c)

t	$f(t)$	t	$f(t)$
1	0.6	11	19
3	1.5	13	36
5	2.6	15	71
7	5	17	137
9	9.8	19	264

(d)

t	$f(t)$	t	$f(t)$
0	22	5	1.9×10^{13}
1	5383	6	4.7×10^{15}
2	1.3×10^6	7	1.2×10^{18}
3	3.2×10^8	8	2.8×10^{20}
4	7.8×10^{10}	9	6.9×10^{22}

Let's close out this chapter with a couple of comments concerning transformations. As you progress through your continued study of mathematics, you may come to realize that being able to work with transformed data and variables can be very handy. The motivation for wanting to transform data will vary from application to application, but overall it provides us with a simpler representation of the data, either visually or algebraically.

But here is the catch: We have to keep reminding ourselves that once we perform a transformation and begin to work with the transformed data plot (called the tranformed "space"), the best fitting line we get from least squares produces model parameter estimates based on the best fit in the *transformed* data set and *not* in the original data. You must plot the exponential model using the parameters you estimate with the original data so that you can visually assess how well your model describes the original data.

Regression provides a means of fitting various types of nonlinear curves to data sets when we have reason to suspect that the underlying behavior conforms to one of these nonlinear function forms. This type of regression could very easily produce different estimates for the model parameters we are after. We'll leave an in-depth study of this topic for a course in mathematical statistics or regression. If it piques your interest now, either of the books on regression that we referenced in Chapter 8 provides good coverage of this more advanced topic.

9.8   SUMMARY

Exponential functions arise in practice when the response changes in proportion to the amount of response present.

The laws of exponents and logarithms provide us with a means of performing algebraic simplifications that allow us to more easily examine the relationship existing between the two.

Logarithmic models are appropriate when the rate of change of the response is proportional to the reciprocal of the predictor.

Data transformation is a very useful technique to use when determining unknown parameters of exponential and logarithmic models. The appropriateness of a model developed using parameters determined from the best-fitting line in the transformed space must be checked against the original data. Remember that the best-fitting line was determined using the transformed data and not the original data.

9.9 PROJECT: HARVESTING FOREST RESOURCES

Let's set the tone: Assume that you are an analyst working for a consulting company in Los Altos, California. The company uses math models to help other companies make intelligent business decisions about their operations. One of the contracts involving natural resource issues, which is your area of expertise, involves a client company called Ny-Com.

Ny-Com has two divisions, an Aluminum Division and a Wood Products Division. It is the Wood Products Division that needs assistance in developing their long-term business strategy. Your task is to develop a math model to help the management of Ny-Com decide on a long term policy for harvesting timber in their Pacific Northwest region.

9.9.1 Background information

In the 1980s, significant controversy started over the management of the old-growth forests on public lands in the Pacific Northwest region of the United States. The controversy really centered upon conflicting uses: harvesting timber for commercial use versus preserving the wilderness.

Ny-Coms Wood Products Division has a business interest in maintaining their access to the public forests that are managed by the U.S. Forest Service, since most of the privately held lands in the region that are leased by Ny-Com have been unable to generate sufficient stock for Ny-Com to satisfy their customer's needs. And, although Ny-Com replants many new trees in all the areas that they cut, the most valuable of these new trees will not reach maturity for many years.

The old-growth forests of this region are a valuable source of high quality wood veneer for Ny-Com, which processes this wood and sells it around the world. These specific forests are also considered a depletable natural resource.

Environmentalists and several federal lobbying groups continue to express concern over the rate of harvesting of old growth forest timber from Washington, Oregon, and California. These forests support a variety of plant and animal life that cannot be found anywhere else in the world. In a complex interaction only beginning to be understood by scientists, the diversity of ecological elements that comprise the old-growth forests of this region are a rich source of clean water, wildlife habitat, and biological diversity.

Additionally, the uniqueness of this region has stimulated the creation of a significant number of wilderness businesses that provide outdoor experiences for visitors, such as camping, hiking, hunting, and fishing.

At best estimate, there are currently 1,590,000 acres of old-growth forests in the Pacific Northwest regions.

Although both Ny-Com and the environmentalist groups see the forest as having great value, one groups goal appears to be in direct conflict with the others. Once old-growth timber is harvested, the delicate ecosystem is gone. To complicate the situation further, even though Ny-Com will replant the same type of trees in the areas that it cuts, it takes 150 to 200 years for the old-growth ecological environment to reform. This is called the forest's *regeneration cycle*.

The current situation:

The management of Ny-Coms Wood Products Division has a meeting with U.S. Forest Service representatives very soon to discuss and renegotiate Ny-Com's harvesting policies for the next 20 year planning horizon. The Forest Service currently permits Ny-Com to use an "even flow" harvest rate. Under this policy, Ny-Com harvests the *same amount* of timber each year. Each acre of old growth yields 44,000 board-feet of this valuable timber. The Forest Service's current even-flow policy allows Ny-Com to harvest 1738 million board-feet of old growth annually. This amount is sufficient to meet their projected customer demand.

Required Analysis_____

9.1. Identifying the assumptions:

    (*a*) The problem description states that there are 1,590,000 total acres. If you decide to use this number as the total amount of old-growth timber present for your model, what assumptions would you be making about the location of old-growth forests currently present in the Pacific Northwest? How reasonable is this assumption?

    (*b*) As the situation is described, what assumption is made about the number of companies harvesting old-growth timber from this area? If you don't use this assumption to build a math model, in what ways would the problem become more complicated?

    (*c*) What assumption is being made about the quality of the old-growth timber throughout the three state region? Do you think that this is a reasonable assumption to use to develop an initial model?

9.2. There is some information that we need to uncover about the current even-flow policy. The conflict between commercial timber business and environmental organizations has existed for quite a few years, and no one group has managed to raise this issue to such a level of attention before. So, under the even-flow policy, something must be going to happen in the future that is objectionable from both a business point of view (Ny-Com) and an environmentalist point of view. What is it, and when is it going to happen? Is the event significant enough for Ny-Com to consider adopting a new strategy? Or, could they continue to pursue the same harvesting strategy that they are currently using? Would this course of action make good business sense? To answer these questions, we need to build a mathematical model that represents the current even flow policy.

(a) Let t represent time in years, S_t represent the amount of old growth stock remaining at the end of year t, R_t equal the amount of old growth timber harvested during time period t. So, S_0 would represent the amount of old growth timber present at the start of the tracking period.

(b) With the current even flow extraction policy in mind, write an equation that describes the number of acres of old-growth timber remaining at the end of each year (S_t) in the future as a function of how much is being harvested annually (R_t). (Hint: Remember that the same amount of timber is being harvested each year under the current policy.)

(c) Plot the model that you come up with.

(d) Examine the plot that you created to answer the questions posed. Keep in mind the fact that it takes 150–200 years for old-growth forests to regenerate.

The proposed strategy:

The current even-flow policy has been useful for several industries that are dependent upon wood products for their livelihood, such as the home building industry, because it tends to restrict radical swings in timber supply from year to year. They currently do a pretty good job of predicting with some degree of accuracy how much timber will be available for their use in any particular year.

Ny-Com expressed to you that it would like to preserve some proportion of the old growth supply for future generations, and still be able to extract enough timber to sustain their Wood Products business during the planning horizon. If it has to switch over to a new product to replace its old-growth veneer business, it does not want to do this before it has time to retrain and re-outfit new production plants, which will take between 8 to 10 years.

Consequently, as opposed to harvesting the same amount of old-growth timber each year, Ny-Com is interested in harvesting the same *percentage of the remaining stock of timber* each year. This strategy inherently dictates that a different amount of timber will be harvested each year, with more being harvested in early years when the stock level is high, and less in later years when the stock level of timber has been depleted.

Ny-Com believes that a new extraction plan such as this is called for based on several important aspects of the environmentalists concerns that it now wishes to recognize. Specifically, Ny-Com would like to have 46% of the current stock of old-growth timber remaining at the end of 60 years, and believes that this goal would accommodate many of the environmentalists goals and concerns.

Required Analysis

9.1. First, let's examine the impact of Ny-Com's goal on the model that we already have developed for the current even-flow policy.

(a) Adjust your previous even-flow model to pass through the point where 46% of the timber resource remains at year 60.

(b) Would this new even-flow model be acceptable to the environmentalists and/or Ny-Com? Explain.

(c) What type of model would be appropriate for the proposed policy? Why?

(d) Would you think that the new model should be discrete or continuous? Why?

9.2. As done previously, let S_0 represent the initial amount of timber stock present, S_t be the amount of timber stock remaining at the end of time period t, and b represent the fixed percentage of harvesting allowed during each period.

(a) Using a recursive set of equations for S_0, S_1, S_2, ..., write an equation that will allow us to predict the level of timber remaining at the end of any time period S_t as a function of the initial amount S_0 and the allowable percent extraction b.

(b) Using a spreadsheet, estimate a value for b in the discrete model you just developed so that 46% of the initial stock is remaining at the end of 60 years.

9.3. Here's a reality check: Ny-Com's stated goal is to have 46 percent of the initial stock of timber remaining at the end of 60 years. However, after 60 years, do they care how much is remaining past that point? That is, do you think that they want us to develop a model that continues to harvest old-growth timber after the 46% mark is reached? Or, do you think that they want to leave 46% of the stock remaining forever? Explain how your answer to these questions effect your model.

9.4. Now, let's see what happens if we develop a continuous model directly from data using the techniques in the last section.

(a) Using the discrete model you just developed, generate a table of data that contains the predictor values (t), and response values S_t over the 60 year period Ny-Com is interested in.

(b) Assuming that the underlying behavior of the harvesting policy followed an exponential model of the form: $S_t = a \exp(bt)$, apply a natural logarithm transformation to the model and state the resulting natural logarithm linear model.

(c) Using linear regression on the transformed data set, estimate the exponential model parameters a and b.

(d) Plot both the original data and the exponential model on the same graph and commment on your assessment of how well the model fits the original data.

(e) Does this new model accomplish Ny-Com's goal? Does it accomplish the environmentalist's goal of preserving 46% of the old-growth timber for future generations of humans to enjoy? Explain.

9.5. Suppose that the model you developed worked just fine for old-growth, and Ny-Com is wondering if they could use it for their other timber harvesting operations. In particular, they would like to use it for examining different harvest strategies for Southern White Pine. How adaptable would your model be to this situation, knowing that (1) Ny-Com replants white pine trees in an area immediately after cutting, and (2) the regenerative cycle for white pine is approximately 40 years? How would you have to change the model to accommodate replanting?

9.10   COMPLEMENTS

One nice treatment of transformations from a modeling perspective is provided in

- *A First Course in Mathematical Modeling*, 2nd edition, by Giordano, Weir, and Fox. Brooks/Cole Publishing, Pacific Grove, California, 1997.

They provide a good coverage of the "Ladder of Transformations" along with some nice examples of modeling applications.

CHAPTER
10

NONLINEAR
MODELS III:
TRIGONOMETRIC
FUNCTIONS

The moon marks off the seasons, and the sun knows when to go down.

Psalm 104

Chapter Goals

⇒ Develop trigonometric models from data.

⇒ Understand the definitions and domains of trigonometric functions.

⇒ Understand radian measure.

⇒ Understand the Pythagorean theorem.

⇒ Understand the behavior of inverse trigonometric functions.

⇒ Model periodic and asymptotic behavior with trigonometric and inverse trigonometric functions.

⇒ Become familiar with a trigonometric change of variables.

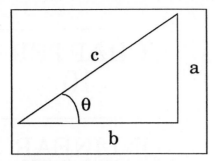

FIGURE 10.1
A right triangle.

10.1 INTRODUCTION

You have probably had a course in trigonometry in your prior studies. As we have done in previous chapters, we will cover some of that material again, but from different perspectives. Our goals are to refresh your skills, apply those skills to develop models, and to point out some of the trigonometric skills which are useful in the study of calculus.

Our experience has been that, of all the prerequisites for calculus students, trigonometry skills are the weakest. When you are done with this chapter, we hope that your skills will be sharpened, that you will recognize situations for which trigonometric models are appropriate, that you can construct trigonometric models, and that you are familiar with some trigonometric changes of variables.

It's not surprising that triangles are useful for modeling; after all, we have seen that the slope of a line can be thought of as the ratio of one side of a triangle (the rise) divided by another side (the run). However, you may be surprised by the wide range of situations for which trigonometric models are useful. The characteristic of trigonometric functions that contribute to their wide adaptability is that they are *periodic*. This ability to capture repeating or cyclical behavior makes them useful for modeling seasonal effects or repeated behavior that we observe, such as sales, tides, and other phenomena.

10.2 TRIGONOMETRIC FUNCTIONS

You recall the definitions of the sine and cosine of an angle. Given a right triangle, such as in Figure 10.1, we see that we have three sides a, b, and c, and an angle θ. By convention, we label the side of the triangle opposite the right angle as c.

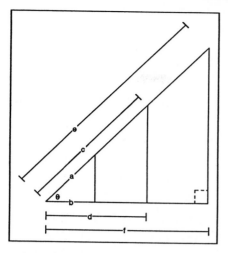

FIGURE 10.2
Similar right triangles with a common angle θ

c is also called the *hypotenuse* of the triangle. We have the following definitions:

Definition 10.1. The Six Trigonometric Functions of an Angle θ. Given a right triangle and an angle θ, as pictured in Figure 10.1, we define

Sine of θ:	$\sin\theta = \frac{a}{c}$
Cosine of θ:	$\cos\theta = \frac{b}{c}$
Tangent of θ:	$\tan\theta = \frac{a}{b}$
Cosecant of θ:	$\csc\theta = \frac{c}{a}$
Secant of θ:	$\sec\theta = \frac{c}{b}$
Cotangent of θ:	$\cot\theta = \frac{b}{a}$

Here's an insight related to geometry. Recall that if we know two of the angles of triangle, the third is determined: they are *similar* triangles. In other words, every right triangle sharing the same acute angle θ is going to have the same value for a trigonometric function of θ. So, in Figure 10.2, it doesn't matter whether we are referring to the smallest or largest of the three triangles shown because the ratio of the sides of the triangles, a/b, c/d, and e/f will be constant. This frees us to focus on θ, and not worry about a particular right triangle.

10.2.1   Radian measure

Before we go any further, we need to decide how we will measure θ. There are two widely used choices: *degree* measure and *radian* measure. You are no doubt

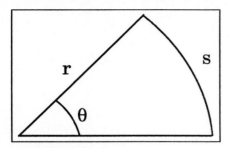

FIGURE 10.3
The relationship between radian measure and arc length of a unit circle.

familiar with degree measure, which says there are 360° in a circle. This measure is very familiar, and the one most frequently used in everyday applications.

RADIAN
MEASURE

However, we are going to use another measure for angles, *radian measure*. Radian measure is used in calculus, as well as physics and engineering, because it greatly simplifies many operations on trigonometric functions, such as integration and differentiation. Recall that we preferred the base e for similar reasons.

Radian measure uses the fact that there are 2π radians in a circle. Whereas a right angle, which is one quarter of the angular measure of a circle, was 90°, we now say it is $\frac{2\pi}{4} = \frac{\pi}{2}$ radians.

Another way of thinking about this is illustrated in Figure 10.3.

There we see that if we construct a circle with radius of length 1, the circumference of the circle is 2π. Then the radian measure of an angle is equal to the corresponding arc length "cut out" from the circle by the angle. In precise language, the radian measure of an angle is equal to the length of the arc of a circle of radius 1 *subtended* by the angle.

By convention, an angle is in standard position if its initial side is on the positive x-axis, with the vertex at the origin. We start measuring arc length at the point $(1, 0)$, and arc length is positive if measured in a counterclockwise direction, and negative if measured in a clockwise direction. (This is because we move "up" initially if we move in a counterclockwise direction from $(1, 0)$.)

This also gives us a handy way to find the arc length of portion of a circle. For example, if we have a circle of radius 2 feet, and we move along the circle through an angle of $\pi/4$ radians, how far have we moved? We have that $\theta = s/r$, where s is the arc length and r is the radius. Solving for s gives

$$s = r\theta \qquad (10.1)$$

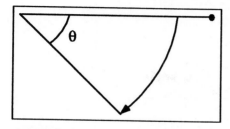

FIGURE 10.4
An example of a negative angle.

For our problem, we have $s = r\theta = \pi/4 \times 2 = \pi/2$ feet.

Notice that s is in the units of feet, and r is in the units of feet. Accordingly, from Equation 10.1, θ must be a dimensionless quantity, since the units cancel.

In general, we can convert from degrees to radians and radians to degrees by referring to how much of a circle is measured by the angle

$$\frac{\text{radians}}{2\pi} = \frac{\text{degrees}}{360} \tag{10.2}$$

By solving for radians, we obtain a formula for converting from degrees to radians:

$$\text{radians} = \frac{2\pi \text{ degrees}}{360} = \frac{\pi \text{ degrees}}{180} \tag{10.3}$$

Similarly, we obtain

$$\text{degrees} = \frac{360 \text{ radians}}{2\pi} = \frac{180 \text{ radians}}{\pi} \tag{10.4}$$

10.2.2 A word on notation

We will use the following two conventions for the rest of the book. First, you may assume all angles are measured in radians, unless we explicitly say otherwise. Second, it is awkward to refer continually to "an angle whose measure is k radians." We will use the more informal wording: "an angle of k radians." **NOTATION ALERT!**

10.2.3 Functions of θ

We can consider $\sin\theta$, $\cos\theta$, etc., to be *functions* of θ. Let's see if they meet the criteria for the definition of a function from Chapter 4. Is there only one value for $\sin\theta$, for a given θ? Yes! As a result, by definition we can consider $\sin\theta$ to be a function.

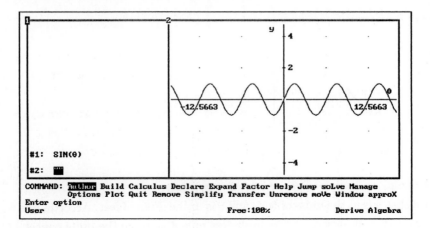

FIGURE 10.5
A plot of $y = f(\theta) = \sin \theta$. Note the range and domain of the function.

What would be the domain and range of $f(\theta) = \sin \theta$? Before we get a graphical answer, let's see if we can reason our way to an analytic answer. First, what are the possible values for the domain? Can we have a negative angle? The answer is yes, and this corresponds to moving downward from our initial position on the unit circle, as shown in Figure 10.4.

Since the measure of an angle can be any real number, positive or negative, for which of these real numbers is $\sin \theta$ defined? If we look at Figure 10.3, we see that a ranges between -1 and 1, and that the $\sin \theta = a$, since $c = 1$. As a result, $\sin \theta$ is defined for all angles, and its range is $[-1, 1]$.

Figure 10.5 shows a *Derive* plot of the function $f(\theta) = \sin \theta$, which illustrates the properties that we are discussing. We leave the determination of the domain and range of the other trigonometric functions to the exercises.

10.2.4 θ as a function of time

We can often think of the angle θ as varying with time. Frequently, the angle varies linearly with time:

$$\theta = bt + c \qquad (10.5)$$

Example 10.1. Consider a pointer spinning on a dial at a constant rate, which points at an angle of 1 radian when time is equal to 0. Say the pointer completes one revolution per minute. Then the angular measure increases by 2π radians every minute. We have as the equation for the angle of the pointer

$$\theta = 2\pi t + 1$$

It is possible to construct other models for θ as a function of time, but the linear model is surprisingly useful.

When we look at Equation 10.5, we can interpret the constant $b = 2\pi$ as the rate of change of the angle, or the *angular velocity*. It tells us how fast the angle is changing per unit time.   ANGULAR VELOCITY

Let's look at this idea from another perspective. If the angular velocity is b, how long does it take to complete an additional full circle, i.e., to traverse 2π radians? To answer this question, we must solve the equation $2\pi = bt$, which results in

$$t = \frac{2\pi}{b} \tag{10.6}$$

The time to traverse one full circle is a useful measure, and we will return to it.

Exploration Exercises _____

10.1. First, here's some practice in moving from measurement in degrees to radian measure.
(a) Convert 30° to radians.
(b) Convert 60° to radians.
(c) Convert 90° to radians.
(d) Convert $\pi/4$ radians to degrees.
(e) Convert $\pi/12$ radians to degrees.

10.2. If you ride on a Ferris wheel with radius 30 feet, and you make 15 complete revolutions during your ride, how far have you traveled? If your ride lasted 90 seconds, what was your average speed? What was your angular velocity?

10.3. In a continuation of the previous exercise, suppose that there are 12 equally spaced benches on the Ferris wheel. The benches are loaded/offloaded one at a time, in sequence. How far does one bench move between loadings?

10.4. Demonstrate that the expression $y = f(\theta) = \sin(\theta)$ is a function by plotting the expression over its domain and interpreting its plot with respect to the definition of a function.

10.5. Demonstrate that the expression $f(\theta) = \cos\theta$ is a function by plotting the expression over its domain and interpreting its plot with respect to the definition of a function.

10.6. Identify the domain and range of $f(\theta) = \tan\theta$ using a plot of this function to support your answer. Describe what happens when $\theta = \pi/2$? Why does this occur?

10.7. Identify the domain and range of $f(\theta) = \csc\theta$ using a plot of this function to support your answer. What happens when θ is an integer multiple of π?

10.8. Find the domain and range of $f(\theta) = \sec\theta$ using a plot of this function to support your answer.

10.9. Find the domain and range of $f(\theta) = \cot\theta$ using a plot of this function to support your answer.

10.10. Use Figure 10.1 to show that $\sin\theta = \cos(\pi/2 - \theta)$. (Hint: We know two angles of the right triangle in Figure 10.1. What must the third angle be?)

10.3 MANIPULATING TRIGONOMETRIC FUNCTIONS

Using trigonometry in modeling requires us to be able to simplify and manipulate trigonometric expressions. In this section, we will develop some of the more common manipulations that arise.

With the use of a computer algebra system (CAS) that has preprogrammed symbolic manipulation routines, it is less urgent for us to know and remember all the possible trigonometric manipulations. Still, understanding the ones presented in this chapter reinforces both our understanding of trigonometry and our modeling skills. Many of these manipulations are also useful in calculus to simplify expressions; learning them now provides both a present and a future payoff.

10.3.1 Identities

Relationships between trigonometric functions which hold for all possible values of θ are called *identities*. Many of them are based on the Pythagorean Theorem:

> **Theorem 10.1. Pythagorean Theorem.** Let a, b, and c be the sides of a right triangle, as pictured in Figure 10.1, with c the hypotenuse. Then
>
> $$a^2 + b^2 = c^2 \qquad (10.7)$$

Until recently, math historians thought that the history of mathematics began with Babylonian and Egyptian arithmetic, algebra, and geometry. However, several researchers[†] have discovered evidence of the Pythagorean Theorem's use in ancient alter constructions in India, the ancient Chinese collection *Nine Chapters of the Arithmetical Art*, and in the construction of the megalithic monuments in Southern England and Scotland.

[†]See *Geometry and Algebra in Ancient Civilisations*, by B.L. van der Waerden. Springer, 1983, pp. xi, 33, 35.

Notice that the Pythagorean Theorem only applies to right triangles, since it's origin was in exploring the relationship between the areas of three squares positioned to be touching at corners to form a right triangle.

The converse of the Pythagorean Theorem is also true: If the sides of a triangle satisfy the relationship that $a^2 + b^2 = c^2$, then the triangle is a right triangle. The proof of this converse dates back to Euclid (his 47th Problem). This converse was used by stone masons in the Middle Ages. They would construct triangles with sides of length 3, 4, and 5, resulting in right triangles. These right triangles were then used to verify that the masons had constructed square corners when they were building various structures.

If we refer back to Figure 10.3, we can see that there is a special relation between a, b, $\sin\theta$, and $\cos\theta$ when $c = 1$. Since $\sin\theta = a/c = a/1 = a$, we have that $\sin\theta = a$, when $c = 1$. In other words, the length of the opposite side is equal to the sine of the angle θ when the hypotenuse of the right triangle has length 1. In the same manner, we also see that $\cos\theta = b$.

Applying the Pythagorean Theorem, we have that

$$a^2 + b^2 = (\sin\theta)^2 + (\cos\theta)^2 = 1 \qquad (10.8)$$

Equation 10.8 holds for all values of θ:

$$(\sin\theta)^2 + (\cos\theta)^2 = 1$$

If we divide both sides of Equation 10.8 by $\sin\theta$, we obtain

$$1 + (\cot\theta)^2 = (\csc\theta)^2 \qquad (10.9)$$

which is another useful relationship. However, does this equation hold for all values of θ? In particular, what happens when $\theta = 0$? We'll let you explore these questions in the exercises.

We can get another useful relationship if we divide both sides of Equation 10.8 by $\cos\theta$. We obtain

$$(\tan\theta)^2 + 1 = (\sec\theta)^2 \qquad (10.10)$$

Again, we leave it for you to explore whether this meets the requirement to qualify as an identity.

There are many identities involving the sum and product of angles. For example, we know from standard trigonometry course that the $\sin(\alpha + \beta) =$

$\sin(\alpha + \beta)$	$= \sin\alpha\cos\beta + \cos\alpha\sin\beta$
$\cos(\alpha + \beta)$	$= \cos\alpha\cos\beta - \sin\alpha\sin\beta$
$\tan(\alpha + \beta)$	$= \frac{\tan\alpha + \tan\beta}{1 - \tan\alpha\tan\beta}$
$\sin(2\alpha)$	$= 2\sin\alpha\cos\alpha$
$\cos(2\alpha)$	$= \cos^2\alpha - \sin^2\alpha$
$\sin\alpha + \sin\beta$	$= 2\sin(\frac{\alpha+\beta}{2})\cos\frac{\alpha-\beta}{2})$
$\cos\alpha + \cos\beta$	$= 2\cos(\frac{\alpha+\beta}{2})\cos(\frac{\alpha-\beta}{2})$
$\tan\alpha + \tan\beta$	$= \frac{\sin(\alpha+\beta)}{\cos\alpha\cos\beta}$

TABLE 10.1
Additional useful trigonometric relations.

$\sin\alpha\cos\beta + \cos\alpha\sin\beta$. For our purposes, we will just acknowledge that these identities exist. If we need to simplify an expression that requires the use of such an identity, we will either use our computer algebra system, or look the identity up. We provide a partial table of these identities in Table 10.1 to cut down on the amount of outside referencing you might need to do.

A more complete listing is available from a standard trigonometry textbook, or a standard mathematics reference such as the *CRC Standard Mathematical Tables.*[‡]

The next example illustrates a graphical way of verifying whether a relationship is an identity.

Example 10.2. Suppose that

$$\sin\theta = 1 - \cos\theta$$

is an identity. Then, by simply moving all the terms of the equation to one side, it will always be true that

$$\sin\theta - 1 + \cos\theta = 0$$

So, if we plot the function $\sin\theta - 1 + \cos\theta$, it should appear as a horizontal line along the θ-axis. Figure 10.6 clearly shows this not to be the case. Therefore the proposed identity must not be true.

This graphical manner of checking the validity of an identity is very useful in general to verify whether a particular algebraic expression is true. We will return to this graphical check in the exercises.

[‡]Check out the excellent chapter on Linear Algebra by P. J. Driscoll in the 30th edition of the CRC tables!

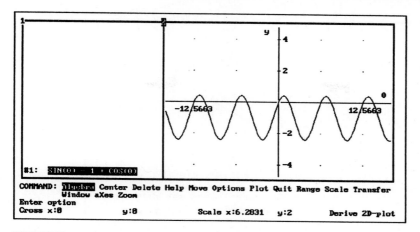

FIGURE 10.6

A graphical check of the proposed identity $\sin\theta = 1 - \cos\theta$ by plotting $\sin\theta - 1 + \cos\theta$.

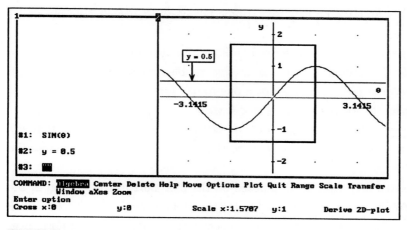

FIGURE 10.7

Restricting the domain for the inverse of $y = f(\theta) = \sin\theta$.

10.3.2   Inverse trigonometric functions

Suppose that we're gathering data on some periodic response and one of the values we measure is $y = 0.5$. If we suspect that the functional relationship is sinusoidal, we might model the behavior using the sinusoidal function $y = \sin\theta = 0.5$. The question is: How can we determine that value of the predictor θ that gave us this response?

Plotting $y = 0.5$ on the same graph as $y = f(\theta) = \sin\theta$, we see that there are an infinite number of values of θ such that $\sin\theta = 0.5$. One such value occurs

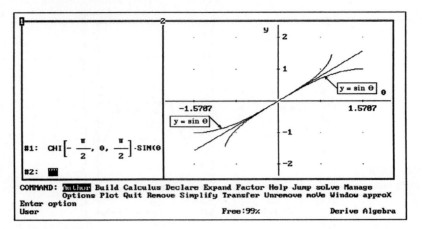

FIGURE 10.8
Finding the inverse of $f(\theta) = \sin\theta$ graphically, after we have restricted the domain of $f(\theta)$.

every time the function repeats its periodic behavior. Figure 10.7 clearly shows this behavior.

In order to find any θ, we need to know the inverse of the function $y = f(\theta) = \sin\theta$. Unfortunately, we face another problem in trying to find $f^{-1}(y)$. The function $y = f(\theta) = \sin\theta$ is not a one-to-one function, so it does not have an inverse over its entire domain $-\infty < \theta < \infty$.

However, notice in the plot of $y = f(\theta) = \sin\theta$ in Figure 10.7 that it's possible to restrict the domain of $f(\theta)$ so that any horizontal line will cross the function only once.

The boxed area that superimposed on the plot isolates the portion of the domain of $f(\theta)$ between $-\pi/2$ and $\pi/2$. On this interval, the function $f(\theta) = \sin\theta$ passes the horizontal line test, and is consequently one-to-one. Therefore, over the interval $-\pi/2 \le \theta \le \pi/2$ we can find its inverse.

Graphically, we can obtain a plot of the inverse function of $y = f(\theta) = \sin\theta$ over the interval $-\pi/2 \le \theta \le \pi/2$ by restricting the plot of the function to this interval and reflecting the plot through the line $y = \theta$. This procedure is shown in Figure 10.8 where we have restricted the domain of the plot region using the *Derive* chi function. Notice that we also changed the scale of the y-axis on the plot to highlight the idea of reflecting across the line $y = \theta$.

Accordingly, we make the following definition.

Definition 10.2. **Inverse Sine Function.** Let $f(\theta) = \sin\theta$. We define $\theta = f^{-1}(y) = \sin^{-1}(y)$ to be the unique value of θ in the interval $[-\pi/2, \ \pi/2]$ such

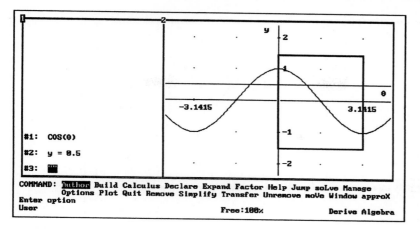

FIGURE 10.9
The graph of the function $f(\theta) = \cos\theta$ along with the line $y = 0.5$. What values of θ satisfy the equation $f(\theta) = \cos\theta = 0.5$?

that $\sin\theta = y$.

Note that this is not an inverse function for all values of θ. While it is true, for example, that $\sin^{-1}(\sin(\pi/3)) = \pi/3$, this does not hold for all values of θ. If we pick a value of θ outside the interval $[-\pi/2,\ \pi/2]$, we will not get the original value back. For example,

$$\sin^{-1}(\sin(4\pi)) = \sin^{-1}(0) = 0 \neq 4\pi$$

Given y, how do we find the value of $\sin^{-1}(y)$? We could approximate the value graphically, using Figure 10.8. However, many scientific calculators, all spreadsheets, and all computer algebra systems allow us to obtain the values of these functions. We took you through the ideas in this section to help you understand why a computer gives the results that it does when you ask for an inverse value using the program's routines.

10.3.2.1 INVERSE COSINE FUNCTION.
Finding the inverse of the cosine function $y = f(\theta) = \cos\theta$ requires us to restrict the domain of the cosine function for exactly the same reasons we restricted the domain of the sine function.

From looking at Figure 10.9, it appears reasonable to restrict the domain of θ to the interval $[0,\ \pi]$, which we have highlighted with a superimposed box. With this choice, $y = f(\theta) = \cos\theta$ will pass the horizontal line test for any

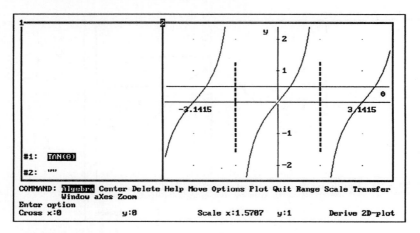

FIGURE 10.10
Our choice of restricted domain for $y = f(\theta) = \tan\theta$ is $\theta \in (-\pi/2,\ \pi/2)$, resulting in a one-to-one function for which we can find an inverse function.

horizontal line. Hence, the function defined over this restricted domain will be one-to-one, and will possess an inverse. We can specify another definition as a result:

> **Definition 10.3.   Inverse Cosine Function.**   Let $f(\theta) = \cos\theta$. We define $\theta = f^{-1}(y) = \cos^{-1}(y)$ to be the unique value of θ in the interval $[0,\ \pi]$ such that $\cos\theta = y$.

Again, we stress that this is a true inverse only if the domain of θ is restricted to be in the interval $[0,\ \theta]$.

10.3.2.2   INVERSE TANGENT FUNCTION.

The last inverse trigonometric function we will examine is the inverse of the tangent function $y = f(\theta) = \tan\theta$. We can see two important characteristics in the plot of the tangent function shown along with the horizontal line $y = 0.5$ in Figure 10.10 that will influence how we define an inverse for this function.

First, the periodic behavior of this function is quite different from that displayed by the sine and cosine functions. Although the pattern of its response for values of θ clearly repeats itself, the function is *discontinuous*. We can see that we'll again have to restrict the domain of $y = f(\theta) = \tan\theta$ if we want to define an inverse function for it. As it stands, the tangent function clearly fails the horizontal line test across all values of θ.

Second, there are several values of θ that the function seems to get close to but never quite reach. In some sense, they're like vertical fences or barriers that the function cannot cross from either side. Figure 10.10 shows these barriers to be occurring where $\theta = n\pi/2$, where n is any odd integer value. We need to know why this is happening. So, let's take a slight side step back to the definition of $\tan \theta$.

As you recall, for any right triangle, such as that shown in Figure 10.1, we define the tangent of the angle θ as

$$\tan \theta = \frac{\text{opposite}}{\text{adjacent}} = \frac{a}{b} \tag{10.11}$$

Now, fix the length of the hypotenuse c. As the angle θ increases, the hypotenuse c swings counterclockwise, stretching out the opposite side a for a while but continuously shrinking the adjacent side b.

As θ approaches the value $\pi/2$, or $90°$, the opposite side a stays just about constant, but the adjacent side b is very, very close to being zero! This makes the fraction of Equation 10.11 get larger and larger in value. Hence, if you zoom out as far as you want on a plot of $y = f(\theta) = \tan \theta$, the range of the function goes off to positive and negative infinity $(-\infty, \infty)$.

However, as the denominator of Equation 10.11 gets closer to zero, the definition of tangent is attempting to divide by zero, which is not defined. And this happens every time the hypotenuse of the triangle approaches the vertical axis of the plot: $\pi/2$, $3\pi/2$, $\ldots$, $n\pi/2$. But, since we also allow the hypotenuse to swing clockwise creating negative θ values, we get the same effect for $-n\pi/2$, $n = 1, 3, 5, \ldots$. So, we can't allow θ to use these values.

Both of these characteristics force us to restrict the domain of $y = f(\theta) = \tan \theta$ to $(-\pi/2, \pi/2)$, which in turn restricts the range of the inverse function to $(-\pi/2, \pi/2)$. This choice means that we will find inverses using only the portion of the graph of $f(\theta) = \tan \theta$ between the dashed vertical lines in Figure 10.10.

We define the inverse tangent function as we have defined the other inverse trigonometric functions:

Definition 10.4. **Inverse Tangent Function.** Let $y = f(\theta) = \tan \theta$. We define $\theta = f^{-1}(y) = \tan^{-1}(y)$ to be the unique value of θ in the interval $(-\pi/2, \pi/2)$ such that $\tan \theta = y$.

We could define inverse functions for the cotangent, secant, and cosecant functions, following the ideas presented above. We will not do so, however, in this book. You should be aware that various authors define the domains of these three inverse functions differently, so it is important to know the exact definition being used if you encounter one of them.

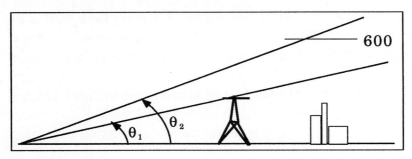

FIGURE 10.11
Constraints for finding a glide path angle.

Why do we care about inverse trigonometric functions? We will use the inverse trigonometric functions primarily in the next section on changes of variables. However, they are useful in their own right for modeling, as the next two examples show.

Example 10.3. One of the tools used by airports to guide arriving planes is called a *glide slope indicator*, or GSI. A GSI projects three beams of high-intensity light colored red, green, and yellow. If an aircraft's angle of approach to the airport landing strip is correct, the pilot will see the green light all the way in. If the aircraft is flying below the correct glide path, the angle of approach will be too shallow and too close to the ground. In this case, the pilot will see a red light. If the aircraft is approaching the landing strip flying above the correct glide path, the pilot will see the yellow beam, indicating that the aircraft should assume a steeper descent.

The light for flying below the correct glide path is red because that means the aircraft has the potential of flying into obstacles or into restricted airspace. Many localities around airports have restrictions about how low aircraft can fly over their areas.

At what angle should the glide slope indicator be set? Let's stand at our planned touchdown point for the airplane, somewhere on the runway. Say the closest obstacle to the airport is a set of high power lines 500 meters from the end of the runway. The lines are 25 meters high. Approaching aircraft will want to clear them, so the angle must be large enough that any incoming aircraft clears them. Let's also say that there is a 10,000 meter buffer zone off the end of the runway. Past that buffer is residential housing, and approaching aircraft are required to fly at least 600 meters above that housing, to reduce the noise that the residents are exposed to. Figure 10.11 shows the constraints.

Additionally, the aircraft should approach the landing strip on the shallowest glide path possible, so as to not discomfort the passengers. We also want to meet our constraints.

The first constraint says that $\tan\theta \geq \frac{25}{500}$, which in turn implies that $\theta \geq \tan^{-1}(0.05) = 0.05 \text{rad} = 2.86°$.

The second constraint says that $\tan\theta \geq \frac{600}{10,000}$, which in turn implies that $\theta \geq \tan^{-1}(0.06) = 0.06 \text{ rad} = 3.44°$.

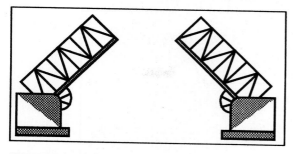

FIGURE 10.12
A schematic of the Montlake Bridge.

Aircraft should approach on the greater of the two angles, or 0.06 radians.
As an aside, aircraft tend to take off at much steeper angles than they land.
Why is this so?

Example 10.4. In the Montlake area of Seattle, close to the University of Washington, there is a drawbridge over the Montlake cut, which connects Lake Washington with Lake Union. The bridge has a length of 186 feet, divided into two sections of 93 feet each, as illustrated in Figure 10.12. The bridge opens as electric motors pivot the bridge deck open. The maximum angle that the bridge can open is 72 deg, or 1.2566 rad. The bridge deck is wider than the canal below it, because the gears that pivot the bridge open are on land. The actual width of the cut is 146 feet.

We'd like to have two pieces of information. First, what is the maximum width of the gap between the ends of the bridge? Second, for a specific gap, what should angle should the bridge deck make with the horizontal position? This second issue is important because a lot of sailboats go through the Montlake cut, and the bridge has to be opened only wide enough to pass the mast through with a sufficient margin. The smaller the angle is, the quicker the operation can be performed.

We find the maximum width by referring to Figure 10.13.

There we see that the gap width, w, is found as

$$w = 2r(1 - \cos\theta) \tag{10.12}$$

Since the maximum angle is 1.2566 rad, we see that the maximum value of $w = 1.3820r$. For the Montlake Bridge, that would be $w_{max} = 1.3820 \times 93 = 129$ feet.

Where does the inverse trigonometry come in? Well, say that we need a gap of only 50 feet. What should the angle be? We must solve

$$50 = 2(75)(1 - \cos\theta)$$

which simplifies to

$$\cos\theta = 1 - \frac{50}{2 \times 75} = \frac{2}{3}$$

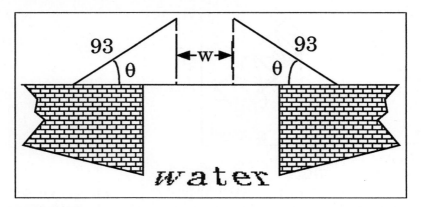

FIGURE 10.13
The Montlake bridge, with notation for modeling.

This means that

$$\theta = \cos^{-1}\left(\frac{2}{3}\right) = 0.8411 \text{ rad} = 48.1897°$$

Notice we have applied the definition of inverse cosine directly. And, as we would encourage you to do, we used our calculator to obtain these values!

In the exercises, we ask you to make a table for the bridge operator, showing the angle of the bridge opening necessary to obtain horizontal clearances of various widths. For additional information, visit the WWW site for the Seattle Engineering Department, at

http://www.pan.ci.seattle.wa.us/seattle/engr/bridge.htm.

10.3.3   Changes of variable

This section is a preview of a very handy technique that arises in calculus. At the heart of this technique is the idea that we can structure a problem's description to resemble the sides of a triangle and then change the variables from measures of length to angle measurement. Why would we ever want to do such a thing?

It turns out that solving calculus integrals involving angles is often much simpler than solving integrals involving expressions with square roots, especially if the square roots are in the denominator of an expression.

This technique is often called a *trigonometric substitution* because we use trigonometric identities to substitute expressions involving angles for the expressions involving the original variable. It is really clever once you understand the basic idea. Let's see if we can give you a feel for it.

Say we have an expression such as $y = 1/\sqrt{1 - x^2}$. Now, picture a triangle that looks like the one in Figure 10.14.

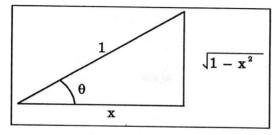

FIGURE 10.14
A triangle showing the change-of-variable scheme.

Here we have a right triangle with hypotenuse equal to 1, and with the side opposite our angle θ being $\sqrt{1-x^2}$. Using the Pythagorean Theorem (here it is again!), you should convince yourself that the adjacent side must have length x. With regard to Figure 10.14, this means that our expression represents

$$y = \frac{1}{\sqrt{1-x^2}} = \frac{\text{hypotenuse}}{\text{opposite}}$$

which is the definition of $\csc\theta$.

So instead of working with our starting expression, which was a function of x, we can work with the equivalent trigonometric function $y = \csc\theta$, which is a function of θ. This technique changes the variables that we are working with; hence, it's called a *change-of-variable* technique.

If we wanted to check to see if our change of variables is correct, we can find an expression for θ and work backward to see if we recover our original expression. From Figure 10.14 we have that

$$\frac{x}{1} = x = \cos\theta \qquad \text{or} \qquad \theta = \cos^{-1}x$$

Then, using our CAS we can substitute this expression for θ into the new trigonometric function $y = \csc(\cos^{-1}x)$, and simplify it. As hoped, we obtain $y = \frac{1}{\sqrt{1-x^2}}$.

We can find changes of variables for other expressions in a similar manner, especially if they involve $\sqrt{1+x^2}$, $\sqrt{x^2-1}$, or $\sqrt{1-x^2}$, which makes it easy to construct the appropriate right triangle. We'll do one more example.

Example 10.5. Consider the expression $y = x^2/\sqrt{x^2-1}$. We wish to change variables using a trigonometric substitution. So, we draw a triangle and label the sides as in Figure 10.15. Since we are working with the term x^2-1, the Pythagorean Theorem suggests that x should be the length of the hypotenuse, since the longest side is always the hypotenuse in a right triangle, and $x >$

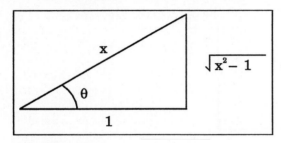

FIGURE 10.15
Finding an appropriate change-of-variables.

since the longest side is always the hypotenuse in a right triangle, and $x >$ $\sqrt{x^2 - 1}$. We choose (arbitrarily) to let the side opposite θ equal $\sqrt{x^2 - 1}$, which makes the remaining side have length 1.

We then use the definition of tangent to link angle measurement to length measurement:

$$\tan \theta = \frac{\sqrt{x^2 - 1}}{1}$$

Notice that we also have $\sec \theta = x/1 = x$. We can put these pieces of information together, so that we have

$$y = \frac{x^2}{\sqrt{x^2 - 1}} = \frac{\sec^2 \theta}{\tan \theta}$$

This form is much easier to work with in a calculus course. (It had better be, to justify the extra work in making the change of variables!)

Exploration Exercises

10.1. Determine whether the following equations are identities.
  (a) $\sin \theta = 1 + \cos \theta$
  (b) $\sin^2 \theta = 1 - \cos^2 \theta$
  (c) $\sin(2\theta) = 2 \sin \theta \cos \theta$
  (d) $\sin(3\theta) = 3 \sin \theta \cos \theta$
  (e) $\cos(2\theta) = 2 \cos \theta$
  (f) $\cos(3\theta) = 3 \cos \theta$

10.2. Solve the following equations for θ, if possible. If not possible, state why not.
  (a) $\sin \theta = 0$
  (b) $\sin \theta = 1$
  (c) $\sin \theta = 2$
  (d) $\cos \theta = 0.5$
  (e) $\sin \theta = \cos \left(\frac{\pi}{2} \right)$
  (f) $\cos^{-1} = \frac{12\pi}{5}$
  (g) $\cos^{-1} = \frac{2\pi}{5}$
  (h) $\tan \theta = 600$
  (i) $\tan \theta = -600$

10.3. We see in our glide slope example that for small values of θ, such as $\theta = 0.05$ and $\theta = 0.06$, $\tan^{-1}(\theta) \approx \theta$. Explore this approximation by plotting the two functions $f(x) = \tan^{-1}(\theta)$ and $g(\theta) = \theta$ on the same plot. Does the same approximation hold for $\sin^{-1}(\theta)$?

10.4. If an approaching aircraft has to clear an obstacle 35 meters high located 6000 meters from its touchdown point, find the minimum glide slope angle θ. Express your answer in both radians and degrees.

10.5. The battleship U.S.S. Missouri ("Mighty MO) has a beam (maximum breadth) of 108 feet. What is the minimum angle θ that the Montlake bridge deck must be raised for the "Mighty MO" to pass through?

10.6. Develop a table for the Montlake bridge operator to use that shows what the angle of elevation must be for the bridge for a specified width of opening. Have entries for 10 feet wide, 20 feet wide, and so on, up to 129 feet wide.

10.7. Develop a second table for the Montlake bridge operator that tells how high the end of the bridge deck has risen for a given angle of elevation. Have entries for 10 feet high, 20 feet high, etc. What is the maximum height for the bridge, given that the maximum angle of elevation remains 72°?

10.8. Use a trigonometric change of variables to rewrite each of the following expressions.
(a) $x^2/\sqrt{1-x^2}$
(b) $x/\sqrt{1-x^2}$
(c) $x/\sqrt{1-x}$ (Hint: Let $x = u^2$.)
(d) $x^{3/2}/(x^2+1)^2$

10.9. Extend the idea of trigonometric change of variables to expressions of the form $a^2 + x^2$, $a^2 - x^2$, and $x^2 - a^2$.

CHALLENGING

10.4 SIMPLE HARMONIC MOTION

We are now going to examine some idealized models, in which the motion of bodies can be represented by trigonometric functions. These models are useful in the physical sciences. The ideas they use can be extended to the social sciences and to business, as well.

Our first order of business will be to discuss simple functions describing how θ varies. We will then discuss sinusoids. Finally, we will use the ideas about functions about the composition of functions, from Chapter 4, to extend our sinusoid model to several interesting applications such as radio broadcasting and sales forecasting.

PERIODIC
FUNCTIONS
The key concept in this section is the idea of a *periodic function*, or one that repeats itself over time. We will examine the implications of periodicity in some detail.

10.4.1   When θ varies

We discussed earlier how θ can often be thought of a linear function of time. For example,

$$\theta = -\frac{2\pi \text{ hours}}{12}$$

could describe the angle the hour hand of a clock makes with its "12 o'clock" position. θ is often modeled this way, as a multiple of time.

This is useful for modeling behavior that repeats itself over time. For example, the sales of some items might vary according to the season of the year, but remain otherwise level from year to year. Another example might be the carrier wave for a radio signal. If it operates at a certain frequency on the dial, then the carrier wave repeats itself at a fixed interval.

The classic example is a mass suspended from a spring, for which we ignore the effects of friction. The spring mass system is said to have *simple harmonic motion*.

10.4.2   Harmonic motion

Many models in physics describe the location of a body as a function of time. The
HARMONIC
MOTION
simplest models describe motion along one axis, such as ball rolling along a groove or the bobbing up and down of a weight at the end of a spring. There are laws in physics that describe these motions, under certain simplifying assumptions.

Analysis of these laws often leads to models that involve trigonometric functions. We are going to look at one such model, and examine its solution in detail.

> **Example 10.6.** Suppose we have a mass suspended vertically from a spring. If we let the mass rest, it will hang at some fixed length, with the spring stretched. Let's say that the height of the mass at rest is $h = 0$. Now, let's lift the mass up a small distance to a point we'll call the initial displacement point. We'll call that point a, with a distance of $|a|$ from the rest point. When we release the mass, what happens? It begins to move down as the spring stretches. It passes through the rest point and continues, until it gets to the same distance a below the rest point. It then rises back through the rest point, compressing the spring, until it reaches the initial displacement point again. And the process repeats.
>
>   *Hooke's Law* from physics can be used to show that the motion of this ideal spring mass system follows the equation
>
> $$h = a\cos(bt + c) + d \tag{10.13}$$

In Equation 10.13, a is called the *amplitude*. The amplitude is defined as the maximum distance above (or below) the rest point that the spring reaches. What is b?

One way to interpret b is to consider how long it will take for the mass to return to its maximum height. We know that it would take a compete rotation through an angle of 2π radians for that to happen. So we have

$$2\pi = bT$$

which tells us that the time between successive maximums is

$$T = \frac{2\pi}{b}$$

This time T is called the *period* of the spring mass system, and it depends on b.   **PERIOD** We'll discuss this more in a later section.

Another way to look at b is to ask how often in a given unit of time the spring returns to its maximum, given that it started there. If the time between   **FREQUENCY** successive maximums is T, they must occur at a rate of $f = \frac{1}{T}$. This rate, f, is called the *frequency* of the spring mass system.

The value c is a constant that allows us to adjust our model if our initial start time was not $t = 0$. The value d allows us to adjust our model if the rest position of the mass is not at the zero point on whatever scale we are using to measure height.

10.4.2.1   MORE ON B.

Every spring has a constant associated with it, k, which measures how resistant the spring is to stretching. High values of k mean that the spring is harder to stretch. One consequence of Hooke's law is that we can find b in terms of k and m, the mass of the spring. The relationship is given by

$$b = \sqrt{\frac{k}{m}} \qquad (10.14)$$

10.5   PERIODIC FUNCTIONS

When you plotted the functions of $y = f(\theta) = \sin\theta$, $y = f(\theta) = \cos\theta$ and the other trigonometric functions, the most salient characteristic of these functions is that they tended to repeat their appearance across the unrestricted domain of θ. That also was true for the simple harmonic motion of the preceding section. We are going to explore this periodic behavior in this section.

First, we need to create a definition.

PERIODIC

FUNCTIONS

Definition 10.5.   Periodic Function. A function is *periodic* if there exists a real value T such that $f(x + T) = f(x)$ for all values of x in the domain of f. If T is the smallest positive value for which this property holds, then the function is said to be periodic with period T.

Example 10.7. The trigonometric function $y = f(\theta) = \sin\theta$ is periodic with period 2π. We can see this by examining the earlier graph of $y = f(\theta) = \sin(\theta)$ in Figure 10.5. Notice that $\sin(\theta + 4\pi) = \sin\theta$, as well, but $T = 2\pi$ is the *smallest* value for which the expression $\sin(\theta + T) = \sin\theta$ is true for all θ. That is why the period is 2π.

Not all periodic functions are trigonometric functions. Here is an example of one that is not.

Example 10.8. Let's define a function using two pieces: $y = f(x) = 1$ if x is an integer, and $y = f(x) = 0$ if x is not an integer. Is this function periodic? If so, what is its period?

First, let's fix k to be an integer. In this case, notice that $f(x + k) = f(x)$ for all x, because if x is an integer, then $x + k$ is also an integer, and if x is not an integer, $x + k$ is also not an integer.

Second, notice that 1 is the smallest positive integer, and that the property $f(x + k) = f(x)$ in this example only holds for integer-valued k's. So by our definition, the period the function $f(x)$ is $T = 1$.

To return to trigonometric examples, we noticed in the preceding section that the period of $h = a\cos(bt)$ was equal to $T = \frac{2\pi}{b}$, although we loosely defined "period." Does this hold for other trigonometric functions? We will answer this

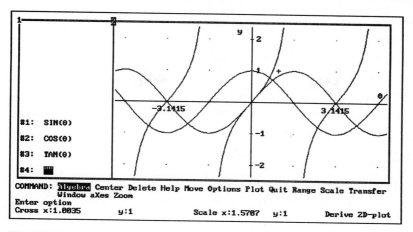

FIGURE 10.16

The graphs of $y = f(\theta) = \sin\theta$, $y = f(\theta) = \cos\theta$, and $y = f(\theta) = \tan\theta$. Notice that the period of $y = f(\theta) = \tan\theta$ is not the same as the period of the other two functions.

in two parts. First, we will find the period of each of the six functions, when $b = 1$. Then we will reason what the period must be when $b \neq 1$.

If we plot $\sin(\theta), \cos(\theta)$, and $\tan(\theta)$, we obtain the graphs in Figure 10.16. We see from this figure that $\sin(\theta)$ and $\cos(\theta)$ have the same period, but $\tan(\theta)$ has a different period. The period of $\tan(\theta) = \pi$, while the period of the other two functions is 2π. Because $\sec(\theta) = 1/\cos(\theta)$, $\csc(\theta) = 1/\sin(\theta)$, and $\cot(\theta) = 1/\tan(\theta)$, their periods are the same. You will be asked to demonstrate these ideas graphically and symbolically in the exercises.

10.5.1 Sinusoids

Consider a function of the form $f(t) = a\cos(bt + c) + d$. We call such a function a *sinusoid*. We know already that a is the amplitude, and b is determines the period. What might be the role of c?

The value c is called a *phase shift*. We can consider its role by looking at the form of a sinusoid again, considering it as the composition of two functions. PHASE
We can write $f(t) = \cos(g(t))$, where $g(t) = bt + c$. Then we see that the effect SHIFT
of c is a translation of g. The effect on f is to translate the graph to the left or right depending on whether the sign of c is positive or negative, respectively. When $c = -\pi/2$, the graph of $\cos(bt - \pi/2)$ is the same as the graph of $\sin(bt)$. The sin and cos functions differ only by a phase constant. This is why we call the sinusoid $f(t) = a\cos(bt + c)$ a sinusoid, even though there is no $\sin(t)$ in the

expression!

Notice that the phase constant does not affect the period, which continues to depend on b only, nor does it affect the amplitude, which continues to depend on a only.

The constant parameter d allows us to raise or lower the sinusoid; it is a translation constant, or the vertical shift. This vertical shift allows us to model situations in which the center of the y range is not zero.

Exploration Exercises

10.1. Show that the following functions have the same period.
   (a) $f(\theta) = \sin\theta$ and $g(\theta) = \csc(\theta)$
   (b) $f(\theta) = \cos\theta$ and $g(\theta) = \sec\theta$
   (c) $f(\theta) = \tan\theta$ and $g(\theta) = \cot\theta$
   (d) $f(\theta) = \sin(\theta + 1)$ and $g(\theta) = \sin\theta$
   (e) $f(\theta) = \sin\theta$ and $g(\theta) = tan(2\theta)$
   (f) $f(\theta) = \sin\theta\cos\theta$ and $g(\theta) = \sin(2\theta)$

10.2. If a sinusoid has a period of 6 hours, find b and the frequency.

10.3. Find the amplitude, period, frequency, phase shift, and vertical shift of the following functions.
   (a) $f(t) = 3\cos(4t - 1) + 3$
   (b) $f(t) = 4\cos(-3t + 3) + \pi$
   (c) $f(t) = -3\cos(3\pi t - 7) + 2$

10.4. Can a polynomial be a periodic function? What would its period be? (Hint: think of a polynomial of degree 0.)

10.5. If $f(t)$ has period 2π and $g(t)$ has period 3π, what would be the period of $f(t) + g(t)$? Or would the sum of two periodic functions be periodic? Why or why not?

10.6   MODELING PERIODIC PHENOMENA

In this section, we will look at some phenomena that can be modeled using trigonometric functions, and especially sinusoids. Our ability to represent these phenomena using trigonometric functions will help our understanding of the trigonometric functions and add additional tools to our modeling tool kit. We will also see some instances where these models need refinement, and we will extend our methods.

10.6.1 Two approaches

We can use two approaches to modeling periodic behavior. The first involves modeling from first principles and our understanding of the behavior. The second involves fitting data with periodic functions. In practice, we often use a mixture of the two methods.

10.6.1.1 FIRST PRINCIPLES.

If we know that the behavior we are attempting to model is periodic, we often can use trigonometric functions to model this behavior. This is especially true when the behavior we are observing appears to be dependent upon time. Of course, there are periodic behaviors that are not well modeled by trigonometric functions, but we'll skip those for now.

> **Example 10.9.** Let us say that this behavior is a response y that apparently depends on the predictor t, which we can think of as time. Let's further suppose that y has a period of 3, and that y has a range between -2 and 2, and that y reaches a maximum when $t = 1$. Can we find $f(t)$?
>
> Let's start with a. The range of y is 4 units, meaning that y varies between $+2$ and -2. Accordingly, the amplitude is 2, and $a = 2$.
>
> We are given that the period, T, is 3. Since we know that $T = \frac{2\pi}{b}$, we can solve for $b = \frac{2\pi}{3} \approx 2.0944$.
>
> How do we find c? We can use the information given and found so far to solve for c. We have that $y_{max} = 2 = 2\cos(\frac{2\pi}{3}1 + c)$. We can solve this using our inverse cosine function, as follows.

$$2 = 2\cos(\frac{2\pi}{3}1 + c)$$

$$1 = \cos(\frac{2\pi}{3}1 + c)$$

$$\cos^{-1}(1) = \frac{2\pi}{3}1 + c$$

$$\cos^{-1}(1) - \frac{2\pi}{3}1 = c$$

$$0 - \frac{2\pi}{3} = c$$

$$c = -\frac{2\pi}{3}$$

> Our final model is

$$y = 2\cos(\frac{2\pi t}{3} - \frac{2\pi}{3})$$

or

$$y = 2\cos(\frac{2\pi(t-1)}{3})$$

What would we have done if y had not varied around $y = 0$ in this example, but had ranged from, say, 1 to 5? One option is that we could have added the center y value, 3, to the right-hand side, and written $y = f(t) = a\cos(bt + c) + 3$, and then proceeded as above. This would give us

$$y = 2\cos(\frac{2\pi(t-1)}{3}) + 3$$

which is an example of a vertical translation, as we discussed earlier and in the chapter on functions.

Information about periodic systems can come to us in many forms. We can use information about the range, period, and a fixed value to find the values of the parameters of the sinusoidal model directly. In other cases, we must use other techniques (such as *differential equations*) that proceed from first principles to find the values of the parameters. Or, we can obtain a data set, and try to fit the parameters empirically.

10.6.1.2 FITTING SINUSOIDS EMPIRICALLY.

If we have a data set with (t, y) pairs, we can plot the data. If it appears to be sinusoidal, we can attempt to fit the data with an equation of the form $\hat{y} = f(t) = a\cos(bt + c) + d$. It will often be the case that the data cannot be exactly fit by a sinusoid, because of either measurement error, or because the underlying behavior is only approximately sinusoidal. Still, this empirical approach to fitting a sinusoidal function form provides models that are often useful.

How do we estimate a, b, c, and d from a data set? We want to obtain values of a, b, c, and d that we can use in the equation $\hat{y} = a\cos(bt + c) + d$, where $\hat{y}$ is our estimated value for y given a particular value of t. As done previously when we worked with linear regression, we'll refer to the values the $\hat{y}$ values our final model will produce as *fitted* values.

There are three approaches we can take, although only two will be available to you for now. Each approach attempts to minimize the sum of the squared errors, where this error is the same as that in linear regression: our observed y value from the data minus the fitted values $\hat{y}$.

All three approaches construct the sum of the squared errors as a function of the parameters a, b, c, and d. We then vary the parameters, searching for combinations that minimize the sum of the squared errors, where each squared

TABLE 10.2
Data for the empirical fitting examples.

t	y	t	y
0	2	6	-2
1	5	7	-1
2	6	8	2
3	5	9	5
4	2	10	6
5	-1		

error amount is calculated as

$$(y - \hat{y})^2 = (y - (a \cos(bt + c) + d))^2$$

Lets consider that we have 11 observations, as given in Table 10.2.

The first approach employs a manual search using, say, a spreadsheet. Writing the t and y data from Table 10.2 in separate columns, we can then define the parameters in different cells and write a third column as the fitted values based on our estimates for the parameters.

We then create a fourth column as the squared difference between y and $\hat{y}$, and sum that column. By graphing the values of (t, y) and $(t, \hat{y})$ in the same plot, and guessing different parameter values, we get different values for the sum of squared errors, and a different graph of $(t, \hat{y})$. This approach is illustrated in Figure 10.17.

We can continue to experiment until we get errors that appear to be the smallest, giving a good set of parameters to use in fitting our model to the data. One approach is to search through the parameter values in turn, each time finding the value that appears to minimize the sum of squared errors for that parameter. This is illustrated in the spreadsheets in Figure 10.18.

A second option is again a manual search, but this time aided by some first principle ideas about the observed data. For example, if we look at the data in Table 10.2, we see that the distance between the maximum y entries appears to be 8. This allows us to estimate that $b \approx 2\pi/8 \approx 0.7854$. Similarly, we see that the range is between 6 and -2, which allows us to guess that a should be around 4. The value d appears to be equal to 2, since the middle value of the range of y is 2. These good initial guesses, from first principles, allow us to smartly iterate our search for good values of a, b, c, and d much more quickly. (That is actually

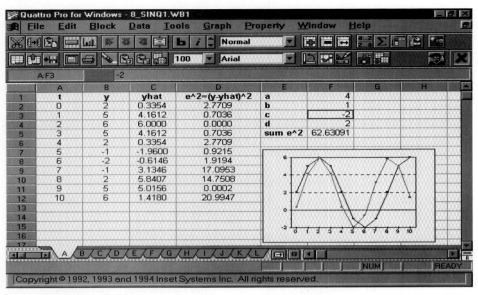

FIGURE 10.17

An initial guess for the values of a, b, c, and d that minimize the sum of $(y - \hat{y})^2$, where $\hat{y} = a\cos(bt + c) + d$. The sum of the squared errors is 62.63091, which is high. We also see that the period seems to be too big, judging from the graph. We can improve our guess by iteration.

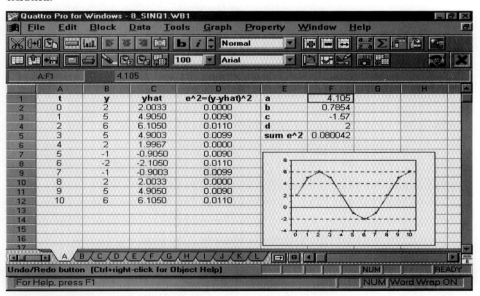

FIGURE 10.18

A much improved guess for values of a, b, c, and d that minimize the sum of $(y - \hat{y})^2$, where $\hat{y} = a\cos(bt + c) + d$. Now the sum of squared errors is only about 0.08. These values for a, b, c, and d are close to the optimal values that we could find using the techniques of calculus.

the approach we took to get the improved values in the second spreadsheet in Figure 10.18.)

There are two problems associated with these first two approaches. First, while we can see that we have good fits, we have no assurance that we have the best fit. Second, we have to iterate repeatedly to improve our estimates, and that takes time and effort.

Surprisingly, what calculus does to answer this challange is, in essence, the same—it allows us to find the parameters that minimize the sum of the squared errors, using a different technique. Calculus techniques allow us to find the best fit in one step without iterating, and to prove that we actually have found the best fit. Calculus also gives us explicit formulas for the estimated parameters. These advantages are chief among the reasons that calculus is such a powerful tool. This third option, based on calculus, must await your future studies.

Notice that if we had just tried to use a first-principle analysis on this data set without empirical improvement, we would have obtained $a = 4$. The sum of the squared errors for the model with $a = 4$ is 0.146463, which is about 80% more than the best fit we display in Figure 10.18.

10.6.1.3 COMMENTS.

Even when we think we know what the parameters of our fitted function should be, based on first principles, we can still often improve the fit of our model to the real data. We should keep this in mind.

We also might find situations where our amplitude or period are functions of t, instead of being constants. We will see an example of this shortly when we discuss radio signals. This, of course, calls for more complicated modeling.

Last, there are behaviors that can be modeled as linear combinations of trigonometric functions, as sums of polynomials and trigonometric functions, and as products of trigonometric functions and other functions. We will present a few such examples in the exercises, to stimulate your appreciation for the power of trigonometric models.

10.6.2   Tides

Since tides rise and fall regularly, we might think they could be modeled with trigonometric functions. Can we find data and construct a model?

There is a Web page dedicated to surfers at http://www.surfinfo.com. One SURFER of the services at this site provides information about tides and waves for various WEB SITE

TABLE 10.3
Some tide data for Portland, Maine, 0600 to 2200 hours, April 25, 1996.

Time	Tide height(ft)	Time	Tide height(ft)
0600	8.4	1400	3.1
0700	7.8	1500	4.5
0800	6.6	1600	5.8
0900	4.5	1700	7.2
1000	3.0	1800	8.0
1100	1.4	1900	7.8
1200	1.3	2000	6.8
1300	1.4	2100	5.0
		2200	3.8

locations in the country, which may be helpful if you are thinking about surfing during a coming vacation.

The Web site is updated daily, and provides a graph of tide predictions for the next 4 days. We obtained a graph from the Web site for the tides for Portland, Maine, that was posted on April 25, 1996. From this graph, we have estimated the tides at various times of day, which we have shown in Table 10.3.

Let's see if we can fit this data with a simple sinusoid. We expect that the fit will not be perfect, because we know that the moon influences tides, and the moon operates on a separate 28-day cycle. Still, let's see what we can do.

We see that the maximum tide height is 8.4 feet, and the minimum is 1.3 feet, which gives us a range of $7.1 = 2 \times 3.65$ and a midpoint of 4.85 feet.

We'll use as our initial guesses that $a \approx 3.65$ feet and $d \approx 4.85$ feet. The two maximum values seem to be about 12 hours apart, so we'll use $b \approx 2\pi/12 \approx 0.52$ as our first guess. Setting time zero as midnight, the maximum seems to occur about one-half period after time zero, so we'll use $c \approx 3.14$ feet as our initial guess for c. This gives us the fit pictured in Figure 10.19.

With iteration, we obtain the fit in Figure 10.20, which appears to be a pretty good fit. Looking at our estimated values for a, b, c, and d, we see that we have estimated a mean sea level of $d = 4.65$, a period between high tides of $T = 2\pi/b = 12.241$ hours, and a maximum tide of $a + d = 8.09$ feet. Our model is off, on average, less than a quarter of a foot.

Since we have ignored major effects, such as the long-term influence of the

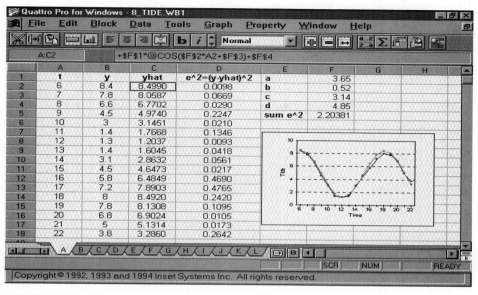

FIGURE 10.19
Our initial guesses for the tide data.

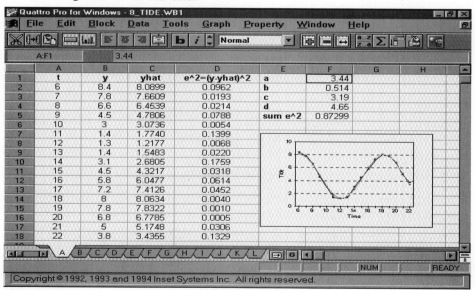

FIGURE 10.20
Our best guess for the tide data.

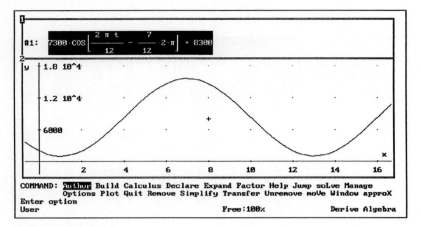

FIGURE 10.21
A graph of the function $s = 7300 \cos(\pi t/6 - 2\pi 7/12) + 8300$, which models lawn mower sales.

moon and other factors, we should be careful about using this model to estimate the tides for times that are very far away from those used to fit the parameters, namely April 25, 1996. Still, we have a very useful tool for estimating tides within that time frame.

10.6.3 Seasonal sales

Imagine that you are a major manufacturer of lawn mowers. Sales of lawn mowers tend to be seasonal, with many sales in, say, March through August, and relatively fewer the rest of the year, especially in the northeastern United States. We are going to attempt to model this sales phenomenon with a simple trigonometric model because of our observation that this sales pattern tends to repeat, year after year.

First, suppose that we sell about 100,000 lawn mowers per year, with our peak sales being in July. During July, we experience sales of about 15,600 lawn mowers. Sales then drop off until January, where they reach a low of about 1000 lawn mowers. Since the sales pattern tends to repeat itself yearly, let's fix the period as 12 months.

For our simple model, we are going to ignore factors such as sales due to the holiday shopping season around Christmas. (So, when was the last time you received a lawn mower as a holiday gift? How big of an assumption is this that we're making?)

From the information given, we can estimate all four of the parameters for a simple sinusoid, $s = f(t) = a\cos(bt + c) + d$, with s equal to monthly sales and t representing the month of the year. Since the amount of sales varies between a high of $15,600$ and a low of 1000 units, the sinusoidal function needs to capture this behavior, which is a range of 7300 units whose average is 8300 units. This means that $a = 7300$ and $d = 8300$. Since this is an annual model, the period is 12 months, which means that $b = 2\pi/12 = \pi/6$.

Lastly, since the model has its maximum in July, which is month number 7, we find that $d = (2\pi 7)/12$, which shifts the maximum 7 months to the right. A graph of the resulting sales function appears in Figure 10.21.

10.6.4   Radio waves: AM

How do radio waves work? We can sketch out the general idea. We have two sets of waves. The first is the carrier wave, which operates at the frequency that you set your radio to on the radio dial. The second is the signal wave. It RADIO is the oscillations of this signal wave, which are picked up by the microphone, WAVES that represent the sound being broadcast. We will represent the signal as a function of time by $s(t)$. The carrier wave is a sinusoid. We will represent it as $c(t) = cos(bt + c)$. The signal wave is not periodic, because the sound does not repeat itself over and over. Still, it can be thought of as the sum of many pieces of sinusoids, each at a slightly different frequency.

For our discussion of radio waves, we will imagine that the signal wave is a constant tone, operating at 1000 hertz, which is a deep bass tone. One hertz is defined as 1 cycle per second. This will simplify our work without affecting our understanding of the process.

"AM" stands for *amplitude modulation*. The basic idea is that the carrier wave operates at a fixed frequency. The amplitude of the carrier wave is shaped by the signal wave, by multiplying the two waves together. This only works if the frequency of the carrier wave is much higher than that of the signal wave. Once you see the picture, the idea is quite clear—so let's look at Figure 10.22.

The AM signal, AM, is represented as

$$AM = \text{signal} \times \text{carrier} = s(t)c(t) = \cos(t)\cos(50t)$$

Notice that the AM signal is the *product* of two functions.

A *tuner* is a device that allows the radio to focus on a precise carrier wave, ignoring others. The radio circuitry then reproduces the signal wave by measuring how much the strength of the AM signal fluctuates.

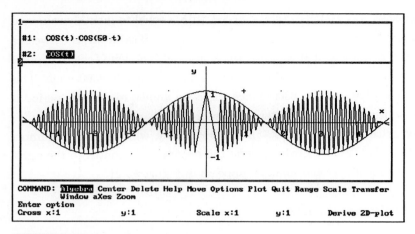

FIGURE 10.22

A carrier wave modulated by a lower frequency signal wave, producing an AM signal. Here the carrier wave is $\cos(50t)$. The signal wave is the much lower-frequency $\cos(t)$. To aid in the picture, we have superimposed the signal wave on the AM signal.

One of the problems with this method of signal transmission is that *static* can distort the response. Static is a random signal that occurs at wildly varying frequencies. If the static happens to occur at a frequency that is near the carrier frequency, it can interfere with the transmission. Similarly, if we are between two stations using the same carrier frequency, they can also interfere with each other.

FREQUENCY MODULATION

Electrical engineers wrestle with the problems of static, and they have devised many clever schemes to reduce its impact. One of them, *frequency modulation,* is discussed in the next section. To reduce interference from multiple stations with the same frequency in the United States, the Federal Communications Commission (FCC) regulates who can broadcast on what frequency, and with what strength. Other nations set their own rules, and treaties assure that the differing national schemes are (one hopes) compatible.

10.6.5   Radio waves: FM

What to do about static? Since static primarily affects the amplitude of a signal, let's try to modulate a different parameter of our sinusoid function. One choice is to vary the frequency of the carrier signal, by adding the signal wave to the parameter b, as opposed to using it as a function multiplier. That is the basic idea behind *frequency modulation,* where our FM signal pictured graphically in

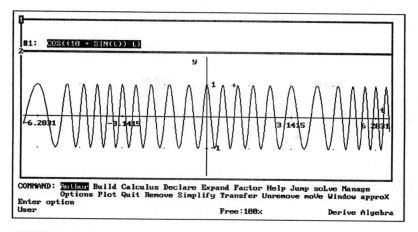

FIGURE 10.23

An FM, or *frequency modulated*, signal. Note how the amplitude is fixed, and the period varies. We have greatly exaggerated the FM effect so that it is visible.

Figure 10.23 is represented as

$$FM = \cos\left[(b + s(t))t\right] = \cos\left[(10 + \sin(t))t\right]$$

where $s(t) = \sin(t)$ represents our signal wave.

As an aside, you might take notice that frequency modulation is a very practical use of the idea of composition of functions, since

$$FM(t) = f \circ g = f(g(t)) = \cos\left[(10 + \sin(t))t\right]$$

where $f(t) = \cos(10 + t)t$, and $g(t) = \sin(t)$.

FM results in much clearer sound, because it is practically immune to static. It comes at a cost, however. FM must operate on carrier waves with much higher frequencies. Because the frequencies are varying, they must be spaced much farther apart so adjoining signals to not bleed over. This results in a less efficient use of the available spectrum of frequencies.

A similar approach is called *phase modulation*. Here, a particular signal is **PHASE** obtained by varying the phase constant c, instead of the parameter b: **MODULA-**

$$PM = \cos\left[(b + s(t))t + c\right] = \cos\left[(10 + \sin(t))t + 10\right]$$ **TION**

An interesting question that effects our signal transmission is "What happens if two signals collide?" The answer to this question is important not only to signal transmissions, but also to occupational safety folks in manufacturing facilities.

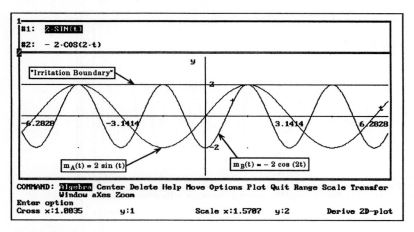

FIGURE 10.24
Two separate transmitted signals remain just below the level at which the noise is irritating.

Example 10.10. Suppose that you are working in a factory that has two low-pitched (rather noisy) machines operating near you that produce constant tones. Let's call these machine A and machine B, just to keep it simple. Most of the time, either one or the other is operating, which can be irritating, but occasionally both are in operation. The question is: Why does this happen? And, is it dangerous to your hearing (besides just being loud)?

Well, suppose that machine A is generating a noise that can be represented by $m_A(t) = 2\sin(t)$, and machine B's tone is given by $m_B(t) = -2\cos(2t)$, where t is given in seconds. Figure 10.24 shows a plot of both of these functions with a label added for clarity. Further suppose that these noises irritate you when the amplitude of a signal reaches 2. So, we've added this "boundary of irritation" as a horizontal line in Figure 10.24.

SUPERPOSITION

When both machines are operating at the same time, an interesting (and sometimes dangerous) phenomena happens, called *superposition*. Both signals are operating at the same time t. So, for each instant in time t, the signal ordinates (or plot points in a graphical sense) are added:

$$M_{A+B}(t) = m_A(t) + m_B(t) = 2\sin(t) - 2\cos(2t)$$

The effect of this superposition is shown in Figure 10.25.

The particular points of this new plot that have our attention are highlighted with small circles in Figure 10.25. Superposition is causing the two individually transmitted signals to reinforce each other every $t = 2\pi$ time units, highlighted by circles on our graph at $t = -3\pi/2$ and $t = \pi/2$. In effect, you are hearing high-amplitude pulses of sound at twice the level that you consider irritating. This is not good.

Equally as interesting are the other points we have circled, at $t = -\pi/2$ and $t = 3\pi/2$. At these instants, superposition causes the signals to cancel out! This is good. Hey, wouldn't be neat to design some kind of small device that you could wear just like headphones that would generate a signal of its own that would cancel out most of both machines' signals? It already exists. Several companies

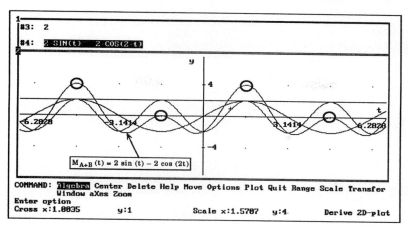

FIGURE 10.25
Transmitted simultaneously, the signals adhere to the principal of superposition.

have such devices for sale for under $200.

From an industrial engineering perspective, we wouldn't want to cancel out all of the signals that a device like the one mentioned above detects. Yes, it would be incredibly quiet. In fact, you probably wouldn't be able to hear someone yell, "Look out!" So, devices like this are designed to cancel only those sounds that are hazardous to your hearing, but to leave human speech frequencies out of the cancellation scheme.

Discussion Ideas

The idea of superposition introduced in the previous example brings up some interesting questions that spill over into other areas besides industrial safety settings. We propose the following focus questions so that you can involve your physics instructor in creating models to get at the information asked.

⇒ Music composers dedicate a large portion of their time in writing music to make sure that it is "in harmony." What does it mean to have music in and out of harmony with regard to signals being transmitted by musical instruments?

⇒ Suppose that you have two keyboards in your band. Is it possible for their individual tones to cancel if both are playing at the same time? Or, does one keyboard have to be "out of tune?" Exactly what does it mean for an instrument to be "out of tune?"

⇒ If you have ever been to an outdoor rock, jazz, rap, reggae, metal, or hip-

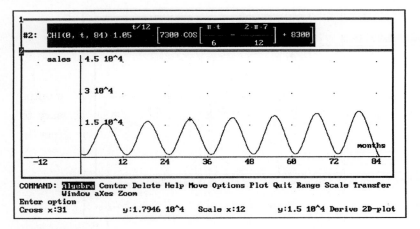

FIGURE 10.26
A graph of our model for seasonal sales with annual growth, represented by $s(t) = 1.05^{t/12}\,(7300\cos(\pi t/6 - 2\pi 7/12) + 8300)$.

hop concert, you may have noticed a tendency of the musicians to turn the instruments up as loud as possible without causing distortion to the music. Or, perhaps you've ridden in a car in which the driver has huge sub-woofers rigged to pump out a car-rattling bass sound. At what level of amplitude should you worry about causing damage to your hearing? Is low-frequency sound or high-frequency sound more damaging?

10.6.6   Mixed models: Seasonal sales with annual growth

In Section 10.6.3, we discussed a model for sales of lawn mowers, which involved a sinusoid with a 1-year period. How would we adjust that model to account for annual growth in sales?

We have some modeling choices, depending on what we mean by annual growth. Do we mean that the average annual sales increases, but that the amplitude remains unchanged? If so, then we would replace d in our equation $s = a\cos(bt + c) + d$ with some function $d(t)$ which reflected that annual growth. A good choice for $d(t)$ would be an exponential model, based on our work in Chapter 9.

Another choice might be that both the amplitude and average sales increase by the same amount. This is the same as a scale change in s. Our model would then be $s(t) = g(t)\,(a\cos(bt + c) + d)$, where $g(t)$ was a function reflecting annual growth. Again, an exponential model would be a good first choice for $g(t)$, since the growth increases as a percentage of the previous year's sales.

Returning to our lawn mower example, let's assume that we have 5% annual growth in sales, and our seasonal fluctuation also proportionally increases. An annual growth of 5% implies that $g(t) = 1.05^{t/12}$. Since t is measured in months and we want the growth to reflect an *annual* increase of 5%, it is necessary to divide t by 12. Otherwise, unit sales would experience a 5% growth each month.

Our new model becomes $s(t) = 1.05^{t/12} \left(7300 \cos(\pi t/6 - 2\pi 7/12) + 8300 \right)$. A graph of this sales function appears in Figure 10.26. The *Derive* crosshair placement shows a peak of the function occuring at month 7, 19, 31, etc., corresponding to July of each year. The difference between the approximate value of the peak at month 31, $17,946$, and the actual peak given by $1.05^3 \times 15,600 = 18,058$ is due to rough screen approximation. Zooming in on the maximum point will confirm the correct peak sales amount each year.

10.6.7   Mixed models: damped oscillation

Earlier, we discussed modeling a *spring-mass* system using a sinusoid. This model is useful, but not fully correct.

Equation 10.13 represents an *ideal* spring. This means that there is no energy lost to air resistance, friction, or the the heat loss from the stretching and contraction of the spring. These sources of energy loss *dampen* the motion of the spring. The model due to Hooke's law says the spring will oscillate forever, DAMPING with constant amplitude. This is not consistent with reality, for we know that the spring will not continue its motion forever. Eventually it stops. So, a model that captures this "eventual stopping" characteristic would more closely resemble reality.

A better model incorporates the damping effects that we just described. The basic idea of damping is that the amplitude of the spring mass system is not constant for all t; it is constantly being reduced by some amount proportional to the current amplitude. The frequency and phase of the sinusoid are not affected.

We know that the exponential function is a useful model for representing quantities that are continuously changing by an amount proportional to the amount present. So, let's model the amplitude of our spring mass system as an exponential function

$$a(t) = A_0 \exp(\alpha\, t) \tag{10.15}$$

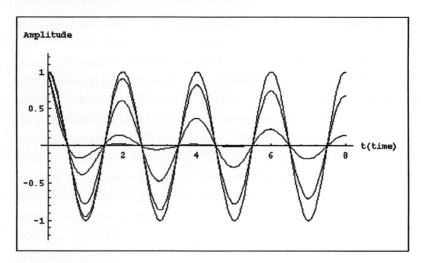

FIGURE 10.27
Plot of damping on the response of a spring-mass system.

This new model representing the energy response for the damped spring mass system now becomes

$$h(t) = A_0 \exp(\alpha t) \cos(bt + c) + d \qquad (10.16)$$

We can see by setting $t = 0$ that A_0 is the initial amplitude. In order for the amplitude to gradually decrease, the new exponential term has to "decay" the amplitude over time. This means that $\alpha < 0$. Notice that if $\alpha = 0$, we recover our previous model in which the amplitude was constant for all t.

For a particular application, we can model α using laws of physics, or estimate it from observations of a particular spring-mass. To estimate the value of α, we would again try to identify the values of all the parameters of our new model that minimized the sum of the squared errors, where each squared error would be calculated using $(h - \hat{h})^2$.

Example 10.11. Figure 10.27 shows a graph in which we have plotted both damped and undamped models for the spring mass system, varying the damping parameter α. We're using Equation 10.16, with the model parameters A_0, b, c and d fixed at $A_0 = 1$, $b = \pi$, $c = 0$, and $d = 0$. This allows us to isolate just the effects of varying the α parameter. We used five values of α: 0, −0.05, −0.25, −1, and −2. Can you identify which plot corresponds to each value of α?

There exists an extensive amount of information concerning damped oscillations. The particular type of damping that we have explored here illustrates the case of *under-damped* oscillatory motion. The study of the other two types, *critically damped* and *over-damped* oscillatory nonforced motion, is part of most differential equations courses or a calculus-based physics course. This more in-depth look at the physical effects of oscillation include models arising when there is an external driving force on the spring. It is these models that are used for designing shock absorbers for automobiles, among other applications, where the amplitude of an oscillation needs to be reduced over time.

10.6.8 So that's why they also make snow blowers

If you are in a business with seasonal sales, you are naturally concerned with your fluctuating demand. There are three basic strategies.

The first involves pacing your production over the course of the year, accumulating inventory in the months with slow sales and selling it off during the months with high sales. This is expensive, because it costs money to carry that inventory.

The second involves varying your production to meet demand. That is very expensive, because it involves idling both plant capacity and workers during low-demand months. This is a poor use of both human and physical capital.

The third involves diversifying into a second product line with seasonal demand that balances the demand for your primary product. For example, if we could make a product that had a high winter demand, we could balance our production of lawn mowers and run at close to an even production level all year. Many lawn mower producers also make snow blowers for that reason. The two products are similar enough that they can be produced on the same assembly lines with a reasonable amount of retooling, and the demand for the two products tends to balance out the seasonal fluctuations.

In the exercises, you will be asked to model the total demand for lawn mowers and snow blowers, and you will see how neatly the demands can balance out.

Exploration Exercises _____

10.1. Using Equations 10.13 and 10.14, model the motion of an ideal spring-mass system with spring constant $k = 1$, mass $m = 4$, and an initial displacement of 30 centimeters.

10.2. In the preceding exercise, what effect would doubling the weight of the mass have on the response of the spring mass system?

TABLE 10.4
Two years sales data for Marie's Swimsuit Company.

Month	Sales	Month	Sales
1/95	300	1/96	305
2/95	450	2/96	420
3/95	610	3/96	600
4/95	800	4/96	830
5/95	1300	5/96	1275
6/95	1400	6/96	1460
7/95	1200	7/96	1250
8/95	750	8/96	800
9/95	400	9/96	410
10/95	275	10/96	250
11/95	250	11/96	225
12/95	275	12/96	280

10.3. In the preceding exercise, identify the model that results if the spring loses 10% of its amplitude each second. (Hint: See the previous chapter for help modeling $a(t)$.)

10.4. If you want to see an interesting effect of damping introduced by the product of two functions, use $y = f(t) = \sin(4t)$ as the signal and $y = g(t) = 3\exp(-2t/\pi)$ as the multiplying damping term. How long does it take for the original signal's amplitude to be less than 0.25 in magnitude?

WEBSEARCH

10.5. Go out on the World Wide Web and find tide data for another U.S. location besides Portland, Maine. Collect the data for a single day and fit a sinusoid to the data using the techniques of this chapter. If you are not connected to the Internet, you can find similar information in an almanac. Is the period you obtain in your model similar to the one in our example? If not, why do you think they might be different?

10.6. Table 10.4 contains some sales data by month for a fictional company Marie's Swimsuits. Plot the data, and then fit a seasonal sales model. Comment on whether you think a sinusoidal model seems appropriate. Using your model, did any months seem to have unusually large or small sales?

10.7. The model that we used in the lawn mower sales example is given by

$$s(t) = 7300\cos(\pi t/6 - 2\pi 7/12) + 8300$$

Assume that we want to have approximately constant demand for the combined sales of snow blowers and lawn mowers each month. What would be a good choice for our snow blower sales function? (Hint: Think about what is being asked, and compare the situation to what happens with the principal of superposition.)

10.8. In our spring-mass model, we initially ignored the effects of friction and heat loss that eventually cause the spring-mass to stop. By introducing a decay term on the amplitude, we could now consider the effect of damping that might be caused by friction and heat loss. In that case, we used an exponential damping term of the form $\exp(\alpha t)$.

Let's now consider modeling the effect of damping in a similar manner as the growth model of earlier. Suppose that the amplitude of a spring mass system decays by a fixed percentage each time period, so that we have $g(t) = k^t$, where $0 < k < 1$. For example, with a 5% loss each time unit, we would have $g(t) = 0.95^t$ as a decay term. This would result in a different model

$$y = f(t) = 0.95^t a \cos(bt + c) + d$$

where base of the exponential term is now introducing decay. What happens to the response $f(t)$ as t gets very large? This is a look at the long-term behavior of this model. Just like we did earlier, you will want to fix the values of certain paramters in order to isolate the effect that you want to explore. Include whatever graphs you need to support your analysis of this long-term behavior. How might we fit k in our model empirically? (Hint: Recall our spreadsheet examples.)

10.7 SUMMARY

Arc length, radius, and radian measure are related for a circle by the formula $x = r\theta$.

Angles can be functions of other predictors, and often are.

Periodic functions must have restricted domains to have inverses.

We learned how to fit trigonometric models by minimizing the sum of squared residuals by iterative methods.

We learned how to construct a change of variables for functions involving $\sqrt{1^2 + x^2}$, $\sqrt{1^2 - x^2}$, and $\sqrt{x^2 - 1^2}$.

We learned the phase-amplitude form of a sinusoid.

10.8 PROJECT: MEASURING THE SPEED OF LIGHT

How do we know the speed of light? The first method of measuring the speed of light, which did not involve astronomical observations, was developed in 1849 by Armand H. L. Fizeau (1819–1896). We will consider a simplified version of the experiment, and develop a model for estimating the speed of light.

Consider a toothed wheel and a mirror, separated by a great distance. Shine a focused bean of light between the two teeth of the wheel. The light goes through the teeth, is reflected by the mirror, and passes back between the teeth. The basic setup is drawn in Figure 10.28.

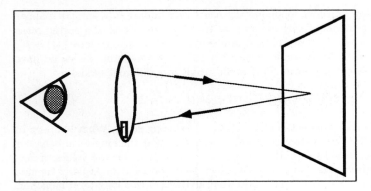

FIGURE 10.28
A simplified schematic of Fizeau's experiment.

What happens if the wheel is spinning? First, if the speed of light is infinite, the beam will return instantly from the mirror. If we are looking along the line of the light, we will see the reflected from the mirror no matter how fast the wheel is spinning.

What happens if the speed of light is finite? Then, if the wheel is spinning fast enough, the light won't come back to the wheel before the next tooth blocks our view. We won't see the light reflected in the mirror, even though the light shines through the toothed wheel continuously.

How do we find the speed of light from these facts? First, we know that the speed of light will equal the distance traveled, divided by the time elapsed. We can measure the distance traveled, which is twice the distance to the mirror (there and back). The spinning wheel gives us a way to calculate the elapsed time.

We find the elapsed time by speeding up the wheel from rest until we can no longer see the light reflected. We then measure how long it has taken for the next tooth to move into position to block our view. The time elapsed will be the number of radians in the angle between the teeth, divided by the radians per second that the wheel is spinning:

$$t = \frac{\theta}{\frac{\text{radians}}{\text{second}}} \tag{10.17}$$

Then the speed of light, c, equals distance divided by time, or

$$c = \frac{2d}{t} = \frac{2d}{\frac{\theta}{\frac{\text{radians}}{\text{second}}}} \tag{10.18}$$

For example, suppose that we have a toothed wheel with 180 equally spaced teeth, with tooth width equal to the gap width. Then the gap between any two teeth is $\pi/180$ radians. Now suppose that we increase the spin rate of the wheel until we can no longer see the light reflected, and that the revolutions per second of the wheel at that point are 41.625 revolutions per second, or $2\pi \times 41.625 \approx 261.5376$ radians per second. Let the distance to the mirror be 5000 meters. Using Equation 10.18, we have can find c, which is left to you as an exercise.

It is possible to construct an apparatus to collect your own data, using an eye-safe laser (such as a pointer) and a spinning wheel connected to a rheostat, to vary the spin rate. If you are interested n the details, check out our Web site.

Many scientific advances have been made using simple models. For another example involving light, you can read about the Michelson-Morley experiment, cited in the references. Your authors were required to actually replicate the Michelson-Morley experiment in their sophomore physics course in college!

Required Analysis

1. Imagine that you have a phonograph player. (Historical note: A phonograph player was a popular sound reproduction system prior to the introduction of the compact disc.) It has a tuning system that allows you to vary the revolutions per minute (rpms). You take an old phonograph record, and notch it, similar to the way the toothed gear was notched. You borrow a small laser pointer (eye-safe), and decide to verify the Fizeau experiment.

   (*a*) How many notches do you need?

   (*b*) How far should the mirror be positioned from the phonograph record? Assume the phonograph spins at 33−1/3 revolutions per *minute*. There is not one unique solution, so try to find one that seems to pass a common-sense test.

10.9 COMPLEMENTS

1. Schaum's outline series is a good reference for trigonometric identities and review of general trigonometric relationships.

- *Schaum's Outline of Theory and Problems of Plane and Spherical Trigonometry 3*, by Frank Ayers. McGraw-Hill, New York, 1994.

2. Most every calculus course will examine sinusoidal motion in detail. We still like Gil Strang's calculus text in this capacity.

   - *Calculus*, by Gilbert Strang. Wellesley-Cambridge Press, Wellesley, Massachusetts, 1991.

3. A quick summary of radio waves is available at

   - http://www.tbi.net/ jjhall/modl.html,

   which is a good start point for further exploration using any Web search application.

4. Additional tide data is available at

   - http://www.surfinfo.com

5. Econometrics and time-series analysis are the academic subjects concerned with modeling sales data. Most universities offer courses in both.

CHAPTER
11

POLAR AND PARAMETRIC MODELS

What matters to me is not merely to impart to the reader what I have to say, but above all to convey to him the reasons, subterfuges, and lucky hazards which led me to my discoveries. When Christopher Columbus, Magelhaen, and the Portuguese relate how they went astray on their journeys, we not only forgive them, but would regret to miss their narration because without it the whole grand entertainment would be lost.

Johannes Kepler

Chapter Goals

⇒ Plot curves using polar coordinates.

⇒ Understand polar representation of conic sections.

⇒ Understand parametric representation of functions.

⇒ Calculate intersection and collision of curves.

⇒ Appreciate the additional modeling power of polar and parametric models.

11.1 INTRODUCTION

So far in the text, we have been concerned with Cartesian coordinates. You recall that Cartesian coordinates are based on a rectangular system for measuring location relative to some fixed origin with perpendicular axes. Cartesian coordi-
POLAR
COORDINATESnates work well for many, many applications, but in some circumstances they can become unwieldy. In particular, many curves can be better represented in other coordinate systems. We will look at one such system called *polar coordinates* in detail. This will have the added benefit of exercising our newly developed trigonometry muscles.

We then move to an examination of parametric equations. In parametric equations, the coordinates themselves are functions of another variable, usually time.

With both of these tools, we will be able to analyze curves and motion along curved paths. We will also get some insights into physics and astronomy.

11.2 POLAR COORDINATES

Imagine that you were on a ship in the middle of the ocean, and you saw another ship approaching you. How would you describe its location? You probably would not use Cartesian coordinates. Rather, you would probably say that the ship was a certain distance from you, at a certain angle (or "bearing").

That is the idea behind polar coordinates. Instead of giving locations by rectangular coordinates, we describe position by a certain distance from the origin, at a certain angle.[†]

Figure 11.1 lays out our system for describing location. For clarity, Figure 11.1 includes the x- and y-axis, as well. We need a way to measure distance and "bearing." Note that the positive x-axis is used for measuring angles—it

---

[†]Polar coordinates were created by Gregorio Fontana (1733–1803), but although "Cartesian coordinates" are named after Descartes, we have no "Fontanian coordinates." The conventions for naming mathematical objects are somewhat arbitrary!

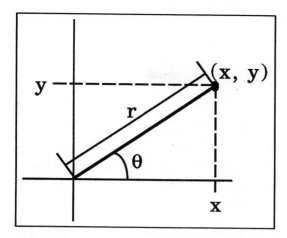

FIGURE 11.1
Polar coordinates and Cartesian coordinates.

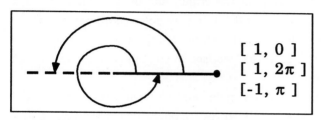

[1, 0]
[1, 2π]
[-1, π]

FIGURE 11.2
Multiple polar coordinates for the point with Cartesian coordinates (1, 0).

is the *polar axis*. As in the last chapter, angles will measured in radians unless we mention otherwise. Positive angles will be measured in the counterclockwise direction. We will measure distance from the origin using the units of our choice.

So how do we describe a point using polar coordinates, now that we have our origin and a way to measure angles? Imagine we have sketched a ray from the origin to our point. This ray has a length, and makes an angle with the polar axis. We will use two variables. The first, r, will be the *radial variable*, measuring RADIAL the directed distance from the origin to the point. By *directed distance*, we mean VARIABLE that distance in the direction of the ray is positive. The second, θ, will be the angle that the ray makes with the polar axis.

To distinguish polar coordinates from Cartesian coordinates, we will write polar coordinates using square brackets instead of parentheses: $[r, \theta]$ instead of (x, y).

At this point, we should say that there are still some details to consider.

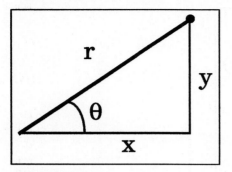

FIGURE 11.3
Conversion between polar and Cartesian coordinates.

First, each point has only one set of Cartesian coordinates but it can have many sets of polar coordinates. Here is why. Consider a point with Cartesian coordinates $(1, 0)$. Since it is one unit from the origin, and on the x-axis, we can describe this point by saying $r = 1$ and $\theta = 0$, giving polar coordinates of $[1, 0]$. We could also say that the point is at $[1, 2\pi]$, or $[1, 4\pi]$, or even $[-1, \pi]$. If we are giving directions, $[-1, \pi]$ means that we face in the opposite direction, but proceed backward. See Figure 11.2.

Second, how do we move between polar and Cartesian coordinates, and back? You may guess that the answer involves trigonometry! If we look at Figure 11.3, we recognize our old friend, the right triangle. Since our Cartesian coordinates are based on perpendicular axes, we see that we can construct a right triangle with one vertex at the origin, and a second at the point in the plane represented by (x, y). The third vertex is at the point $(x, 0)$. The hypotenuse of this right triangle has length

$$r = \sqrt{x^2 + y^2} \tag{11.1}$$

The angle that the hypotenuse makes with the positive x axis is found by

$$\tan \theta = \frac{y}{x}$$
$$\theta = \tan^{-1}\left(\frac{y}{x}\right) \tag{11.2}$$

Equation 11.1 and Equation 11.2 permit us to convert from Cartesian coordinates to one set of polar coordinates for a point.

How to we convert from polar coordinates to Cartesian coordinates? Let's reexamine Figure 11.2. If we know r and θ, how would we use trigonometry to find x and y? Applying the definitions, we see that

$$\sin\theta = \frac{y}{r} \tag{11.3}$$

$$\cos\theta = \frac{x}{r} \tag{11.4}$$

From Equations 11.3 and 11.4, it follows that

$$x = r\cos\theta \tag{11.5}$$

$$y = r\sin\theta \tag{11.6}$$

Using Equations 11.5 and 11.6, we can convert from polar coordinates to Cartesian coordinates.

Let's try a few quick examples.

Example 11.1. If the Cartesian coordinates for a point are given by $(x,y) = (1,1)$, the polar coordinates for the point are given by

$$\begin{aligned}[r,\theta] &= \left[r = \sqrt{1^2+1^2}, \quad \theta = \tan^{-1}\left(\tfrac{1}{1}\right)\right]\\ &= \left[\sqrt{2}, \pi/4\right]\end{aligned}$$

If the polar coordinates for a point are given by $[3, \frac{5\pi}{4}]$, then its Cartesian coordinates are given by

$$\begin{aligned}(x,y) &= \left(3\cos\left(\tfrac{5\pi}{4}\right), \quad 3\sin\left(\tfrac{5\pi}{4}\right)\right)\\ &= \left(\tfrac{-3\sqrt{2}}{2}, \quad \tfrac{-3\sqrt{2}}{2}\right)\end{aligned}$$

Exploration Exercises _____

11.1. Convert the following Cartesian coordinates to polar coordinates.
   (a) $(1,1)$
   (b) $(-1,1)$
   (c) $(-1,-1)$
   (d) $(1,-1)$
   (e) $(0,1)$
   (f) $(-4,6)$
   (g) $(\pi,-e)$
   (h) What do you thing will happen when you try to apply Equations 11.1 and (refe9-2) to the point $(0,0)$? What polar coordinates make sense for the origin?

11.2. Convert the following polar coordinates to Cartesian coordinates.
   (a) $[1,1]$
   (b) $[-1,\pi]$

(c) $[1, -\pi/4]$

(d) $[2, \pi/3]$

(e) $[0, \pi]$

(f) $[\pi 0]$

(g) $[\pi, e]$

(h) $[e, \pi]$

11.3. Imagine that you are located at the point $(1,1)$ on the (x,y)-plane, and there is another person located at the point $(3,2)$. Identify both locations in polar coordinates. Next, find the distance between the two locations, and the angle between the two locations.

11.4. Suppose that you are located at the origin. You turn until you are facing along the polar angle $3\pi/4$, and move out smartly a distance of 100 units. What is your ending location in (a) polar coordinates, and (b) Cartesian coordinates?

11.3 POLAR FUNCTIONS AND MODELS

We can define functions in polar coordinates, as we do in Cartesian coordinates. We will most often consider θ as the independent variable, and r as the dependent variable, and write $r = f(\theta)$. To plot these polar functions, we will use our computer algebra system. (If we didn't have such a system, we could construct a table of $[r, \theta]$ values, plot those points, and "connect the dots.")

11.3.1 Simple polar functions

We examine some simple polar functions in this section, to develop our appreciation for working in polar coordinates.

Let's start with some very simple polar functions, the constant functions. $r = 1$ is a constant function, which says regardless of what θ is, $r = 1$. The graph of this function is a circle of radius 1, centered at the origin. We can confirm this by plotting, by tables, or by converting back to (x, y) coordinates.

To convert the equation $r = 1$ to Cartesian coordinates, we substitute our conversion formula for r, obtaining

$$r = \sqrt{x^2 + y^2} = 1$$

which we recognize as the equation of a circle with radius 1, in Cartesian coordinates.

Notice that the equation of the circle in Cartesian coordinates is *not* a function, while the equation in polar coordinates *is* a function. This is one major advantage of working with the curves using polar coordinates—you can often get equations for the curves as functions of the θ.

A second example of a constant polar function is the equation $\theta = 1$. Substituting our equation for θ, we obtain

$$\tan^{-1} \frac{y}{x} = 1$$

which simplifies to

$$y = \tan(1) \times x$$

which we recognize as a line through the origin with slope equal to $\tan(1) \approx$ 1.5574. Let's fix the value of θ at some value, say θ_o. Similarly, for the equation $\theta = \theta_o$, we obtain

$$y = \tan \theta_o \times x$$

This works well, unless $\theta_o = \frac{(2k+1)\pi}{2}$, in which case $\tan(\theta_o)$ is undefined.

What would be the polar equation for a line that doesn't go through the origin? In Cartesian coordinates, we have

$$y = mx + b$$

Substituting our polar equations for x and y, we have

$$r \sin \theta = m(r \cos \theta) + b$$

We can manipulate this algebraically to arrive at

$$r = \frac{b}{\sin \theta - m \cos \theta} \qquad (11.7)$$

Here there is no apparent advantage to working in polar coordinates, and there is a cost. In Cartesian coordinates, the domain of x is not restricted. However, if $x = r \cos \theta$, then x is between $-r$ and r inclusive. (We write this domain restriction as $x \in [-r, r]$). So we not only have a more unwieldy equation for the line; we have also lost a portion of our domain and range.

For these simple functions, we don't need any sophisticated plotting aids. There are others for which we will need computer-generated graphics.

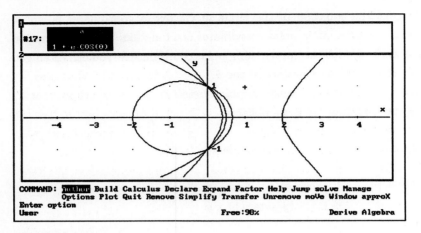

FIGURE 11.4
The ellipse, parabola, and hyperbola that result when e is 0.5, 1, and 1.5, respectively.

11.3.2   Conic sections in polar coordinates

You may have seen in an earlier course that there are three types of conic sections: ellipses, parabolas, and hyperbolas. These curves are called *conic sections* because they can be obtained by slicing a cone at different angles. Apollonius introduced these curves, and an early mathematician named Hypatia expanded on the work, before she was killed by a mob in A.D. 415.

CONIC SECTIONS

All three of these shapes have the same general form of a polar equation:

$$r = \frac{a}{1 + e \cos \theta} \tag{11.8}$$

ECCENTRICITY

where a is a scaling parameter, and e determines the *eccentricity* of the conic section.

What is eccentricity? If $0 \leq e < 1$, then Equation 11.8 describes an ellipse with one focus at the origin, in which the length of the semimajor axis is equal to a. As a special case, if $e = 0$, Equation 11.8 describes a circle centered at the origin with radius a. If $e = 1$, Equation 11.8 describes a parabola. If $e > 1$, we get a hyperbola.

In a sense, e measures how unlike a circle a conic section is: If $e = 0$, the conic section *is* a circle. If e is very small, the resulting ellipse is nearly circular.

In Figure 11.4, we've plotted an ellipse, a parabola, and a hyperbola with eccentricities of 0.5, 1, and 1.5, respectively.

The conic sections are interesting polar functions, especially in light of Kepler's three laws. Kepler's first law states that the planets travel in elliptical orbits around the sun, with the sun at one focus. We will return to Kepler's laws in the project. It is also interesting to note that Gauss developed the method of least squares to fit the orbits of the planets, or in other words to find the exact equations for the elliptical orbits. It is also of note that a meteor that flies by the sun or by a planet results in one of three possible orbits: an ellipse if it is captured by the gravitational field of the larger body, a hyperbola if it flies by or strikes the larger body, or a parabola. As a result, conic sections occupy a central position in the study of astrodynamics.

You may be familiar with conic sections in Cartesian coordinates. We leave it as an exercise to show that the polar equation is equivalent to the Cartesian equations for the various conic sections.

11.3.3   Cardioids and other polar functions

The idea of polar functions has been around for a long time. Well, at least long enough for many different looking curves to be discovered and recorded. And, although we aren't going to introduce any really strange ones here, we highly encourage you to take the time to explore the effects of changing parameters, introducing new terms, and extending the ideas into three-dimensional plots. Playing with the function forms will allow you to develop some degree of understanding of how scaling and translation affect polar plots.

There are many polar functions that we could examine. In fact, if you find yourself getting bored with the ones here, we suggest to visit the Famous Curves Index Web site at:

http://www-groups.dcs.st-and.ac.uk/ history/Curves/Curves.html

If the website has changed its location by the time that you get to this portion of the book, you will be able to link to it through our McGraw-Hill Web site listed in Chapter 1.

Let's take a look at the equations for several interesting polar functions here, and leave the exploration of their properties for the exercises.

11.3.3.1   CARDIOIDS.

A cardioid is a heart-shaped curve that is described by the equation

$$r = a(1 - \cos\theta)$$

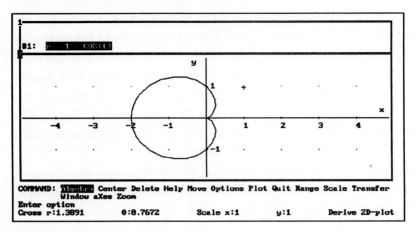

FIGURE 11.5
The cardioid given by $r = (1 - \cos\theta)$.

The cardioid is our first example of a curve that is much easier to draw using CARDIOII polar coordinates instead of Cartesian coordinates. In the exercises, we want you to show that the corresponding Cartesian equation for a cardioid is given by

$$x^2 + y^2 = \sqrt{x^2 + y^2} + x$$

A plot of a cardioid is in Figure 11.5. We also mention that the equations $r = a(1 - \cos\theta)$ and $r = a(1 \pm \sin\theta)$ produce cardioids oriented in different directions.

11.3.3.2 LIMAÇON.

A cardioid is a special case of a more general polar curve called a *limaçon*, which was discovered by Blaise Pascal. The general form of a limaçon is

$$r = a\cos\theta + b$$

When the parameters $a = b$ in this expression, the resulting curve is a cardioid. When $a > b$, the result is a curve that has two loops. When $a < b$, we get a LIMAÇON curve with one loop, similar to a cardioid but flatter. In the exercises, we ask you to graph the limaçon, to find the corresponding Cartesian equations, and to discuss the orientation of the other equations for limaçons.

11.3.3.3 ROSE.

If we let $r = a\sin(k\theta)$, with the parameter k being an integer, we obtain a rose. If k is odd, the resulting plot is a *rose* with k petals. If k is even, the resulting plot is a rose with $2k$ petals. In the exercises, we ask you to graph these roses, to find their equations in Cartesian coordinates, and to discuss how to change the orientation of the rose.

We can also obtain roses if we let $r^2 = a^2 \sin(2\theta)$, as we ask you to verify. The special case $r^2 = a \sin(2\theta)$ is called the *Lemniscate of Bernoulli*.

Exploration Exercises

11.1. Verify that Equation 11.7 is the correct equation for a line in polar coordinates. Plot the line using polar coordinates, and comment on the appearance of the graph.

11.2. Why do we say that $\tan\left(\frac{(2k+1)\pi}{2}\right)$ is undefined?

11.3. Convert Equation 11.8 from polar to Cartesian coordinates, and simplify. Show that when $e = 1$, a parabola results. Show that if $e > 1$, an ellipse does not result.

11.4. Graph the polar function $r = \theta$, and describe its appearance.

11.5. Graph the polar function $r = \theta^{-1}$, and describe its appearance. What is the function's domain and range?

11.6. Verify that $r = a(1 + \cos\theta)$ can be written in Cartesian coordinates as $x^2 + y^2 = \sqrt{x^2 + y^2} + x$. Can you solve for y?

11.7. Verify that there are, in fact, two loops produced in the expression $r = a\cos\theta + b$ when $a > b$.

11.8. Graph the following limaçons, and comment on the shape when a/b is large or small.
  (a) $r = \cos\theta + 1$
  (b) $r = \cos\theta + 2$
  (c) $r = \cos\theta + 10$
  (d) $r = \cos\theta + 100$
  (e) $r = 2\cos\theta + 1$
  (f) $r = 10\cos\theta + 1$
  (g) $r = 100\cos\theta + 1$

11.9. Find a formula for the number of petals (as a function of k) for the roses given by
  (a) $r = \sin(k\theta)$
  (b) $r^2 = \sin^2(k\theta)$
  What happens if you introduce noninteger values for k?

11.10. Consider an ellipse with its corresponding polar equation. We know that e defines the eccentricity of the ellipse.
  (a) What does the parameter a represent? To identify an answer to this question, consider a line segment that passes through the points $[r, 0]$ and $[r, \pi]$. These two points are the closest and farthest points of the ellipse from the polar origin, respectively. This line is called the *major axis* of the ellipse. Let's say its length is $2d$. What is the relationship between a and d? (d is the "semimajor axis length".)
  (b) Now, consider the line segment connecting the polar points $[r, \pi/2]$ and $[r, 3\pi/2]$. This segment is called the *minor axis*, and we will say its length

is l. (We're running out of letters ...). Express l as a function of a and e.

(c) Where do the major and minor axes intersect? This point is the *center* of the ellipse.

11.4 PARAMETRIC FUNCTIONS AND MODELS

Once we know that the planets travel in elliptical orbits, the next reasonable question might be where a planet is at any given time—to predict its location on the orbit. Kepler's second law states that the line connecting the sun to a planet sweeps out equal areas over equal times. To use Kepler's first and second laws to obtain an exact equation for the location of a planet as a function of time is very hard, and requires advanced calculus. However, the general question is still interesting: If we know the shape of the path along which an object is traveling, can we model its location as a function of a time parameter? That modeling is **PARAMETRIC** the idea behind *parametric functions*. For our planetary example, we would want **FUNCTIONS** an equation for θ as a function of time: $\theta(t) = f(t)$, and we could then substitute this equation for θ into our equation for r. This *composition of functions* results in $r(\theta(t)) = r(t)$. We then have our polar coordinates as functions of time:

$$[r(t), \theta(t)]$$

The hard part, of course, is finding $\theta(t)$. Gauss developed his method of least squares to find $\theta(t)$ empirically; that is, by fitting an equation to the data. Exact solutions had to wait for Isaac Newton.

However, there are simpler systems than planetary orbits with which to work. We will look at a few in this section.

11.4.1 Intersections and collisions

Imagine two cars driving through an intersection, as pictured in Figure 11.6. Clearly their paths intersect. Do the cars collide? Only if the cars are at the intersection point at the same time.

The issue of intersecting versus colliding paths arises in many fields. We might be interested if the path of the earth intersected that of a large meteor; we would be *very* interested if the meteor and the earth arrived at the intersection point at the same time.

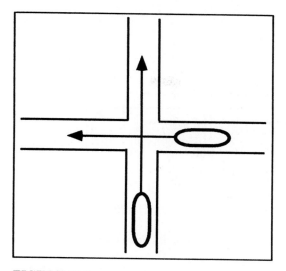

FIGURE 11.6
Two cars pass through an intersection. Do they collide?

Again, to answer the collision question, it is necessary to model the components of location as functions of time. Those components could be $(x(t), y(t))$ or $[r(t), \theta(t)]$.

How did we determine where two curves intersected? To do so, we generally eliminate the parameter, if possible, resulting in two equations: $y_1 = f_1(x)$ and $y_2 = f_2(x)$. Setting $f_1(x) = f_2(x)$ and solving gives the x coordinates of the points of intersection. A second approach is to plot both curves and find the point of intersection graphically.

How would we find out whether the paths collide? Let's think a moment about what a collision means. To collide means that both objects arrive at the intersection point at the same time. Since time is important, we can not eliminate the time parameter as we did in the previous paragraph.

Assume the location of the first object as a function of time is given by $(x_1(t), y_1(t))$ and the second object by $(x_2(t), y_2(t))$. If both objects are at the same point at the same time, then we must have

$$x_1(t) = x_2(t) \tag{11.9}$$

$$y_1(t) = y_2(t) \tag{11.10}$$

We solve for all values of t that satisfy *both* Equations 11.9 and 11.10. Of course, we can have 0, 1 or many solutions to a system of nonlinear equations.

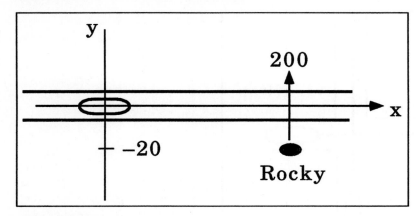

FIGURE 11.7
Rocky Raccoon takes his life in his hands by crossing to our front. We've included a coordinate scheme.

Once we have all the times of collision, if any, it is trivial to substitute back in to find the points of collision. Let's do a few examples.

Example 11.2. We are driving down the highway at a constant speed. Rocky Raccoon decides that he will dash across the road in front of us. Is there a collision? See Figure 11.7.

We set our coordinate system so we are traveling along the x-axis at a constant speed of 88 feet per second. For convenience, we will say at time $t = 0$ we are at the origin. Our position is then given parametrically as

$$(x_{us}(t), y_{us}(t)) = (88t, 0)$$

Rocky is located at $(200, -20)$, or 200 feet to our front, and 20 feet to our right. At $t = 0$, Rocky heads across our front at 15 feet per second. His position is then given parametrically by

$$(x_{Rocky}(t), y_{Rocky}(t)) = (200, -20 + 15t)$$

Do we hit Rocky, if we both proceed at the same speeds on the same paths? We will use Equations 11.9 and 11.10 to find out. If we collide, then

$$x_{us}(t) = x_{Rocky}(t)$$

which means that $88t = 200$. So if we do hit Rocky, it will be at $t = 200/88$ seconds. If we do hit Rocky, then

$$y_{us} = y_{Rocky}$$

or $0 = -20 + 15t$. If we substitute in $t = 200/88$, which is the only possible time for a collision, we obtain $0 \neq -20 + 15(200/88) = 34.0909$. In other words, when we draw even with Rocky's positions, he will already be 34.0909 feet across the road. We and Rocky both breathe sighs of relief.

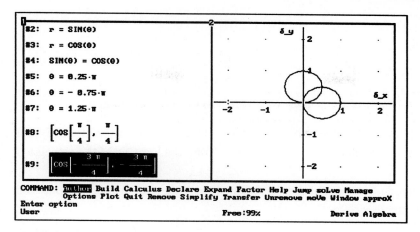

FIGURE 11.8
Graph of the two polar circles $r_1 = \sin\theta$ and $r_2 = \cos\theta$.

Example 11.3. Lets say we have two circles given by polar coordinates, as pictured in Figure 11.8. Their equations are given by

$$r_1 = \sin\theta \tag{11.11}$$

$$r_2 = \cos\theta \tag{11.12}$$

We see from the graph in Figure 11.8 that the curves clearly intersect at the origin and also at a point with Cartesian coordinates $(0.5, 0.5)$. Now, let's imagine that the angle θ is a function of time. First, let's set $\theta_1 = \theta_2 = t$. Do objects on these paths collide?

If we solve the system of equations given by

$$t = t \tag{11.13}$$

$$\cos t = \sin t \tag{11.14}$$

on the interval $[-\pi, \pi]$, we obtain $t = \frac{-3\pi}{4}$, $t = \frac{\pi}{4}$, and $t = \frac{5\pi}{4}$. The three values of t all plot to the same point, which has Cartesian coordinates $(0.5, 0.5)$. So the curves have two intersection points, but only one collision point. The curves don't cross the origin at the same time.

We can also work these examples in three dimensions, where we add a $z(t)$ to indicate the object's vertical position. Then to find collisions, we solve to three equations in t simultaneously:

$$x_1(t) = x_2(t)$$

$$y_1(t) = y_2(t) \tag{11.15}$$

$$z_1(t) = z_2(t)$$

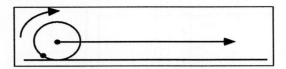

FIGURE 11.9
The painted tire moves down the road. What path does the spot travel along?

If there is no solution, then the objects do not collide. Each solution gives a different time of collision, which can be used to find the location of the associated collision.

We include some problems involving three dimensional intersections and collisions in the exercises.

11.4.2 Cycloids

Let's now consider a problem that involves the sum of different functions which describe the motion of an object. We have in mind an automobile tire rolling along the road. Imagine that we have painted one spot on the outer rim of the tire, and we watch it roll along. (See Figure 11.9.) What path does the spot take?

To answer this, we break the motion of the painted point into two pieces. First, the point moves around the center of the tire. Second, the center of the time moves down the road. We will describe each in turn, beginning with the second.

Let's assume that the road is flat, the tire perfectly round, and the center moving straight down the road at a constant speed. Let's put the center of the tire at the point $(0, r)$ when $t = 0$, where r is the radius of the tire. Let's also assume that the painted spot is at the origin $(0,0)$ at $t = 0$. Let's say the center moves at the constant rate of k unites per second. Then the location of the center is given parametrically by

$$(x_c(t), y_c(t)) = (kt, r)$$

We see that the y component of the location does not change, as a consequence of assuming a flat road and perfectly round tire.

Now, what happens as the painted point moves around the tire? First, the circumference of the tire is $C = 2\pi r$. For each revolution of the tire, the tire center moves $2\pi r$ units, since that is how much pavement the tire rim rolls along. (Now we are also assuming no slippage between the tire and the road.) If the tire is rotating at a rate of ϕ radians per time unit, the total distance traveled

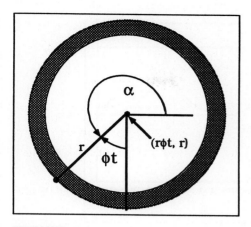

FIGURE 11.10
Schematic for converting the angle ϕ relative to the vertical axis to an angle α relative to the horizontal axis.

in a given time will be $d = r\phi t$. Since the tire center is also moving at the rate of k units per unit of time, we have that $d = kt$. We can use these two equations to obtain

$$r\phi = k \tag{11.16}$$

Using our trigonometry, we see that we can model the motion of the painted spot relative to the center of the wheel quite easily as a function of time, using Equation 11.16 and Figure 11.10.

In Figure 11.10, there are two angles drawn, α and ϕt. We see that $\phi t + \alpha = \frac{3\pi}{2}$, so $\alpha = \frac{3\pi}{2} - \phi t$. We know that the arc length kt is equal to $r\phi t$, which in turn gives us $\alpha = \frac{3\pi}{2} - \frac{kt}{r}$. We get

$$
\begin{aligned}
x_p(t) &= r\cos\alpha \\
&= r\cos\left(\frac{3\pi}{2} - \frac{kt}{r}\right) \\
&= -r\sin\left(\frac{kt}{r}\right)
\end{aligned}
\tag{11.17}
$$

$$
\begin{aligned}
y_p(t) &= r\sin\alpha \\
&= r\sin\left(\frac{3\pi}{2} - \frac{kt}{r}\right) \\
&= -r\cos\left(\frac{kt}{r}\right)
\end{aligned}
\tag{11.18}
$$

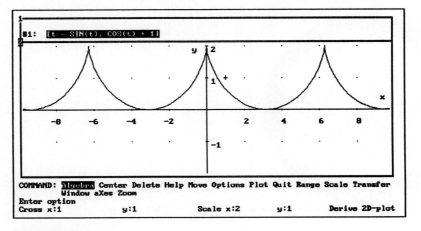

FIGURE 11.11
Graph of the cycloid given by Equation 11.19, with $r = k = 1$.

Adding the motion of the center of the wheel and that of the point on the wheel, we have

$$(x(t), y(t)) = (x_c(t) + x_p(t), y_c(t) + y_p(t))$$

$$= \left(kt + \left(-r\sin\left(\frac{kt}{r}\right) \right), r + \left(-r\cos\left(\frac{kt}{r}\right) \right) \right)$$

$$= \left(kt - r\sin\left(\frac{kt}{r}\right), r\left(1 - \cos\left(\frac{kt}{r}\right) \right) \right) \qquad (11.19)$$

The parametric *Derive* plot in Figure 11.10 has $k = r = 1$.

CYCLOID   This parametric curve is called a *cycloid*. It was first studied in 1501 by Charles de Bouelles.[‡] Many famous mathematicians, such as Galileo, Pascal, and the Bernoullis (Jean and Jacque) studied the curve. It has several interesting properties. Turn the curve upside down, and examine the portion of the curve pictured in Figure 11.12.

The cycloid describes the fastest path for a sliding body to get from A to B under the influence of gravity. The fastest path is *not* a straight line. Equally amazing: the time to reach the bottom point B is the same regardless of where you start on the curve! To find curves with these properties (called a *brachistochrone* and *tautochrone* respectively) occupied many of the great minds of mathematics, including Newton, Leibniz, L'Hopital, and the Bernoullis.

[‡]D. E. Smith, *History of Mathematics*, Vol. 2. NY: Dover, 1958, p. 327.

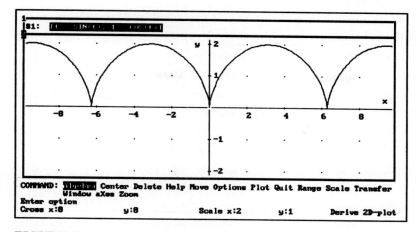

FIGURE 11.12
The inverted cycloid. This curve has many interesting properties.

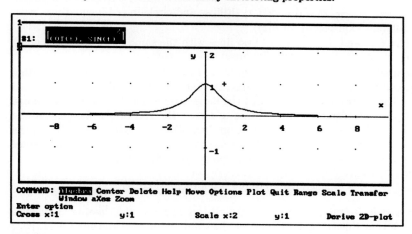

FIGURE 11.13
  The Witch of Agnesi.

A good calculus course will explore the properties of this curve in great detail. It is a fascinating piece of work.

11.4.2.1 WITCH OF AGNESI.

The equations for a very interesting curve involving trigonometric functions are

$$x = a \cot t \qquad\qquad (11.20)$$

$$y = a \sin^2 t \qquad\qquad (11.21)$$

where the parameter a is used as a scaling constant.

The resulting parametric curve was first described by Maria Gaetana Agnesi, who was the chair of mathematics at the University of Bologna for a period in the 1700s. She wrote the first three-semester textbook for the calculus in 1748. The text was translated into English in 1801, and the name of the curve was mistranslated as "witch." Unfortunately, that memorable misnomer has become permanently attached to the name of the curve.

If $a = 1/\sqrt{\pi}$, the curve can be shown to be the *Cauchy density*, which is a very useful curve in the study of probability and statistics.

In the exercises, we ask you to find some of the properties of this curve.

Exploration Exercises _____

11.1. Graph, and then find the points of intersection and/or collision for the following pairs of parametric curves.
   (a) $(t, \frac{1}{1+t^2})$ and $(t, 2t + 1)$ (Witch of Agnesi and a line)
   (b) $[\frac{2}{1+0.5\cos(2t+1)}, 2t + 1]$ and $[1, t]$ (Ellipse and circle in polar equations, with different expressions for $\theta(t)$)
   (c) $(t, t + 1)$ and $(t + 1, t + 2)$ (Two lines with the same slope and intercepts)
   (d) $(t, 1)$ and $(t, 2)$ (Two parallel lines)

11.2. A train wheel does not have a flat bottom. Instead, the wheel has a protruding edge, called a *flange*, that extends past the flat bottom of the wheel. The actual wheel surface rests on the rail, but the flange on the inside of the wheel keeps the train from derailing. Let's place a dot on the rim of the flange. Let the radius of the wheel base (which rests on the rail) be 0.5 meters, and that of the flange be 0.55 meters. The curve that the dot will trace out as the train wheel rotates is called an *epicycloid*. It is given parametrically by

$$(x(t), y(t)) = (a\theta - b\sin\theta, a - b\cos\theta)$$

with $a < b$. In our problem, $a = 0.5$ meters and $b = 0.55$ meters. Convince yourself that this is a good model for the train wheel. Plot the epicycloid. Now let $\theta = kt$ and then answer the question, "When a train moves forward, what part of the train moves backward?"

11.3. Consider the train wheel of the previous exercise. Now we will place a dot halfway between the axle and the edge of the wheel on the rail. The radius of the wheel remains 0.5 meters, and the dot is 0.25 meters from the axle. The curve that this dot traces out as the train wheel rotates is called a *hypocycloid*, and is given parametrically by

$$(x(t), y(t)) = (a\theta - b\sin\theta, a - b\cos\theta)$$

with $a > b$. This is the same equation as for the epicycloid, but with $a > b$ instead of $a < b$. Convince yourself that this is a good model for the location of the new dot. Plot the hypocycloid. Now let $\theta = kt$, and decide if this dot ever moves backward, ever stops, or if it moves forward continuously.

11.4. Decide if the 3D parametric curves (t, t^2, t^3) and (t, t, t) intersect or collide.

11.5   SUMMARY

We have studied two different ways to describe curves in this chapter. First, polar coordinates allowed us to simply describe motion around a fixed point, such as orbits, that would have been difficult to model using Cartesian coordinates. We learned how to move between coordinate systems using the relationships

$$
\begin{aligned}
r &= \sqrt{x^2 + y^2} \\
\theta &= \tan^{-1}\left(\tfrac{y}{x}\right) \\
x &= r\cos\theta \\
y &= r\sin\theta
\end{aligned}
$$

We studied new curves using polar coordinates, including

- LINES. $\theta = 1$; $r = \frac{b}{\sin\theta - m\cos\theta}$
- CIRCLES. $r = 1$; $r = \pm a\sin\theta$; $r = \pm a\cos\theta$
- CONIC SECTIONS. $r = \frac{a}{1 \pm e\cos\theta}$; $r = \frac{a}{1 \pm e\sin\theta}$
- CARDIOID. $r = a(1 \pm \cos\theta)$; $r = a(1 \pm \sin\theta)$
- ROSE. $r = \pm a\sin(k\theta)$; $r = \pm a\cos(k\theta)$

We then studied new curves using parametric curves, where the coordinates we plotted were functions of an independent parameter. This allowed us to solve problems of intersection and collision. We were also introduced to some parametric curves, including

- CYCLOID. $\left(kt - r\sin\left(\tfrac{kt}{r}\right), r\left(1 - \cos\left(\tfrac{kt}{r}\right)\right)\right)$
- WITCH OF AGNESI. $\left(a\cot t, a\sin^2 t\right)$

These new tools expand our ability to model behavior mathematically.

11.6   PROJECT: PLANETARY MOTION

In this project, we would like you to consider the difficulties faced by early astronomers when they tried to obtain their models of planetary motion. We know that each of the planets moves around the sun in ellipses with one focus at the

Planet	a	e
Mercury	0.3871	0.2056
Venus	0.7233	0.0068
Earth	1.000	0.0167
Mars	1.524	0.0934
Jupiter	5.203	0.0482
Saturn	9.519	0.0539
Uranus	19.28	0.0050
Neptune	30.17	0.0050
Pluto	39.76	0.2583

TABLE 11.1
A table of the orbital characteristics of the planets. a is the scaling constant and is in Astronomical Units (AU) where 1.000 is the average distance of the earth from the sun. e is the eccentricity of the elliptical orbit. Source: American Ephmeris and Nautical Almanac, 1969. Washington, D.C., U.S. Government Printing Office, 1967.

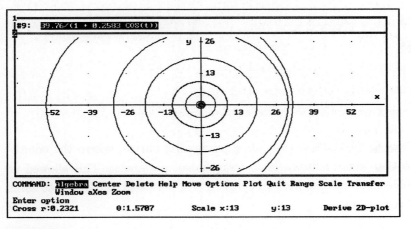

FIGURE 11.14
The nine planet orbits, in polar coordinates. One unit equals one AU, the mean distance from the earth to the sun.

sun, and we will assume that all the planets move in the same plane (which is almost true, with the exception of Pluto.) In this project, we will give you enough information to plot the different orbits of the nine planets around the sun. We will also ask you to investigate what the motion of one planet must look like when observed, not from the sun or a fixed point, but from another moving planet!

Take the data in Table 11.1, and plot the orbits of the nine planets on the same graph, using polar coordinates. You should obtain a graph which looks like the one in Figure 11.14.

When we look at Figure 11.14, we see several features. First, the scale of the solar system is very interesting. The first four planets, including Earth, are fairly close to the sun. The next two are farther out; and the last three are quite a long distance. This makes scaling the graph to capture all 9 planets hard—if we see Pluto, we must necessarily crunch the first four planets very close together. Second, most of the planets have nearly circular orbits, except Mercury and Pluto—the planets nearest and farthest from the Sun.

We also note that without information about how the angle θ changes for the polar orbit of each planet, we cannot determine where a planet is on its orbit at any given time. We need a parameterization of θ for the truly interesting problem of animating the orbits, so we can see where the planets are relative to each other as function of time. With the polar orbits, we can answer some interesting questions.

Required Analysis

1. What is the closest any planet gets to the sun?

2. What is the farthest any planet gets from the sun?

3. Which planet has the most nearly circular orbit?

4. What is the difference between the closest distance between Pluto and the Sun, and the farthest distance between Pluto and the Sun? Between Mercury and the Sun?

5. Imagine you are on the earth, watching the motion of another planet. What other factors would you have to include in a model to be able to describe the motion of another planet relative to you, the observer? Do you think this simplifies or complicates the modeling process?

6. Discuss how you would go about collecting data to fit the polar equations for the orbits of the planets. How would you fit the equations, once you obtained your data?

11.7 COMPLEMENTS

1. An undergraduate text which describes the motion of the planets, and uses polar coordinates as well as calculus, is

   • *Fundamentals of Astrodynamics*, by Roger R. Bate, Donald D. Mueller, and Jerry E. White. Dover Publishing, New York, 1971.

   The authors were on the faculty of the Department of Astronautics and Computer Science, United States Air Force Academy, and were uniquely qualified to write on the subject.

2. We continue to recommend the *History of Mathematics*, by D. E. Smith, previously cited, for background information about the men and women whose discoveries we study.

3. Information on Hypatia can be found on the World Wide Web at

   • http://www.scottlan.edu/lriddle/women/hypatia.htm

   This site includes references to a biography and two biographical articles. It also links to information on 84 other women mathematicians.

4. A gallery of curves discussed in this section, with pictures and historical notes, is available on the WWW at

   • http://www-groups.dcs.st-and.ac.uk/ history/Curves/Curves.html

5. If you are interested in astronomy, there is a huge collection of references at the *AstroEd* Web site at the University of Washington:

   • http://www-hpccc.astro.washington.edu/scied/astro/astroindex.html

CHAPTER 12

LOOKING AHEAD TO CALCULUS

I know not what I may appear to the world, but to myself I seem to
have been only like a boy playing on the sea-shore, and diverting myself
in now and then finding a smoother pebble or a prettier shell than
ordinary, whilst the great ocean of truth lay all undiscovered before me.

Isaac Newton

Chapter Goals_____

⇒ Summarize the precalculus course.

⇒ Introduce the idea of instantaneous rates of change.

⇒ Introduce the concept of accumulation and area.

⇒ Introduce the concept of limits.

⇒ Reflect on our mathematical education and goals.

One of the goals of this text is to introduce various topics in the context of modeling that will support your study of calculus. So it seems fair that the last chapter should talk about some of the ideas a calculus course will introduce. You will be pleased to learn that many of the themes that we built into our explorations and exercises directly carry over to calculus. Many of the ideas that we have been developing in the exercises are pieces of the calculus puzzle. Most important, the modeling approach we used—a preditor-response orientation—will be very helpful in calculus, with the simple substitution of the term "independent variable" for "predictor," and "dependent variable" for "response."

There are three primary themes in every calculus course, regardless of whether it calls itself a traditional calculus course or a reform calculus course: limits, rates of change, and accumulation. In most cases, these three ideas are introduced in exactly this order. We'll discuss them in a slightly different order so that we can highlight what we have learned so far, and see how it fits into the "big picture." Let's start with rates of change.

12.1   RATES OF CHANGE

What is speed? Speed is the rate of change of distance, with respect to time—miles per hour, feet per second. Speed is our most familiar rate of change.

However, how do we measure speed? We may know that it takes 1 hour to go from St. Joseph, Missouri, to Kansas City, Missouri, a distance of 55.5 miles. Our average speed must be

$$\text{speed} = \frac{\text{distance}}{\text{time}} = \frac{55.5 \text{ miles}}{1 \text{ hour}} = 55.5 \text{ miles per hour}$$

That doesn't tell us how fast we are going at any given moment on the trip. We could watch the mileposts go by, and use a watch to time how long it takes to travel a mile, but that would just give our average speed for that mile. What is our speed at any given instant?

You are probably saying, "Hey, to measure my speed at any given moment while traveling in a car, I'll just look at the *speedometer*." OK, humor us here, and pretend that you don't have a speedometer to look at. Maybe you're way in the back of a van on a class trip, or the speedometer is broken. Whatever. The point is that we want to start with a familiar setting before we move to one that doesn't have built-in measuring devices!

We introduced one approach to answering this question for the special case of exponential functions in Chapter 9. As you will now see, it was no coincidence that we examined the slope of a tangent line to the exponential curve at a particular value of x to get at this information. Calculus tackles this problem by using a tangent line, but in a slightly different manner; one that uses the idea of a *limit*.

LIMIT

At the heart of the question we are posing is the mathematical issue of how rapidly one variable changes with respect to making changes in another. This question arises in many different places. How fast do interest rates fall when inflation is falling? How much does the arc length of a circle change when the radius is changing? What is the effect on sales for spending an additional dollar on advertising?

These are questions about the properties of a model. We can gain much from knowing how much of a change in our response results from a change in one or more of our predictors. The simplest case is the linear model with one predictor, and it forms the basis for determining rates of change for all other models. That is where we will start, after we review a little notation.

12.1.0.2 NOTATION.

Let's review our notation. We will have a response variable, usually y. Initially, y is a function of some predictor variable, x. We would like to know the rate of change of y as x changes.

We label a change in y as Δy, and a change in x as Δx. We are looking, initially, at the ratio

$$\frac{\Delta y}{\Delta x} \tag{12.1}$$

which is the amount of change in y divided by the amount of change in x. We call this ratio the *difference quotient*. Dividing the change in y by the change in x scales the changes to the same units, and allows us to compare answers for different size changes in x at different initial values of x.

DIFFERENCE QUOTIENT

For example, consider a car rolling down the highway. Its location is given by $p(t)$. Its difference quotient is given by

$$\Delta = \frac{p(t_1) - p(t_0)}{t_1 - t_0}$$

The units for Δ are distance per time, usually miles per hour for cars.

How do we use these difference quotients? We might like to know what our change in position might be for a 1-hour change in time. How far will our car travel in the next second? We might like to know what our change in sales would be for a $10,000 change in advertising. How much does the taste of a cup of coffee improve for an additional 20 seconds of brewing?

Of course, the value of the difference quotient can depend on the value of x. As an example, an additional 20 seconds of brewing might help the taste of a cup of coffee if the brewing time was less than the optimal time, but hurt the taste if the coffee was already over brewed. An extra $10,000$ for advertising might have a very large impact on sales if the initial advertising budget is small, and less of an impact for a company that already has a $10,000,000$ advertising budget.

More generally, we might like to know the values of x where y is increasing or decreasing. We might also like to know those values of x where y is a maximum or a minimum. We have found graphical answers to these questions earlier in the book. Now we would like symbolic and numerical answers.

We'll find approximate answers to these questions, and then indicate how calculus will give exact answers.

12.1.1   Linear functions

We start with the most useful of functions, the line. From our earlier knowledge of lines, we recall that the *slope* of a line is given by Equation 12.1. In fact, we found in Chapters 4 and 5 that a constant difference quotient was the central property of a linear function.

We'll run through the calculations for the linear case with an example. This will set the stage for our nonlinear models.

Example 12.1. We begin with the slope-intercept form of a line $y = f(x) = mx + b$. What is the ratio change in the output, y, for a change in the input, x? We will designate two x values: the initial one, x_0, and the subsequent one, x_1. Then

$$\Delta x = x_1 - x_0 \tag{12.2}$$

$$\Delta y = y_1 - y_0$$
$$= (m(x_1) + b) - (m(x_0) + b)$$
$$= m(x_1 - x_0) \tag{12.3}$$

Then, combining Equations 12.1, 12.2, and 12.3, we obtain

$$\frac{\Delta y}{\Delta x} = \frac{m(x_1 - x_0)}{(x_1 - x_0)} = m \tag{12.4}$$

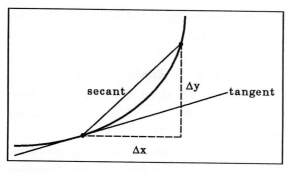

FIGURE 12.1
Secant and tangent lines for a non-linear function.

Equation 12.4 tells us, just as we already know, that the rate of change of y with respect to x is always m, regardless of the size of the change of x, the direction of change of x—increasing or decreasing—or the initial value of x.

We can rewrite Equation 12.4 slightly to obtain the useful equation

$$\Delta y = m\Delta x \qquad\qquad (12.5)$$

Equation 12.5 says that if we know the slope of the line and Δx, we can find the corresponding change in the response, Δy. This is of fundamental importance and is the basis for many approximation schemes in science and engineering.

12.1.2   Nonlinear functions

What happens if $f(x)$ is nonlinear? We can still find the difference quotient, but its value will depend *both* upon the initial value of x and the size and direction of Δx.

Geometrically, the difference quotient gives the slope of the line segment connecting the points $(x_0, f(x_0))$ and $(x_1, f(x_1))$. As we noted previously, and as Figure 12.1 illustrates, this line segment is called a *secant line.*

An interesting effect can be seen by zooming in on the graph of a smooth, nonlinear curve. When the magnification is high, every smooth, nonlinear curve looks linear. This *local linearity* property gives us the ability to use lines to LOCAL approximate the the nonlinear curve in a very small *neighborhood* around some LINEARITY particular point on the curve. We're using the term *neighborhood* to mean exactly as you might suspect: points in a neighborhood of some particular point on a curve "live" in close proximity, or only a short distance from that point.

As we zoom in on a nonlinear curve, we eventually see a line. What is the slope of that line? We can estimate it in two ways, and we can identify its value exactly by a third technique.

To estimate the slope of this approximating tangent line, we could first estimate its value based on our zoomed-in graph, using the ratio of rise-over-run. Or, we could estimate the ratio of the rise-over-run numerically by finding $\Delta y/\Delta x$ for very small, but nonzero, values of Δx.

Calculus gives us the ability to find the slope of this tangent line *exactly*, by observing the behavior of the ratio $\Delta y/\Delta x$ as Δx approaches zero. Recalling that the slope of this tangent line at some point on the nonlinear function is the same as the instantaneaous rate of change of the function at that point, we can say that calculus gives us the ability to routinely calculate the instantaneous rate of change of any function, linear or nonlinear. This is a very powerful tool to have in your possession.

Back to another issue: Why would one want to use a line to approximate a curve? Lines are very easy to work with. We already obtained results for lines in the previous section. If we work with a linear approximation to a curve, we then can assume that $\Delta y/\Delta x = m$, a constant slope.

This makes estimation easy. For example, say we approximate $f(x)$ with a line, $l(x) = mx + b$. Then, as a direct result of Equation 12.5, $\Delta y \approx m\Delta x$, or

$$y_1 \approx y_0 + m\Delta x$$

Of course, the trick is finding the best line to approximate the curve—*and the tangent line is best*. This is again what calculus does—it gives us the slope of the tangent line to a curve at a given point. We can then use the point-slope form of a line to find the equation of the tangent line (but all we usually need is the slope).

TANGENT APPROXIMATION Take a look at Figure 12.2, and recreate it in your CAS. As we zoom in and out, notice that this best line is *tangent* to the curve. Our best linear approximation is a *tangent line approximation*.

12.1.3 Planes and surfaces

Let's recall the equation for a plane: $z = m_1 x + m_2 y + b$. For our line of the preceding section, we had two choices of direction for change in the predictor. We could increase or decrease. When we have more than one predictor, we have

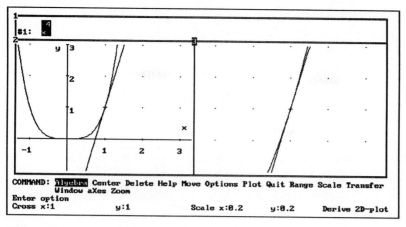

FIGURE 12.2
The best linear approximation to a curve at a point is the tangent line.

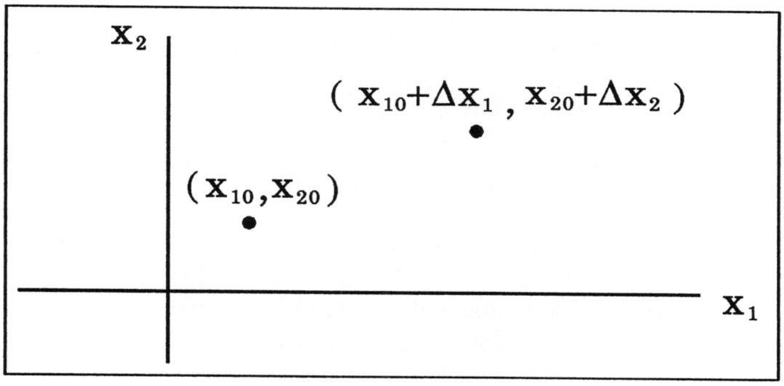

```
                 X₂
                       ( X₁₀+ΔX₁ , X₂₀+ΔX₂ )
                              ●

          ( X₁₀,X₂₀ )
                ●


                                            X₁
```

FIGURE 12.3
Changing predictors by the amount Δx in the x direction and Δy in the y direction.

many more choices of direction. For two predictors, we can move in any direction in the (x, y)-plane—along any line segment from our initial point.

Let's consider movement parallel to the axes first. If we fix, say y, we can vary x alone. Then our change in z is due strictly to our change in x. We find

$$\frac{\Delta z}{\Delta x} = \frac{z_1 - z_0}{x_1 - x_0} = \frac{(m_1 x_1 + m_2 y + b) - (m_1 x_0 + m_2 y + b)}{x_1 - x_0} = m_1 \qquad (12.6)$$

If we move strictly in the y direction, we obtain a similar result:

$$\frac{\Delta z}{\Delta y} = m_2 \qquad (12.7)$$

What if we move in a direction different from one parallel to the axes? Then we will have a move that is equal to the triangle with legs of Δx and Δy.

See Figure 12.3. What is Δz? We see that

$$\Delta z = z_1 - z_0$$
$$= (m_1 x_1 + m_2 y_1 + b) - (m_1 x_0 + m_2 y_0 + b)$$
$$= m_1(x_1 - x_0) + m_2(y_1 - y_0)$$
$$= m_1 \Delta x + m_2 \Delta y \qquad (12.8)$$

TOTAL DIF-
FERENTIAL
Equation 12.8 is called the *total differential*. It describes the change in z as a linear function of the change in x and the change in y.

One of the interesting things about the total differential is that we can use it to find directions on the plane where there is *no* change in z as we change predictors, as well as the directions of *maximum* increase and decrease. We will demonstrate with an example.

Example 12.2. We will imagine a plane given by the equation

$$z = f(x,y) = x + y + 1 \qquad (12.9)$$

For this equation, $m_1 = 1$, $m_2 = 1$, and $b = 1$. What is Δz if $\Delta x = 1$ and $\Delta y = -1$? By Equation 12.8, we have

$$\Delta z = 1(\Delta x) + 1(\Delta y) = 1(1) + 1(-1) = 0 \qquad (12.10)$$

In other words, even though we have changed our predictors, our response has not changed. This is like walking sideways on a hill—you can move without going up or down, an idea that we introduced earlier in this book.

How do we find the direction of steepest ascent or descent? To begin with, we should compare moves of equal length, say one unit of distance. Moving from an initial point a distance of 1 in any direction gives us a circle of possible subsequent points with radius 1, centered at our initial point. Applying basic trigonometry, we have that $\Delta x^2 + \Delta y^2 = 1$ for all moves of total length 1. Solving for Δy, we have $|\Delta y| = \sqrt{1 - \Delta x^2}$. We substitute those values into Equation 12.8 with $m_1 = 1$ and $m_2 = 1$, and obtain

$$\Delta z = 1(\Delta x) \pm 1(\sqrt{1 - \Delta x^2}) \qquad (12.11)$$

The $\pm$ sign is in Equation 12.11 to reflect that Δy can be positive or negative.

We plot both expressions for Equation 12.11 in Figure 12.4. From this figure, we see that Δz has a maximum when $\Delta x = 1/\sqrt{2}$ and $\Delta y = 1/\sqrt{2}$. We also see that Δz has a minimum when $\Delta x = -1/\sqrt{2}$ and $\Delta y = -1/\sqrt{2}$.

It is not a coincidence that the ratio of the values of Δx and Δy is the same as the ratio of the values of m_1 and m_2.

You will see in calculus that the steepest ascent is always in the same direction as (m_1, m_2), the steepest descent is in the direction $(-m_1, -m_2)$, and that the contours of "no change" run in the directions $(-m_1, m_2)$ and $(m_1, -m_2)$.

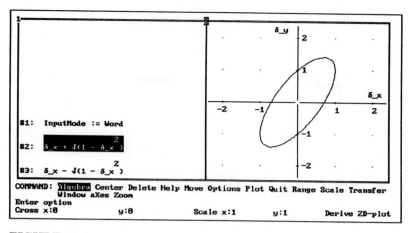

FIGURE 12.4
Plot of the expressions for Δz. The values of Δz lie on an ellipse, with the two expressions forming the upper and lower halves, respectively. Note maximum at $\Delta x = 1/\sqrt{2}$ and minimum at $\Delta x = -1/\sqrt{2}$, seen by looking at the crosshairs' position.

The tangent line is the best linear approximation to a curve in two dimensions. What about surfaces in three (or more) dimensions?

- The *tangent plane* is the best linear approximation for the surface at a given point.

- For each point on the (smooth) surface given by $z = f(x, y)$, we can find the unique tangent plane.

Again, calculus enables us to find the coefficients of the plane, m_1, m_2, and b. We can use the tangent plane, and the properties of planes, to get approximate results for the underlying *response surface*, $z = f(x, y)$. In particular, we can find directions of greatest increase and decrease, directions of no change, and estimates of the amount of increase in *any* direction: directional slope.

12.1.4 Implications

There are two immediate implications of the ability to easily find tangent lines and planes to non-linear functions.

First, if the tangent line is increasing or decreasing, we *cannot* have a maximum or a minimum. A necessary condition for a maximum or a minimum is that the tangent line either have zero slope, or not exist. This gives us a quick way to find *extrema*—extrema being maximums or minimums: Check all the points where the tangent line is horizontal or fails to exist.

This is so important that we say it again: *to find the maximum or minimum value of a function, check all the values where the tangent line is horizontal or does not exist.* If they exist, the maximum will be one of those values and the minimum will be another.

This condition generalizes to surfaces and tangent planes: A necessary condition for a surface to have a maximum or a minimum is that the tangent plane be horizontal (all slopes equal to zero) or not exist. *To find the maximum or minimum value of a function of two variables, check all the values where the tangent plane is horizontal or does not exist.*

Second, we can use the tangent line or planes to approximate the behavior of the underlying function. This is particularly helpful when we want to avoid extensive computations. It is also useful for investigating the properties of functions.

The ability to find and use these tangents is a very powerful tool of calculus, and constitutes what is called the *differential calculus*.

Exploration Exercises _____

12.1. Graph $y = x^2$. Find the location of the minimum value of y. Convince yourself that the tangent line to the curve is horizontal at that point.

12.2. Let $y = x^2$. Let $x_0 = 0$. What is the value of the difference quotient for small positive and negative values of Δx? Compare your answer with your answer to the previous problem.

12.3. Let $y = x^3$. Convince yourself that the tangent line at $x = 0$ is horizontal, but that there is not a maximum or minimum at $(0, 0)$. Explain how this can be.

12.4. Graph $y = \sqrt{x}$. Estimate the slope when $x = 64$. (Hint: You should get $m \approx 1/16$.) Use that estimated slope and Equation 12.5 to approximate $\sqrt{65}$. Compare your answer with the answer provided by your calculator for $\sqrt{65}$. How accurate is your answer?

12.5. Use the method of the preceding problem to estimate $\sqrt{64.05}$. How accurate is your answer? Compare the ease of this method with finding square roots by hand.

12.6. Consider the plane given by $z = 3x + 2y - 7$. Place a point at $(1, 1, -2)$. Find the direction of steepest ascent and descent on the plane. Then find the direction of no change.

12.7. Let $z = f(x, y) = \sin(xy)$. Let $(x_0, y_0, z_0) = (\pi/2, 1/2, 1/\sqrt{2})$. The tangent plane at (x_0, y_0, z_0) is approximately given by

$$z = 0.3353x + 1.1107y - .4036$$

Estimate $f(1.7, .4)$. What is the direction of steepest ascent?

12.8. Write a short paragraph that explains to a friend why tangent lines and planes are useful.

12.2   ACCUMULATION

Many of our models gave us information about the state of a system at a particular place or time. For example, we created many models that allowed us to predict the sales of a product for a given time. We created models for sales that increase linearly, exponentially, and even vary seasonally.

Knowing the sales predicted for a given time is useful, but often we would like to know the accumulated sales for a period of time. We might have a model that gives us daily sales, and want to know the monthly or yearly total.

We also created models that gave us the position of falling bodies, planets, or other moving objects as functions of time. We might want to know how far the objects have moved over a given interval of time, or what their accumulated displacement is.

As another type of accumulation, for any curve of the form $y = f(x)$, we ACCUMULATION might be interested in the area between the curve and the x-axis.

Questions of accumulation are the second major topic treated by calculus. To handle them, we will need a wee bit more notation.

12.2.1   Notation

To accumulate some quantity, we add. So, let's review our notation for sums because if you're not working with this notation on a frequent basis, it's easy to forget how to work with it.

Consider a sequence of numbers to be added, say x_1, x_2, x_3, x_4 and x_5. To add them, we could write

$$x_1 + x_2 + x_3 + x_4 + x_5$$

However, if this is cumbersome for five terms, it becomes a nightmare for larger numbers of terms. We need a better notation; some shorthand symbol, perhaps.

The notation we use to represent the process of summing is called *series notation*. There are three pieces. A capital Greek letter Sigma (Σ) stands for SERIES summation. The second piece is an *index*, which identifies the different terms to NOTATION be added. Usually the index ranges over some set of integers, and the index is customarily represented by the letters i, j, or k. The third piece is the *summand*, which is the expression being added. It's time for an example.

Example 12.3. Consider the summation notation given by

$$\sum_{i=1}^{n} x_i \tag{12.12}$$

This notation says to add all the terms x_i, with i ranging from 1 to n. The letter i is the index, and the lower limit (1) is on the bottom of the Σ. The upper limit (n) is on the top.

Of course, we have to know each summand x_i to actually do the addition in this last example. We often have $x_i = f(i)$, a function of the index. Strictly **SEQUENCE** speaking, the x_i's form a *sequence* of numbers, and a series is the sum of a sequence.

Example 12.4. In Equation 12.12, we will let $x_i = i$ and $n = 5$. Equation 12.12 is then asking us to add

$$\sum_{i=1}^{5} i = 1 + 2 + 3 + 4 + 5 = 15 \tag{12.13}$$

If $x_i = i^2$ with $n = 5$, then Equation 12.12 represents

$$\sum_{i=1}^{5} i^2 = 1 + 4 + 9 + 16 + 25 = 55 \tag{12.14}$$

Our strategy for modeling accumulation will be to break the independent variable into small pieces, and index each piece. We then will represent the individual contribution of the dependent variable to the sum as a function of the index. We then will need a way to add all the pieces up easily.

We will tackle the easy cases first.

12.2.2 Horizontal lines

The easiest case is perhaps the horizontal line, $y = f(t) = b$. This could represent a constant rate of sales, b units per day, with time measured in days. If we wanted to know the total sales, we could accumulate the daily sales.

Let S represent the total sales, and d_i be the sales for the ith day. For monthly sales, we might have i as an integer between 1 and 30. (Quick: For what months is the range of this index appropriate? Do you remember the rhyme?)

To capture this addition, we write

$$S = \sum_{i=1}^{30} d_i$$

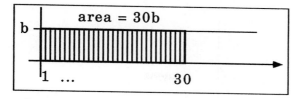

FIGURE 12.5
Accumulated sales for a constant sales function.

Since we have said that the sales for each day is a constant b, we can write

$$S = \sum_{i=1}^{30} b = 30b$$

because $b + b + b + b + \cdots + b = 30b$.

We are going to dwell on this point and draw a graph to represent this sum, because it will set a helpful precedent in this regard.

In Figure 12.5, we have divided up the independent variable, time (t), into 30 segments. Each segment has width of 1 day. Above each segment we have drawn a rectangle, whose width is 1 day and whose height equals b sales per day. The area of each rectangle is given by

$$\text{base} \times \text{height} = 1 \times b = b$$

which represents b units sold on that day.

To find the total sales over these 30 days, we add up the area of each of the 30 rectangles, obtain the result $30b$.

You might observe that finding the total sales was exactly like finding the area under the line. This is a *very* astute observation on your point, because that is exactly the process we are trying to get at. You might also observe that we are able to find an exact expression, $S = 30b$, for the sum that represents the total sales. We will often look for such expressions.

Of course, to find the area under a line it's not necessary to subdivide the area into small rectangles. We can consider the area under the line as one large rectangle with base of 30 days and height of b units per day, and, calculating the area of this big rectangle, we again get a total sales of $30b$ units.

Notice that we have been very careful in this example to specify the units, and to make sure that the units agree. This is a handy technique to avoid mistakes.

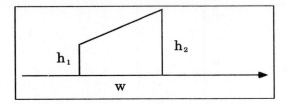

FIGURE 12.6
The area under a line with nonzero slope is that area of a trapezoid.

12.2.3   Other lines

For our second easy case, let's consider lines with nonzero slope. How do we find the area under such a line?

Look at Figure 12.6. We see that the area under a line forms a geometric shape—a trapezoid, in which the height of each side is different. The area of a trapezoid with base w and heights of h_1 and h_2 is known from geometry to be given exactly by the formula

$$A = \frac{w(h_1 + h_2)}{2} \qquad (12.15)$$

We could consider the area under the line to be the sum of many small trapezoids, just as we did with rectangles, and through accumumation we would get the same exact result.

This formula for trapezoids is more useful that a formula for rectangles because the top of the trapezoid is not restricted to be flat like the top of rectangles. We'll use it again in order to estimate the area under curves just for this reason. When using a sum of trapazoids to estimate the area under a curve, we will not get an exact result, but if we use enough really thin trapezoids, our answer will be a decent approximation to the exact area.

12.2.4   Parabolas

We will outline one more exact result, using some more facts from geometry. Consider the parabola given by the equation

$$y = f(x) = ax^2 + bx + c$$

Choose some interval of x values with end points x_0 and x_2, so that $x_0 \leq x \leq x_2$, and let the midpoint of this interval be given by $x_1 = \frac{x_0 + x_2}{2}$.

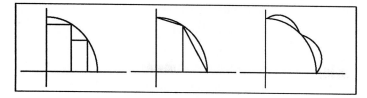

FIGURE 12.7
Approximating the area under the curve $y = \cos x$ with rectangles, trapezoids, and parabolas.

The area between the parabola and the x-axis is then given by

$$A = \frac{(x_2 - x_0)\left(f(x_0) + 4f(x_1) + f(x_2)\right)}{6} \qquad (12.16)$$

Equation 12.16 is similar to the trapezoidal rule: We multiply the width of the interval $(x_2 - x_0)$ times a weighted average of the height of the interval.

This formula allows us to find the *exact* area under a parabola, just so long as we know the values of the parabola at its end points and midpoints. Notice that it is not necessary to know or explicitly solve for a, b, and c in the equation of the parabola to apply Equation 12.16. All that we need are the response values, y.

Like the trapezoidal rule, this parabolic rule is useful. It allows us to approximate the area under curves by summing the area under a collection of parabolas. This is much more accurate than using rectangles or trapezoids, because now the top of our approximating figure does not even have to be a straight line.

12.2.5   Other curves

The reason we developed the methods of rectangles, trapezoids, and parabolas was to use them to approximate the area under other curves, curves without standard area formulas. Let's try an example.

Example 12.5. What is the area under the curve $y = \cos x$, when x is between 0 and $\pi/2$?

We can not find an exact answer without calculus, but we can get a pretty good approximation with the tools we have developed so far. We will try all three approaches: approximating with rectangles, trapezoids, and parabolas. Figure 12.7 illustrates these three approximation methods. For our first set of trials, let's subdivide the interval $[0, \pi/2]$ into four equal pieces, with endpoints 0, $\pi/8$, $\pi/4$, $3\pi/8$, and $\pi/2$.

12.2.5.1   RECTANGLES.

When working with rectangles to approximate area, we are faced with a choice. What should the height of the rectangle be? The dilemma occurs because we

have to pick the point at one top corner or the other to lie exactly on the curve. The usual convention is to pick either the height at the right-hand endpoint or the left-hand endpoint, and to stay consistent. One choice gives the *right-hand rule*, the other gives the *left-hand rule*. We'll try both.

Example 12.6. For our first interval, $[0, \pi/8]$, we pick the height at left-hand endpoint equal to $\cos(0) = 1$. The height at the right-hand endpoint is

$$\cos(\pi/8) = \sqrt{\sqrt{2}/4 + 1/2} \approx 0.923879$$

For our second interval, $[\pi/8, \pi/4]$, we have the height at lefthand endpoint equal to $\cos(\pi/8) \approx 0.923879$. The height at the right-hand endpoint is $\cos(\pi/4) = 1/\sqrt{2}$.

For our third interval, $[\pi/4, 3\pi/8]$, we have the height at left-hand endpoint equal to $\cos(\pi/4) = 1/\sqrt{2}$. The height at the right-hand endpoint is

$$\cos(3\pi/8) = \sqrt{1/2 - \sqrt{2}/4} \approx 0.382683$$

For our fourth interval, $[3\pi/8, \pi/2]$, we have the height at left-hand endpoint equal to $\cos(3\pi/8) \approx 0.382683$. The height at the right-hand endpoint is then $\cos(\pi/2) = 0$.

The area of each rectangle is bh, or base times height, as noted earlier. All the intervals have the same width

$$\frac{\pi/2}{4} = \frac{\pi}{2 \times 4} = \pi/8$$

For the left-hand rule, we can write the height as a function of the interval number

$$h_l(i) = \cos\left(\frac{(i-1)\pi}{2 \times 4}\right) \tag{12.17}$$

For the right-hand rule, we get a similar rule:

$$h_r(i) = \cos\left(\frac{i\pi}{2 \times 4}\right) \tag{12.18}$$

Using Equations 12.17 and 12.18, we can write the approximate area using our summation notation:

$$A = \sum_{i=1}^{n} h(i)b$$

$$A_l = \sum_{i=1}^{4} \cos\left(\frac{(i-1)\pi}{2 \times 4}\right) \frac{\pi}{2 \times 4} \tag{12.19}$$

$$A_r = \sum_{i=1}^{4} \cos\left(\frac{i\pi}{2 \times 4}\right) \frac{\pi}{2 \times 4} \tag{12.20}$$

n	A_l	A_r
10	1.07648	0.919403
100	1.00783	0.992125
1000	1.00078	0.999214

TABLE 12.1
Approximations for the area under the curve $y = \cos(x)$ between $x = 0$ and $x = \pi/2$, using left- and right-hand rectangles with n subintervals.

Using *Derive* and Equations 12.19 and 12.20, we obtain our approximate areas:

$$A_l = 1.18346 \tag{12.21}$$
$$A_r = 0.790766 \tag{12.22}$$

You might ask why we bothered to put our equations for the area in the series notation of Equations 12.19 and 12.20. Well, it was really for convenience. With one small change, we can use the same equations regardless of how many pieces of our interval we use.

Example 12.7. In the last example, we used 4 intervals in the summation. If we substitute n everywhere we see 4 in Equations 12.19 and 12.20, we can rewrite these expressions as

$$A = \sum_{i=1}^{n} hb$$

$$A_l = \sum_{i=1}^{n} \cos\left(\frac{(i-1)\pi}{2n}\right)\frac{\pi}{2n} \tag{12.23}$$

$$A_r = \sum_{i=1}^{n} \cos\left(\frac{i\pi}{2n}\right)\frac{\pi}{2n} \tag{12.24}$$

We going to ask you to verify this result in the Exercises.

Equations 12.23 and 12.24 give us a series representation for our approximate area that depends only on n, the number of intervals used. By changing n, and evaluating the equations on a computer algebra system, we can improve our area approximations very easily. This is illustrated in Table 12.1.

We find that it is also very easy to implement these approximations using a spreadsheet. Looking at Figures 12.8 and 12.9, notice that as we increase n, our approximation appears to be getting closer and closer to 1.0. However, as we increase n we have to contend with increasing computation time and increased

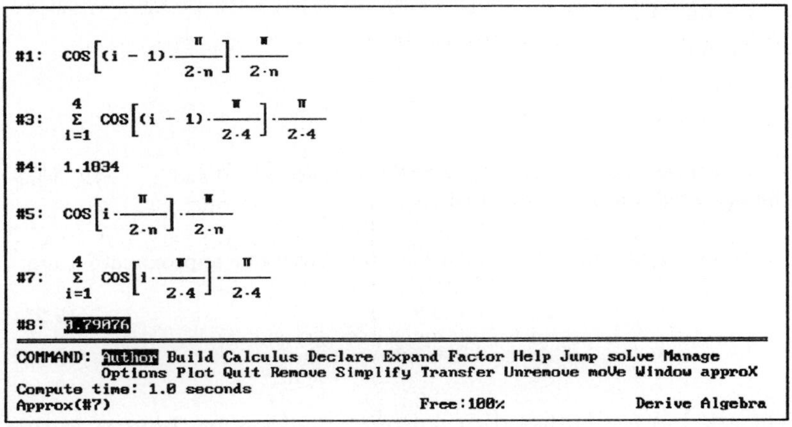

#1: $\cos\left[(i-1)\cdot\frac{\pi}{2\cdot n}\right]\cdot\frac{\pi}{2\cdot n}$
#3: $\sum_{i=1}^{4}\cos\left[(i-1)\cdot\frac{\pi}{2\cdot 4}\right]\cdot\frac{\pi}{2\cdot 4}$
#4: 1.1834
#5: $\cos\left[i\cdot\frac{\pi}{2\cdot n}\right]\cdot\frac{\pi}{2\cdot n}$
#7: $\sum_{i=1}^{4}\cos\left[i\cdot\frac{\pi}{2\cdot 4}\right]\cdot\frac{\pi}{2\cdot 4}$
#8: 0.79076
COMMAND: Author Build Calculus Declare Expand Factor Help Jump soLve Manage
Options Plot Quit Remove Simplify Transfer Unremove moVe Window approX
Compute time: 1.0 seconds
Approx(#7)
Free:100%
Derive Algebra

FIGURE 12.8
Calculations to approximate the area under the curve $f(x) = \cos x$ between $[0, \pi/2]$ using rectangles with $n = 4$, using *Derive*.

Quattro Pro for Windows - C12-8.WB1
File Edit Block Data Tools Graph Property Window Help
Normal
100
Arial
A:D14
NUM
READY
Start
CD Playe...
HiJaak P...
HiJaak Br...
DERIVE
Quattro...
PCTeX fo...
4:48 AM

	A	B	C	D	E	F	G
1	x	f(x)	f(x)*delta				
2					left hand rule		1.183465
3	0	1	0.392699		right hand rule		0.790766
4	0.392699	0.92388	0.362807				
5	0.785398	0.707107	0.27768				
6	1.178097	0.382683	0.150279				
7	1.570796	6.1E-17	2.4E-17				

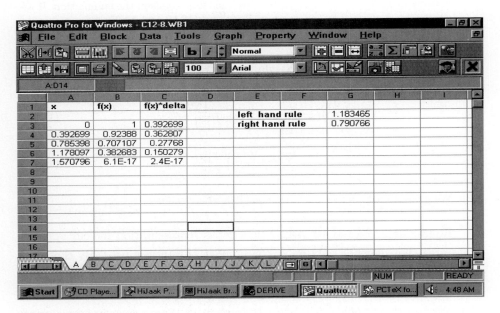

FIGURE 12.9
Calculations to approximate the area under the curve $f(x) = \cos x$ between $[0, \pi/2]$ using rectangles with $n = 4$, using QuattroPro.

error due to rounding and truncation. Of course, if we had a function that gave us the value of the sum exactly, such as we had for the area under a line, we would not have to worry about computation time, or computational error.

12.2.5.2 TRAPEZOIDS.

We are going to use a shortcut for our trapezoid calculations, since we have already done the right-hand and left-hand rectangle calculations.

What is the average of the left-hand and the right-hand rectangles? We add them together and divide by 2, and get

$$\text{Average} = \frac{bh_1 + bh_2}{2} = b\frac{h_1 + h_2}{2}$$

which is the trapezoid area. We can use the average of the left-hand rectangles and the right-hand rectangles to obtain the trapezoidal approximation. It follows that we can average the area approximations from the right-hand rule and the left-hand rule to obtain the area approximation using the trapezoidal rule. In other words, once we have done the right-hand and left-hand approximations, the trapezoidal approximation is essentially free.

With this shortcut, we have

$$A_t(n) \quad = \frac{A_l(n) + A_r(n)}{2}$$

$$A_t(4) \quad = 0.987115$$
$$A_t(5) \quad = 0.991761$$
$$A_t(10) \quad = 0.997943$$
$$A_t(100) \quad = 0.999979$$
$$A_t(1000) \quad = 0.9999997943$$

Again we see that the area approximations appear to be getting closer and closer to 1. also, we see that the trapezoidal rule seems more accurate than either of the rectangle approximations.

12.2.5.3 PARABOLAS.

So far, we have estimated the area under $f(x) = \cos x$ using rectangles and trapezoids. Let's now give it a go using parabolas. Since we are approximating a curve with sections whose top is curved, we expect that we should be able to get a better fit with fewer points.

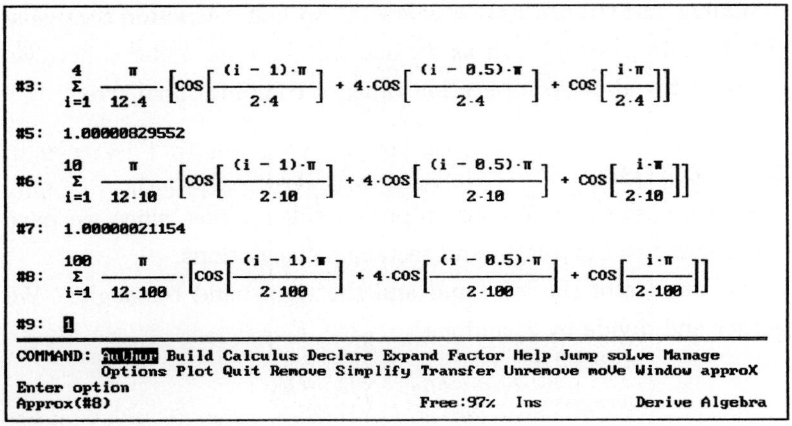

#3: $\displaystyle \sum_{i=1}^{4} \frac{\pi}{12\cdot4}\cdot\left[\cos\left[\frac{(i-1)\cdot\pi}{2\cdot4}\right] + 4\cdot\cos\left[\frac{(i-0.5)\cdot\pi}{2\cdot4}\right] + \cos\left[\frac{i\cdot\pi}{2\cdot4}\right]\right]$

#5: 1.00000829552

#6: $\displaystyle \sum_{i=1}^{10} \frac{\pi}{12\cdot10}\cdot\left[\cos\left[\frac{(i-1)\cdot\pi}{2\cdot10}\right] + 4\cdot\cos\left[\frac{(i-0.5)\cdot\pi}{2\cdot10}\right] + \cos\left[\frac{i\cdot\pi}{2\cdot10}\right]\right]$

#7: 1.00000021154

#8: $\displaystyle \sum_{i=1}^{100} \frac{\pi}{12\cdot100}\cdot\left[\cos\left[\frac{(i-1)\cdot\pi}{2\cdot100}\right] + 4\cdot\cos\left[\frac{(i-0.5)\cdot\pi}{2\cdot100}\right] + \cos\left[\frac{i\cdot\pi}{2\cdot100}\right]\right]$

#9: ▊

COMMAND: Author Build Calculus Declare Expand Factor Help Jump soLve Manage
Options Plot Quit Remove Simplify Transfer Unremove moVe Window approX
Enter option
Approx(#8)   Free:97% Ins   Derive Algebra

FIGURE 12.10
Derive screen showing the manipulations to approximate the area under $f(x) = \cos x$ between $x = 0$ and $x = \pi/2$, using parabolas.

Suppose that we use 4 intervals initially. This means that we use one parabola estimate between $x = 0$ and $x = \pi/8$, a second between $x = \pi/4$, and so on.

Example 12.8. For the first parabola, we have

$$A_p(1) = \frac{(\pi/8 - 0)(\cos(0) + 4\cos(\pi/16) + \cos(\pi/8))}{6}$$

and for the ith parabola we have

$$A_p(i) = \frac{\pi/2}{6n}\left(\cos\left(\frac{(i-1)\pi}{2n}\right) + 4\cos\left(\frac{(i-1/2)\pi}{2n}\right) + \cos\left(\frac{i\pi}{2n}\right)\right) \qquad (12.25)$$

The point $[(i-1/2)\pi]/2n$ is the midpoint of the ith interval.

Don't panic yet—there is a point to all this algebra. We can now write our parabolic approximation to the total area as the sum of these individual parabolic pieces, giving

$$A = \sum_{i=1}^{n} A_p(i)$$

$$= \sum_{i=1}^{n} \frac{\pi/2}{6n}\left(\cos\left(\frac{(i-1)\pi}{2n}\right) + 4\cos\left(\frac{(i-1/2)\pi}{2n}\right) + \cos\left(\frac{i\pi}{2n}\right)\right) \quad (12.26)$$

And finally, we enter Equation 12.26 into *Derive* or a spreadsheet to evaluate our area estimates. The corresponding *Derive* screen is shown in Figure 12.10.

We obtain the following results. When $n = 4$, our estimate for the area is 1.000008925. When $n = 10$, our estimate is 1.000000211. When $n = 100$, our estimate is 1, within the limits of the machine precision.

Clearly our parabolic approximations are getting closer to 1 faster than the other methods. But, absent some theory, we still can't be sure that the true answer is exactly 1 instead of, say, $1 + 10^{-9}$.

Enter calculus, which provides us the theory we need.

12.2.6   Exact expressions

We would like to have exact expressions for these areas. As we take thinner and thinner intervals for our independent variable, we get a better fit with each method, although the fit improves quicker with trapezoids than with rectangles, and quicker still with parabolas. Still, evaluating those sums is a chore. It would be much nicer to have a simple function that gives us the area under the curve once we specify the endpoints.

Integral calculus allows us to find exact expressions for these areas, by taking infinitely thin intervals and adding up the summands. This process is the second great accomplishment of the calculus. For example, integral calculus tells us that the area under the curve $y = \cos x$ between x_0 and x_1 is given exactly by the formula

$$A = \sin(x_1) - \sin(x_0) \qquad (12.27)$$

This formula for the area is certainly much easier to work with than our geometrical approximations, and provides the exact answer! For our example, where $x_0 = 0$ and $x_1 = \pi/2$,

$$A = \sin\left(\frac{\pi}{2}\right) - \sin(0) = 1$$

In the exercises, we ask you to discuss how close our various approximations were to the true value, and to comment on the trade-offs involved.

It is a sad, but true, fact that *not every area problem has an exact functional solution* such as the one in Equation 12.27. In those cases, we *must* use methods such as the ones in this chapter to approximate the area. These techniques are called *numerical integration.*

12.2.7   Implications

We worked an area problem to demonstrate the idea of accumulation. There are many, many other types of accumulation problems—volumes, work, surface area, total sales, and arc length, to name a few. But the general approach remains the same: we divide the total into little pieces, estimate each piece, and then add them back together. If the small pieces are well estimated, then our approximation methods work well.

We have three open issues. First, how can we be sure that our approximations get closer and closer to the true value as we increase n? Second, how large does n have to be to within a certain distance of the true (but possibly unknown) area? And last, when do exact expressions exist for the accumulation, and when must we use approximations?

LIMITS   The first issue is addressed by the theory of *limits*. The second is addressed by error estimates for each of the approximation methods, which are developed using tools of calculus. The third is answered simply: If we can find an exact expression, we use it. If we can't, we approximate.

Exploration Exercises _____

12.1. Write $1^2 + 2^2 + 3^2 + 4^2 + 5^2 + 6^2$ using series notation, as in Equation 12.12.

12.2. Write a paragraph explaining what steps were used to obtain Equation 12.20.

12.3. Verify the result expressed in Equation 12.24.

12.4. Approximate the area under the following curves between $x = 1$ and $x = 2$. Use the specified method and number of intervals. Show your work, and use *Derive* or a spreadsheet as appropriate.
  (a) $f(x) = \exp(x)$, left-hand rectangles, $n = 4$
  (b) $f(x) = \exp(x)$, right-hand rectangles, $n = 4$
  (c) $f(x) = \exp(x)$, trapezoids, $n = 4$
  (d) $f(x) = \exp(x)$, parabolas, $n = 4$
  (e) $f(x) = \ln(x)$, left-hand rectangles, $n = 8$
  (f) $f(x) = \ln(x)$, right-hand rectangles, $n = 8$
  (g) $f(x) = \ln(x)$, trapezoids, $n = 4$
  (h) $f(x) = \ln(x)$, parabolas, $n = 2$
  (i) $f(x) = (2\pi)^{-0.5} \exp(-x^2/2)$, left-hand rectangles, $n = 10$
  (j) $f(x) = (2\pi)^{-0.5} \exp(-x^2/2)$, trapezoids, $n = 10$
  (k) $f(x) = (2\pi)^{-0.5} \exp(-x^2/2)$, parabolas , $n = 10$

12.5. What goes wrong with the approximation methods in this section when we try to approximate the area under the curve $y = f(x) = x^{-0.5}$ between $x = 0$ and $x = 1$?

12.6. Discuss the trade-offs between using the rectangular, trapezoidal, and parabolic approximations. In particular, for a fixed n, what are the sizes of the relative errors? What is the number of additions and multiplications involved for each method?

12.3   LIMITS

We have been tip-toeing around the issue of limits for much of the book. We
don't want to rob the calculus course of its ability to excite and to intrigue by
giving away all its secrets—and understanding the limiting process is surely one
of the keys to success at calculus. We do want to hint at where you will use
limits, and why they are so fundamental.

There are two fundamental applications of the limiting process in calculus.
The first is used to find the tangent line to a curve, as we discussed earlier in
this book and in the first section of this chapter. The second is used to find exact
answers to area problems.

We approximated the slope of a tangent line by the slope of a secant line.
In other words, we said the slope was approximately equal to the "rise divided
by the run" or the change in y for small changes in x, which is the slope of the
corresponding secant line. We can take smaller and smaller values for the change
in x, but we eventually end up dividing zero by zero. What to do?

We also approximated the area under a curve as the sum of geometrical
regions. To get better area approximations, we added more, smaller pieces. These
smaller pieces result in a more *fine* approximation. Eventually, we end up adding
an infinite number of infinitely skinny regions to get an exact answer. How do
we do that?

Whenever we use a fine discrete approximation to a continuous process,
we are faced with the questions we just asked. Very small quantities are called
infinitesimals, and they require relatively careful handling. Adding large num-   INFINITESIMALS
bers of small quantities, as in an area approximation, and taking ratios of very
small quantities, as in a tangent approximation, can be tricky. In addition to the
underlying mathematical difficulties, there are real issues of computational error
due to rounding, truncation, and machine error.

12.3.1   Convergence

One goal of calculus is to determine if the sequence of values produced by succes-
sively finer approximations does *converge* to one number, and if so, to determine   CONVERGENCE
that number. This requires precise definitions (limit, sequence, convergence) and

theorems—in other words, more collegiate mathematics.

We claimed before that we can get exact answers for these limits. For example, we claimed that the sequence of approximations we constructed to estimate the area under $f(x) = \cos x$ converged to a limit of 1 as we let n get larger and larger. But we claimed even more: We said that we could find a function that found those limits based on the endpoints of our interval! In many cases, we can find these functions that give us the exact area. Finding these functions, when they exist, and evaluating their properties are more key tasks of calculus.

Exploration Exercises

12.1. Not all difference quotients converge to a limit as $\Delta x \to 0$. For the following functions, decide if the difference quotient converges.

    (a) $f(x) = x^2$, at $x_0 = 0$
    (b) $f(x) = |x|$ at $x_0 = 0$ (look at both sides of x_0)
    (c) $f(x) = \cos x$ at $x_0 = \pi$
    (d) $f(x) = \tan x$ at $x_0 = 0$
    (e) $f(x) = \sqrt{|x|}$ at $x_0 = 0$

12.2. Consider the function $f(x) = \sin(x)/x$. Why is $f(0)$ not defined? What happens to the value of $f(x)$ as $x \to 0$? (Hint: Plot a graph).

12.3. Consider the function $f(x) = \cos(x)/x$. Why is $f(0)$ not defined? What happens to the value of $f(x)$ as $x \to 0$? (Hint: Plot a graph.)

12.4. Consider the function $f(x) = x \cot(x)$. Why is $f(0)$ not defined? What happens to the value of $f(x)$ as $x \to 0$? (Hint: Plot a graph.)

12.5. We approximated the area under $\cos(x)$ using trapezoids. Argue that the area under the curve is finite. (Hint: Show that it is less than the area of some other simple geometric figure.) Then argue that every time we increase the number of subintervals in this approximation, the sum increases. Must an increasing, bounded sequence of approximations converge? Does it have to converge to the true value? What do you think?

12.6. Find out what beginning calculus textbook your school uses. Scan through the table of contents and then through the book. What topics look familiar? Which problems look familiar? Do you feel ready?

12.7. Find out what beginning physics textbook your school uses. Scan through the table of contents and then through the book. What topics look familiar? Which problems look familiar? Do you feel ready?

12.3.2   Summary

We have created many useful models in this course. We have explored many of their properties, using numerical, graphical, and symbolic tools. We have learned much about our models, and gained strong insights into the corresponding and underlying real world phenomena—but there is much more to be learned.

Rates of changes, amounts of accumulations, limiting behaviors: these three topics are the core of calculus and unlock its powers for your use in the sciences and engineering.

Beyond calculus, there are more areas of mathematics. Some involve modeling based on rates of change (*differential equations*); others involve study of properties of real numbers necessary to prove theorems about limits (*real analysis, topology*). There are many more. We hope that you have the opportunity to pursue studies in these fields, should your interests turn that way. In all of these areas, a good foundation in the ideals of modeling will serve you well.

12.4 PROJECT: COMPASS CHECK

We believe that it is important to place each mathematics course in perspective. In this project, we ask you to answer some hard questions about where you have been, where your are, and where you are headed. We call this a *compass check*. We think that it will be useful to you in understanding this course, and its role in your larger life plans.

We are asking you to write a four part essay. We'd like you to address the following topics.

1. What mathematics have you learned so far in your life?
   - What mathematical skills do you have?
   - What was your most useful course prior to this one? Why?
   - What were your strengths and weaknesses, mathematically, prior to this course?
   - What was your favorite mathematical course? Nonmathematical course?

2. What did you learn in this course?
   - Review the table of contents for this book. Summarize what you have learned.
   - What do you think are the useful things you learned? What was less useful?
   - What are your mathematical strengths and weakness now?

3. Where are you headed in your life? What are your goals?

4. To reach your goals, will you need more mathematics? Will you study more mathematics? How will you take advantage of your mathematical strengths and address your mathematical weaknesses?

We hope that you find this essay useful, and that this self–assessment helps focus your future mathematics education.

12.5 COMPLEMENTS

1. The parabolic approximations we use are called *Simpson's Rule*, after Thomas Simpson, 1710–1761. Simpson was a private tutor and an itinerant lecturer who taught in London coffee houses. In addition to his work on numerical integration, during his life he also wrote mathematics texts, worked on probability theory, and edited the *Ladies Diary*.

2. There are hundreds of calculus books to which you can refer for more information about limits, rates of change, and accumulation. We especially like

   • *Calculus* by Gilbert Strang. Wellesley Cambridge Press, Wellesley, Massachusetts, 1991.

APPENDIX
A

TECHNICAL
REPORT
FORMAT

The simple technical report based on the five-stage modeling process will suffice for most reports that you will have to write during this course. However, in the event that one of your projects expands to include an actual client, you will need to use a more suitable format.

The generic format is the one required of Mathematical Modeling students at the U.S. Military Academy at West Point for both paper-copy and Web-based technical reports. We purposely designed it to be more scientifically oriented than most formats to emphasize the more subtle elements of the modeling process to students. We also recommend this format for use with the COMAP High School Mathematical Contest in Modeling (HiMCM) currently in development and due to be implemented in 1999.

Once you understand the key and essential ingredients that must go into every technical report, we encourage you to customize your reports, adding creativity and flair to your report writing style. As a suggestion, you should always keep a copy of your reports to use as a template for future reports.

Report Format

1. **TITLE PAGE.** This should contain the title of the project, the course number and title, the date, and a listing of the team members. Center this information, and use bold 14 point font.

2. **EXECUTIVE SUMMARY PAGE.** The purpose of the executive summary page is to provide an efficiently presented encapsulated picture of the project for someone who does not have time to read the actual report in its completeness. This page is typically written with upper management in mind. For this reason, most technical reports use an executive summary. This summary should be a *stand alone* document in that it should be able to be detached from your report and still make sense.

   Some guidelines to adhere to:

   - Try to keep your summary between 350 - 400 words.
   - Assume that your reader is technically proficient, although perhaps not as well versed in the techniques and approach that you took.
   - Write in the active voice, using the pronoun "we" where appropriate (i.e., "We have found ..." or "We demonstrate ..." as opposed to "It was found ..." or "It was demonstrated ...")
   - The content of the executive summary should
     (*a*) Briefly describe the problem and specify the context in which it occurs.
     (*b*) Summarize your approach in general to give the reader some idea as to how you chose to examine/attack the problem.
     (*c*) Summarize the results that you were able to obtain, both positive and negative as appropriate. Comment on the significance of these results (immediate, future, or both) as you see it.
     (*d*) State briefly whether this problem should be further examined, what direction future research should take, and why it should follow this direction.
     (*e*) Avoid mathematical equations and expressions, if possible.
     (*f*) Try to make the executive summary easy to understand.

3. **TABLE OF CONTENTS.** Use 1-1/2 spacing between entries, making dots to the page numbers. Use the same font as the main body.

4. **MAIN BODY.** Use 1-1/2 inch spacing, 10 point Times New Roman (or Bookman) font for text, with no smaller than 1 inch margins. Adjust the font size to either 11 or 12 point if you suspect that the 10 point font will cause reading difficulty for the client.

(*a*) PROBLEM DESCRIPTION. This section contains a description of the problem that you were faced with, and sets the stage for the rest of the information in the report. The underlying structure of the information that you present in this section should narrow the focus of the reader from the general setting of the problem to the specific aspect that you were asked to analyze. In modeling terms, you use this section to communicate your perspective of the problem as you sorted out the mess you were faced with.

This section is often used to cite the work of other people who have tackled a similar problem, or whose work is closely related to yours. If you do this, cite the work in chronological order, such as "Jones (1978)," and "Sherali et al. (1986)," etc. You exit this section leaving the reader with a clear understanding of what your challenge was.

(*b*) ASSUMPTIONS. State any assumptions you felt were necessary to model and solve the problem. You must do more than simply list the categories where you made assumptions. You need to explain what the assumption was, *why* you need to make it, and its impact on the problem. The reader needs to understand why *YOU* think you need to make an assumption. Don't leave it up to the reader to guess.

(*c*) ANALYSIS. This section presents your detailed solution to the problem.

> *i*) Definition of variables and symbols. This is a simple listing and explanation of the unknown quantities that you are working with in your model. In some cases, such as when taking a graphical approach to network modeling, the variables are implied by the edges of a graph, the vertices of a drawing, etc. When this occurs, you should still highlight the unknown quantities that you are trying to determine.

> *ii*) Methodology. Use this section to describe the general mathematical approach that you took in solving the problem. For example, "The problem faced by the client is a version of a scheduling problem faced by the airlines industry called the crew scheduling or assignment problem. In this report we adopt a common approach to solving this type of problem, called a relaxation method, that relies on several "best guess" or heuristic methods to obtain a starting solution and then proceeds to use this starting solution to obtain an exact solution."

(*d*) MODEL. Use this section to present the specific mathematical model(s) you developed for the problem at hand. Include all relavent calculations, tables, diagrams, and charts within the text, not as separate inclosures. If you have a significant amount of calculations, consider presenting a small example in this section just to give the client a feel for how they are performed, and put the rest of the supporting calculations in an appendix. Label all your charts and diagrams in sequential order with a short caption. All tables should be labeled in sequential order with a short caption. You should also use this section to present all the objective output of your model, but hold off interpreting these results until the next section.

(e) DISCUSSION AND RESULTS. This section is where you interpret and analyze the output of your model relative to the assumptions you made in building the model. This is the section that clearly indicates the degree to which you understand the true nature of the problem you were dealing with, the model you developed, and the meaning of the output of the model.

(f) SENSITIVITY ANALYSIS. The valid conclusions that we can draw from all mathematical models rests heavily on the assumptions that go into building the model. These assumptions typically include fixing the values of some of the quantities we need (e.g., budget amount available, number of acres of rainforest, expected discount rate, average number of customers, etc.) so that we can develop and test the workings of our model. This section's focus is answering "What if" questions that we anticipate the client will ask. For example, "What if the operating budget that you used was $11 million less than the number we gave you?" Or, "What happens to your recommended dining table layout for our restaurant if the number of customers is about 50% more than you have planned for?" Or, "What happens to your results if the assumption you made about the planets revolving around the Earth is incorrect?" (This was probably the question posed to Copernicus.) It is in this section that we systematically check how robust our conclusions are by experimenting with changing key values and assumptions that we used and seeing how our results change.

(g) CONCLUSIONS. Because the preceding section clearly states your analysis, this section should be used to wrap things up. Do not introduce new material in this section. Directly answer the focus question posed by the client again in this section. If you think further work is needed that you did not have the resources to complete, you should make a recommendation to the client as to what direction to take, and why you think this would be wise.

(*h*) ACKNOWLEDGMENTS. In a professional paper, this section is used to thank those who made significant contributions to your work but are not listed as co-authors. It is also used to cite the specific organization that funded your work (National Science Foundation, etc.). Follow your school's guidelines for documenting assistance you receive from others.

(*i*) REFERENCES. The point that we continue to stress, and will continue to stress, is that references *DO NOT* dilute the strength of your work. Quite the contrary, the depth and breadth of your reference listing gives the reader a feel for how knowledgable you are with the problem area you are addressing. Often, if your reference listing does not include what the experts in the field consider to be the "classic" or definitive works, your report is already off to a shaky start. As a student of precalculus, this is not as critical as later on in your education and professional practice. If your reference is of the typical type (paper, article, etc.), then use the appropriate format recommended at your school. If you have obtained information from an Internet resource via Netscape, Mosaic or some other browser, it needs to be documented using the following format.

- TITLE OF WEB PAGE (typically found in bold, large letters at the top of the web page), WEB PAGE OWNER NAME (Is it a company's page? Or someone's individual page?), WEB PAGE AUTHOR NAME (typically found at the bottom of the page as the person responsible for updating the page, or the person to whom comments should be sent), WEB PAGE ADDRESS (the "http:" address of the Web site), and the DATE that you acquired the information.

The client should have the ability to go to each web site location to check the accuracy of the information that you are including in your report.

(*j*) APPENDICES. This is not the dumping ground of your report. You use these to include information that you think will be important if someone wants to check your work, adapt your work to include parameters they did not want you to know, or extend your results to a new problem. This is where computer code, computer output, extensive data lists, and other supportive information finds a home.

INDEX